D1258263

HEATH MATHEMATICS
CONNECTIONS

Edward Manfre
James M. Moser
Joanne E. Lobato
Lorna Morrow

HEATH

D.C. Heath and Company
Lexington, Massachusetts / Toronto, Ontario

HEATH MATHEMATICS CONNECTIONS

Edward Manfre

Edward Manfre is a former elementary, intermediate, and secondary schoolteacher who has for over twenty years created classroom materials that encourage thinking. He has also conducted workshops on instructional methods and problem solving.

James M. Moser

James Moser has been a teacher of mathematics at several levels, a teacher educator, researcher, curriculum developer, and a state mathematics consultant. He is the author of mathematics textbooks for elementary, secondary, and college students. Currently he is Executive Director of the Wisconsin Mathematics Education Coalition.

Joanne E. Lobato

Joanne Lobato teaches mathematics at Alameda High School in Alameda, California. She has worked as a designer of mathematics software for grades K-8. Joanne conducts research on elementary schoolchildren and frequently presents teacher workshops.

Lorna Morrow

An instructor of mathematics at the University of Toronto, Lorna Morrow has also taught at both the elementary and secondary levels and has written extensively—books, articles, and curriculum materials—on topics in mathematics.

ACKNOWLEDGMENTS

Executive Editor Carol DeBold, **Supervising Editor** Sylvia Clark, **Level Editor** Barbara Kelley, **Product Manager** Sara Conkright, **Design Manager** Robert H. Botsford, **Production Coordinator** Donna Lee Porter, **Permissions** Dorothy Burns McLeod **Outside Editorial Assistance:** Patricia M. Dagle, Justine D. Dunn, Susan B. Sizer

The Fraction Bars illustrated and used in this book were created by Professor Albert B. Bennett, Jr., of the University of New Hampshire and Dr. Patricia S. Davidson of the University of Massachusetts, Boston. Decimal Squares were created by Professor Bennett.

ABOUT THE COVER
Cover Design: Linda Fishborne

Cover Photography: Bruno Joachim Studio, (Central Image)
R. Dahlquist / Superstock
Theme: The importance of geometry is shown through a series of realistic examples and symbolic representations. A hands-on approach to this subject makes it come alive for students.

Published simultaneously in Canada
Printed in the United States of America
International Standard Book Number: 0-669-11903-2
2 3 4 5 6 7 8 9 0

CONTENTS

Exploratory   Discovery   Linking
Symbolic   Application   Problem Solving

iii

CHAPTER

4

COLLECTING, ORGANIZING, AND USING DATA

● Exploratory	◐ Discovery	◖ Linking
◑ Symbolic	◔ Application	● Problem Solving

CHAPTER

5

MEASUREMENT AND GEOMETRY

CHAPTER
6

MULTIPLICATION OF DECIMALS

CHAPTER
7

DIVISION OF DECIMALS

| ⬤ **Exploratory** | ◐ **Discovery** | ◐ **Linking** |
| ◐ **Symbolic** | ◐ **Application** | ⬤ **Problem Solving** |

CHAPTER

8

GEOMETRY

CHAPTER

9 FRACTIONS AND MIXED NUMBERS

| ● Exploratory | ◐ Discovery | ◐ Linking |
| ◐ Symbolic | ◐ Application | ● Problem Solving |

CHAPTER

12

RATIO, PERCENT, AND PROBABILITY

Chapter Opener · Connections to Science *348*

| ● Exploratory | ◐ Discovery | ◐ Linking |
| ◐ Symbolic | ◐ Application | ● Problem Solving |

CHAPTER

13 AREA AND VOLUME

HANDBOOK

● Exploratory   ◐ Discovery   ◑ Linking
◑ Symbolic   ◑ Application   ● Problem Solving

ADDING AND SUBTRACTING WHOLE NUMBERS AND DECIMALS

Critical Thinking

Check Your Receipts Have you ever helped with the shopping? Groceries are a big expense for most families. Some people use a calculator when they shop. As they pick each item, they punch in the price. They may know their total even before they reach the checkout.

Some people watch as each item is added to the total. A mistake of one decimal place can make a big difference. For example, a $0.59 item could be read as $5.90. How much would a mistake like this cost?

Computer checkouts have helped to prevent some mistakes. However, some people still check their receipts very carefully. The next time your family brings home a grocery receipt, check the total with a calculator. You should also read each item to check for other mistakes. What other mistakes might be found on a grocery receipt?

NUMBERS AROUND US

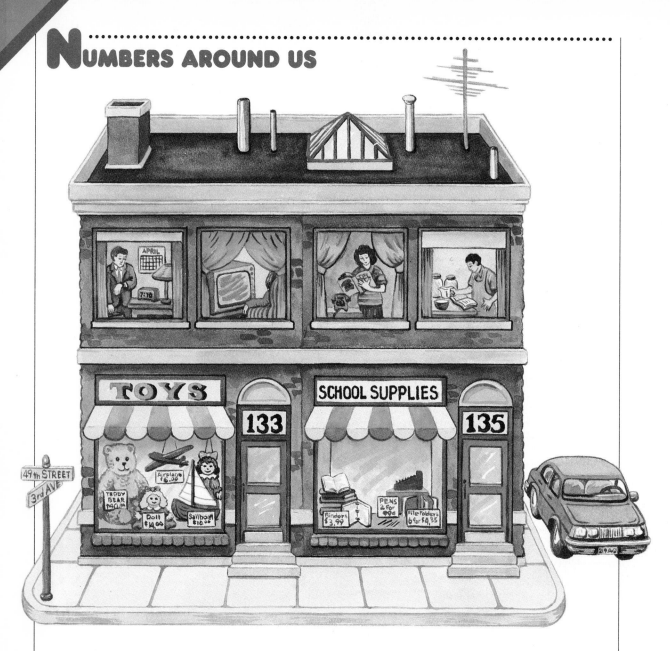

1. In what ways are numbers used in the picture above?

2. In what ways are numbers used at home? List three.

3. Describe three ways you used numbers today.

Describe one way each person would use numbers.

4. doctor

5. carpenter

6. gas-station attendant

7. teacher

8. artist

9. photographer

Write the letters of the numbers these people might use in their jobs. Explain.

a. 160 miles per hour	b. $2\frac{1}{2}$ lb
c. 13,356,827 miles	d. 35¢ each
e. 10 seconds	f. 98.6°

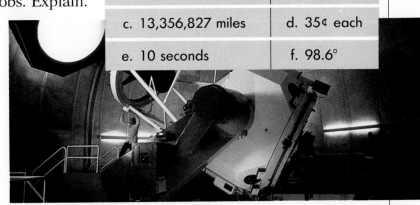

10. sprinter

11. store clerk

12. astronomer

13. nurse

14. race car driver

15. post office clerk

Would you need numbers to do the task? Write *yes* or *no*. Explain.

16. count your money

17. find a show on TV

18. put on your hat and coat

19. play a game of baseball

20. get ready for bed at your bedtime

21. walk the dog

Write an example of the kind of numbers each person might use.

22. a car salesperson

23. an airline pilot

24. a sportscaster

25. an archeologist

26. an office worker

27. a disk jockey

28. a truck driver

29. an architect

PROJECT • Cooperative Learning

Work in small groups. You will need poster board, crayons, construction paper, scissors, and paste.

Choose one of the sports listed. Find three or more ways you would use numbers in that sport. Make a poster to share with the class.

soccer gymnastics

basketball baseball

PLACE VALUE

In 1988, the San Diego Zoo and Wild Animal Park was visited by nearly 4,900,000 people.

Use the place-value chart to help you understand this number.

Billions			Millions			Thousands			Ones		
Hundreds	Tens	Ones	Hundreds	Tens	Ones	Hundreds	Tens	Ones	Hundreds	Tens	Ones
			4	9	0	0	0	0	0		

The number 4,900,000 can be written in different ways.

Short word form: 4 million, 900 thousand

Expanded form: 4,000,000 + 900,000

Standard form: 4,900,000

Think

• What is the value of the greatest place in an 11-digit number?

Other Example

Billions			Millions			Thousands			Ones		
Hundreds	Tens	Ones	Hundreds	Tens	Ones	Hundreds	Tens	Ones	Hundreds	Tens	Ones
		3	0	0	0	7	0	1	9	2	0

3 billion, 701 thousand, 920

3,000,000,000 + 700,000 + 1000 + 900 + 20

3,000,701,920

GUIDED PRACTICE

Write the number in standard form.

1. 307 thousand

2. 26 million, 347 thousand, 28

3. 200,000,000 + 20,000 + 6000 + 2

4. 3,000,000,000 + 400,000,000 + 80,000 + 700 + 30 + 7

Write the number in short word form.

5. 45,000,700,000

6. 375,262

7. 400,000 + 20,000 + 1000 + 500 + 30

8. In the number 333,333, how many times greater is each digit as you move from right to left?

INDEPENDENT PRACTICE

Write each number in standard form.

9. 140 million

10. 600,000 + 40,000 + 1000 + 20

11. 40 billion, 2 hundred

12. 277 billion, 645 million, 2 thousand, 6

Write each number in short word form.

13. 27,555

14. 375,002

15. 4,019,200

16. 88,305,000

Find the digit in the greatest place. Write the value of that digit in short word form.

17. 44,000

18. 2,757,203

19. 16,000,327

20. 231, 459

21. 147,523,472

22. 608,325,422,112

23. Use each digit in the box once to write the
   a. largest number.
   b. closest number to 394,041.

5		0		3	
	9		7		2

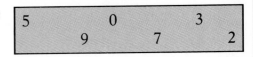

● **Mixed Practice**

Write the answer.

1. 828
   + 53

2. 826
   − 353

3. 3712
   + 2765

4. 6000
   − 911

DECIMAL SENSE

In this lesson, you will use area models to explore decimals. You will need the recording sheet.

▶ Big Bend National Park in Texas covers 700,221 acres. Try to imagine one tenth of this area.

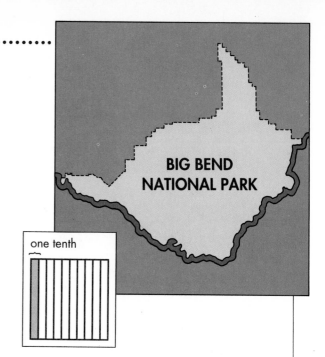

The area model to the right can help you understand one tenth. Notice that one strip represents one tenth of the whole square.

one tenth

1. Would one tenth the area of Big Bend National Park be more than half or less than half of the total area of the park?

2. Look at the model. How many strips are shaded? How many tenths does this represent?

You can write tenths as a fraction or as a decimal.

$$\text{three tenths} = \frac{3}{10} = 0.3$$

3. On the models on your recording sheet, shade:

   a. $\frac{5}{10}$ b. 0.8   c. 0.4

   Write the numbers from least to greatest.

4. Which of the models in exercise 3 also represents the fraction $\frac{1}{2}$? Circle it.

one hundredth

▶ The 10 × 10 area model at the right can help you to understand hundredths. Each small square represents one hundredth of the large square.

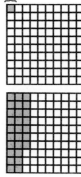

5. Look at the model to the right. How many hundredths does the shaded part represent?

You can write hundredths as a fraction or as a decimal.

twenty-seven hundredths = $\frac{27}{100}$ = 0.27

6. On the models on your recording sheet, shade:

   a. $\frac{34}{100}$ b. 0.50   c. 0.68

   Write the numbers from least to greatest.

7. How many whole tenths are shaded for 0.68?

8. Which of the models in exercise 6 also represents the fraction $\frac{1}{2}$? Circle it.

9. What number would be represented if the model had no squares shaded? All squares shaded?

10. Shade 0.7 on the model on your recording sheet. Compare it to your model that represents $\frac{1}{2}$. Is 0.7 less than or greater than $\frac{1}{2}$? How do you know?

11. Shade 0.48 on the model on your recording sheet. Is 0.48 less than or greater than $\frac{1}{2}$? How do you know?

12. Shade the area models on your recording sheet. Write whether the number is closer to 0, $\frac{1}{2}$, or 1.

    a. 0.6   b. 0.17   c. 0.3   d. 0.92

13. Shade the area models on your recording sheet. Is 0.5 greater than or less than 0.07? How can you tell?

SUMMING IT UP

14. How are fractions and decimals alike?

15. Look at the decimals to the right.

    a. Which are close to zero?

    b. Which are close to $\frac{1}{2}$?

    c. Which are close to 1?

| 0.2 | 0.38 | 0.57 | 0.77 |
| 0.9 | 0.05 | 0.49 | 0.4 |

Number Sense

Both whole numbers and decimals can be shown as numbers on a number line. In this lesson, you will use number lines to find relationships between decimals and whole numbers. You will need a centimeter ruler.

▶ Draw a number line by drawing a line segment 11 centimeters long. Mark off 10 spaces, each 1 centimeter long. Label the number line as shown below.

0   10   100

1. Locate and label 50 on your number line.

2. Next, locate 5, 25, 32, and 85 on your number line. Draw an arrow and label each number.

▶ Make another number line. Label the last mark on the left 0 and the last mark on the right 1. Label the rest of the number line by tenths, beginning with 0.1.

0   1

3. Which decimals on the number line are greater than 0.1 and less than 0.5?

4. Is the decimal 0.3 closer to 0 or closer to 1?

▶ Look back at your number line labeled 0.1 to 0.9. The tenths spaces can also be divided into hundredths. For example, the hundredths between 0.3 and 0.4 are 0.31, 0.32, 0.33, 0.34, 0.35, 0.36, 0.37, 0.38, and 0.39.

Divide the segment between 0.3 and 0.4 on your number line into 10 equal parts. You can use the millimeter markings on your ruler to do this.

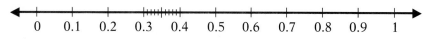

0   0.1   0.2   0.3   0.4   0.5   0.6   0.7   0.8   0.9   1

5. Locate and label 0.38 on your number line.

6. Is 0.38 closer to 0.3 or to 0.4?

7. Is 0.38 closer to 0 or closer to 1?

8. What are the hundredths between 0.6 and 0.7?

9. Find and label 0.04 on your number line. Compare it with 0.4. Which number is larger?

10. Copy the chart below. Place each number from the box at the right in the correct column on the chart.

| 0.2 | 0.37 | 0.81 | 0.75 | 0.09 |

between 0 and 0.5	between 0.5 and 1

11. Think of another number that could be written in each column in the chart. Write the numbers in the chart.

SUMMING IT UP

12. Sort the numbers at the right into three groups: less than 0.1, between 0.1 and 1, and between 1 and 10.

0.45	0.08	2	2.75
6.61	0.21	5.7	0.03

13. Write a rule that helps you tell whether a number between 0 and 1 is closer to 0 or 1.

14. Write a rule that helps you tell whether a number between 0 and 0.1 is closer to 0 or 0.1.

READING AND WRITING DECIMALS

▶ The number 5.302 is a decimal. Use the place-value chart to help you read the number.

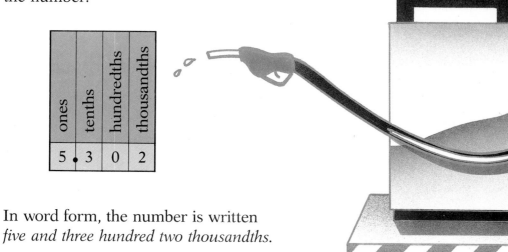

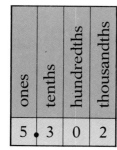

ones	tenths	hundredths	thousandths
5 •	3	0	2

In word form, the number is written *five and three hundred two thousandths.*

Some other examples:

Standard Form: 0.005
Word form: five thousandths

Standard form: 387.46
Word form: three hundred eighty-seven and forty-six hundredths

> **Write the word *and* for the decimal point.**

▶ Writing zeros at the end of a decimal does not change the value of the number.

The decimals 0.60 and 0.6 have equal value. They are equivalent decimals.

Write equivalent decimals for 1.58 and 32.020.

1.58 = 1.580   32.020 = 32.02

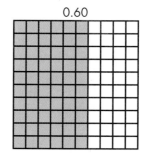

0.60

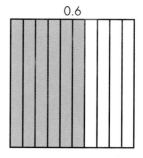

0.6

Think

• Are the word forms of 8.9 and 8.90 the same? Are they equivalent decimals?

GUIDED PRACTICE

1. Write the value of each blue digit.
   a. 2.936   **b.** 7.001   **c.** 1026.5   **d.** 6.841

Write the letter of the answer that best completes each sentence.

2. Three and sixteen thousandths is written as ▨.
   a. 0.316   **b.** 3.16   **c.** 3.016   **d.** 3.0016

3. The word name for 1.062 is ▨.
   a. one and sixty-two thousandths
   b. one and sixty-two hundredths

4. Write two equivalent decimals for exercise 1c.

....

INDEPENDENT PRACTICE

5. Write the value of each blue digit.
   a. 5.067   **b.** 351.386   **c.** 27.593   **d.** 0.46

6. Write the word name for each decimal.
   a. 6.11   **b.** 10,000.001   **c.** 0.453   **d.** 39.01

7. Write each decimal.
   a. fourteen and six thousandths
   b. one hundred and fifty-five thousandths
   c. two and one hundred twelve thousandths

8. Write an equivalent decimal.
   a. 6.04   **b.** 5.2   **c.** 8.170   **d.** 1324.4

9. Use the digits in the circle to fill each box. Do not use a digit more than once.
   a. the greatest decimal □.□□□□
   b. the least decimal □.□□□□

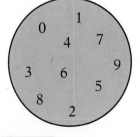

MATH LOG

How is place value to the right of the decimal point different from place value to the left of the decimal point? How is it similar?

COMPARING AND ORDERING

On Tuesday, Angie traveled 5200 kilometers and Laurie traveled 5310 kilometers, Who traveled farther?

5310 KILOMETERS

▶ Compare: 5200 km and 5310 km

● Line up the numbers by place value.	● Compare the digits. Begin with the greatest place.	● Continue comparing if you need to.
5200 km 5310 km	5200 km 5310 km 5 = 5	5200 5310 2 < 3

So, 5200 < 5310. Laurie traveled farther than Angie.

▶ Compare: 41.72 and 41.26

● Line up the numbers by place value.	● Compare the digits. Begin with the greatest place.	● Continue comparing if you need to.
41.72 41.26	41.72 41.26 4 = 4	41.72 41.26 1 = 1 41.72 41.26 7 > 2

So, 41.72 > 41.26.

▶ Order from greatest to least: 0.3, 0.005, and 4

● Line up the numbers by place value.	● Compare to find the greatest number.	● Continue comparing if you need to.
0.3 0.05 4	4 > 0.3 and 4 > 0.05 So, 4 is the greatest number.	0.3 > 0.05

The order from greatest to least: 4, 0.3, 0.05.

Think

- Compare 0.412 and 0.67. Does the decimal with the greater number of digits have the greater value? Explain.

GUIDED PRACTICE

Compare. Write <, >, or =.

1. 0.31 ● 0.299   **2.** 799 ● 801   **3.** 62.4 ● 62.4   **4.** 5.10 ● 5.01

Order the numbers from greatest to least.

5. 83.29, 83.2, 84, 83.21   **6.** 2017, 2017.3, 995.999, 2100

7. 0.07, 0.5, 6, 0.008   **8.** 0.98, 1, 0.099, 0.1

9. Since 9 > 5, is 0.09 > 0.5? Explain.

INDEPENDENT PRACTICE

Compare. Write <, >, or =.

10. 4562 ● 4472   **11.** 0.22 ● 0.221   **12.** 302.1 ● 320.9   **13.** 7.62 ● 7.62

14. 0.2 ● 0.09   **15.** 0.32 ● 0.088   **16.** 6.5 ● 6.50   **17.** 0.99 ● 1

Order from least to greatest.

18. 301, 311, 310, 300   **19.** 6579, 6573, 6755, 6753

20. 0.75, 7.05, 0.77, 0.755   **21.** 24.8, 42.8, 24.888

Problem Solving Use the women's Olympic times for the 100-meter run in the Almanac section of your Data Book in the back of the book.

22. Who had the best time?

23. Who had the second-best time?

24. How many runners had times less than 11.5 seconds?

25. Which runner's time was between 11.25 and 11.75 seconds?

26. Which runner's time was closest to 11 seconds?

SUMS AND DIFFERENCES

▶ Finding an exact answer to a math problem without using paper and pencil is called **mental math**.

Place-value names can help you add and subtract mentally.

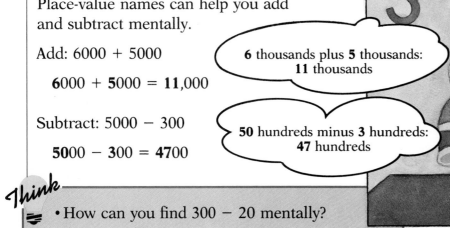

Add: 6000 + 5000

6000 + **5**000 = **11,000**

> **6** thousands plus **5** thousands:
> **11** thousands

Subtract: 5000 − 300

5000 − **300** = **4700**

> **50** hundreds minus **3** hundreds:
> **47** hundreds

Think
- How can you find 300 − 20 mentally?

▶ Sometimes you can find sums with many addends mentally. Look for sums like 100 or 1000.

Add: 50 + 40 + 60 + 50

            100

        100

> **Look for sums of 100.**

100 + 100 = 200

So, 50 + 40 + 60 + 50 = 200

Think
- Write an addition exercise that you can solve mentally. Use three addends.

Other Examples

624 + 500	520 + 70	17,000 − 9000
11 hundred 24, or 1124	**59** tens, or 590	**8** thousand, or 8000

Add or subtract. Use mental math.

1. 600 + 300   **2.** 8000 − 2000   **3.** 60 + 70   **4.** 140 − 70

5. 4000 − 200   **6.** 3025 + 6000   **7.** 5400 + 300   **8.** 50 + 60 + 50

9. How did you find the sum in exercise 8?

INDEPENDENT PRACTICE

Add or subtract. Use mental math.

10. 500 + 200   **11.** 4000 + 5000   **12.** 80 + 20   **13.** 600 + 800

14. 90 − 30   **15.** 7000 − 3000   **16.** 110 − 90   **17.** 1200 − 600

18. 300 − 10   **19.** 500 − 40   **20.** 6000 − 200   **21.** 7000 − 400

22. 530 + 300   **23.** 670 − 100   **24.** 840 + 50   **25.** 3000 + 2500

26. Write each pair of numbers whose sum is 100.

40	90	30	70	50
50	20	80	10	60

27. Write each pair of numbers whose sum is 1000.

800	100	400	300	200
700	500	600	900	500

Add. Use mental math.

28. 50 + 30 + 50   **29.** 400 + 700 + 600   **30.** 35 + 30 + 70

31. 200 + 300 + 150   **32.** 30 + 70 + 20 − 80   **33.** 90 + 30 + 10 + 20

CHALLENGE • Problem Solving

GAME BOARD

When you travel on the game board at the right, you collect points. For example, when you travel from A to B you get 40 points.

List 3 different ways to travel from GO to END so that you collect exactly 150 points.

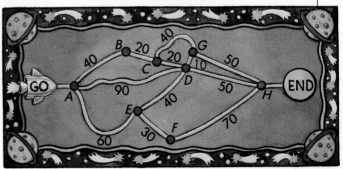

SUMS

Was the total attendance for all three games more than or less than 8000 people?

Baseball Game Attendance	
Game 1	4248
Game 2	895
Game 3	3167

▶ You can answer this question by estimating, using a method called **front-end estimation**.

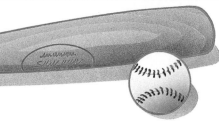

● **Add the digits in the greatest place.**

$$4248$$
$$895$$
$$+\ 3167$$

Rough Estimate: 7000

● **Look for groups of about 1000 in the remaining digits.**

$$4248$$
$$895$$ about 1000
$$+\ 3167$$

Adjusted Estimate: 7000 + **1000** = 8000

● **Answer the question by looking at the remaining digits.**

Since 200 + 800 = 1000, then 248 + 895 > 1000.

This means the total attendance was more than 8000.

▶ Here's another example of front-end estimation.
Estimate: 1240 + 4582 + 537

1240 + 4582 + 537   **Rough Estimate:** 5000

1240 + 4582 + 537

about 1000   **Adjusted Estimate:** 5000 + 1000 = 6000

This estimate did not use the 240, but it could have. For example, 6000 + 240 = 6240. Both 6000 and 6240 are reasonable estimates.

Think

• Will the actual sum always be greater than the front-end rough estimate? Explain.

Other Examples

$24.67 about $10
36.24
+ 9.38 — about $10

Rough Estimate: $50
Adjusted Estimate: $50 + **$20** = $70

5.92 — about 1
2.43
0.42 about 1
+ 1.28

Rough Estimate: 8
Adjusted Estimate: 8 + **2** = 10

GUIDED PRACTICE

Write your estimate. Remember to adjust.

1. 3223 + 429 + 468

2. 543 + 63 + 317 + 95

3. $3.04 + $0.72 + $1.13

4. 2.06 + 1.75 + 3.38

5. Is the exact sum in exercise 3 greater than or less than $5.00? How can you tell?

INDEPENDENT PRACTICE

Write your estimate. Remember to adjust.

6.
```
   512
    87
   353
 +  51
```

7.
```
  1017
   245
   491
 + 4247
```

8. 5412 + 679 + 2208

9. $32.23 + $24.87 + $4.56

10. 3.52 + 1.57 + 2.87

Estimate. Write < or >.

11. 3625 + 479 ● 7000

12. 638 + 75 + 349 ● 1000

13. 2567 + 538 + 1602 ● 8000

14. $45.87 + $9.42 ● $50.00

15. 2.36 + 1.72 + 2.58 ● 6.00

16. 5.26 + 3.38 ● 10.00

Problem Solving Use estimation.

17. Was the total attendance for all five games more than or less than 10,000?

18. Was the total attendance for the last three games more than or less than 6000?

19. Which two games had a combined attendance between 1000 and 2000?

20. Were there more people at games 2 and 5 combined or at game 3?

Baseball Game Attendance	
Game 1	4248
Game 2	895
Game 3	3167
Game 4	262
Game 5	2805

ESTIMATION

DIFFERENCES

▶ The Bernstein Ticket Agency has 5875
tickets to sell for a benefit rock concert.
They have sold 2648 tickets so far.
About how many tickets do they have
left to sell?

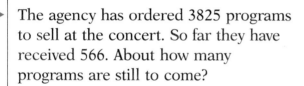

You can use front-end estimation.

$$
\begin{array}{r}
5875 \\
- 2648 \\
\end{array}
$$
Estimate: 3000

They have about 3000 tickets left to sell.

▶ The agency has ordered 3825 programs
to sell at the concert. So far they have
received 566. About how many
programs are still to come?

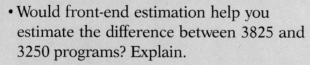

● Use front-end estimation to make a rough estimate.	● You can get a closer estimate by subtracting the digits in both the hundreds and thousands places.
$\begin{array}{r} 3825 \\ - 566 \\ \end{array}$ Estimate: 3000	$\begin{array}{r} 3825 \\ - 566 \\ \end{array}$ Closer Estimate: 3300

There are about 3300 programs still to come.

 Think

• Would front-end estimation help you
estimate the difference between 3825 and
3250 programs? Explain.

Other Examples

$29.55	4462	9463 mi
− 3.89	− 817	− 2594 mi
Estimate: $26.00	Estimate: 3600	Estimate: 7000 mi

GUIDED PRACTICE

Estimate. Which two numbers have a difference of:

1. about 4500?   2. about 4300?

3. about 200?   4. about 4800?

5. Make up two numbers that have a difference of about 2300.

5014		743	
	528		262

....

INDEPENDENT PRACTICE

Write the letter of the closer estimate.

6.   6787
    − 259

   a. 6000
   b. 6500

7.   82,951
    − 6,827

   a. 76,000
   b. 80,000

8. $34.95
    − 7.08

   a. $27
   b. $30

9. $60.38
    − 4.47

   a. $60
   b. $56

Estimate. Which two numbers have a difference of:

10. about 6500?   11. about 4000?

12. about 2700?   13. about 500?

7008		3246	
	521		
	365		839

Which number is a reasonable estimate? Write *a* or *b*.

14. 7468 − 239   a. 5000 b. 7200   15. 9621 − 684   a. 9000 b. 3000

16. $64.80 − $4.67   a. $20 b. $60   17. 322 − 27   a. 300 b. 100

18. Ron has just finished his homework. Estimate to help him find his five mistakes. Write the letter of each incorrect item.

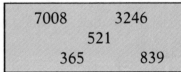

a. 886	b. 4352	c. $25.62	Name: _Ron_
−579	− 867	− 3.49	
37	3485	$ 22.12	

d. 7538 − 442 = 3118   e. 6273 − 4182 = 2091
f. 6425 − 237 = 4055   g. $56.60 − $3.47 = $21.90
h. $40.00 − $6.94 = $33.06   i. $38.43 − $22.67 = $61.10

PROBLEM SOLVER'S GUIDE

There are no magic rules to make solving problems easy. But the Problem Solver's Guide can help.

One time we used the Guide to help build a stone border around a garden.

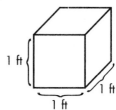

OUR PROBLEM

We planned to put 1-foot blocks of stone side by side to make the border. Each side of the square border was to be 6 feet long. We wanted to know how many blocks we would need.

1 ft
1 ft
1 ft

OUR SOLUTION

UNDERSTAND

What is going on? ———————→ We're making a border of blocks.

What do we know? ———————→ We know the size and shape of the border and the blocks.

What do we need to find out? —→ We need to find out the total number of blocks.

TRY

We were not sure how to start.

We tried drawing a picture.

We saw that each side would have 6 blocks, for a total of 24 blocks.

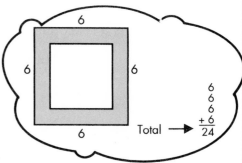

$$\begin{array}{r} 6 \\ 6 \\ 6 \\ +6 \\ \hline 24 \end{array}$$

Total →

LOOK BACK

We checked to see if our answer made sense. We realized we had not thought about the problem carefully enough. We were counting the corner blocks twice.

We **tried** again. This time we used a picture that showed the blocks. We saw that we needed a total of only 20 blocks.

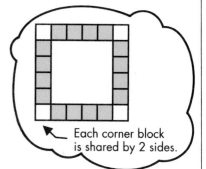

Each corner block is shared by 2 sides.

We **looked back** again.
Our answer made sense.

Work in groups to solve each problem. Use the Problem Solver's Guide to help you.

1. From the camp, Rob hiked 3 miles east, then 2 miles north, then 1 mile east, then 2 miles south. How far and in what direction should he walk to go directly back to the camp?

2. Rob hikes 2 miles each hour. He left the camp at 9:30 A.M. About what time will he return if he takes the route described in exercise 1?

3. At halftime, 12 rows of the marching band form design *A*. They move 3 rows and change to design *B*. How do they do it?

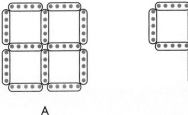

A   B

4. Joan plans to run each day through the State Park to train for a race. She wants to run 700 yards from point *A* to point *H* and then 700 yards back. How can she do this without running along the same path twice?

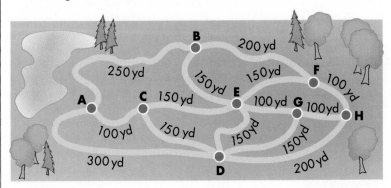

5. What is the shortest route that begins and ends at point *A* and includes points *A, B, C, D,* and *E*? How long is it?

6. Ann, Bob, Cal, Deb, and Ed have 50 minutes to play a new computer game. Only 2 can play at a time. Set up a schedule so they each play for the same amount of time.

ADDITION

A very useful mental-math strategy is to break up numbers into other numbers that are easier to work with mentally. For example: add 26 to 25.

Here are two ways to mentally break up the addends.

Break up one number into tens and ones. In this case, break up 26 into 20 + 6. Now add all three addends.

Break up both addends. Add the tens: 20 + 20. Then add the ones: 5 + 6.

25 + 26

= 25 + 20 + 6
That's 45 + 6, which is 51.

25 + 26

= 20 + 5 + 20 + 6

=   40   +   11
That's 51.

Think

• What other way can you think of to add 25 and 26?

INDEPENDENT PRACTICE

Write the sum. Use mental math.

1. 54 + 26
2. 39 + 11
3. 44 + 55
4. $64 + $28

5. 41 + 39
6. $32 + $52
7. 15 + 78
8. 25 + 65

9. $36 + $18
10. 54 + 29
11. 52 + 35
12. 68 + 27

13. 23 in. + 48 in.
14. 52 cm + 25 cm
15. 69 m + 21 m
16. 57 ft + 35 ft

SECTION REVIEW

for pages 2–22

Write the answer.

1. Frank's bicycle cyclometer showed the following mileages for five different trips: 0.4, 0.65, 0.59, 0.49, and 0.25 mile. Which trips were longer than 0.5 mile?

2. In 1986, Detroit had a population of 1,086,220; Dallas, a population of 1,003,500; and San Diego, a population of 1,015,196. Write these cities in order from greatest to least population.

Which row has numbers ordered from least to greatest?

3. 0.620, 0.26, 6.252, 0.521
   a. 0.26, 0.521, 0.620, 6.252
   b. 0.620, 0.521, 6.525, 0.26
   c. 6.252, 0.620, 0.521, 0.26

4. 20.3, 2.33, 230, 23.04
   a. 230, 20.3, 2.33, 23.04
   b. 23.04, 2.33, 20.3, 230
   c. 2.33, 20.3, 23.04, 230

Write each number in standard form.

5. 200 thousand, 7

6. 35 billion, 2 million, 7 thousand, 25

7. 4,000,000 + 200,000 + 4

8. 625 million, 40 thousand

Write each number in short word form.

9. 3,421,007   10. 65,895   11. 100,002

Write the letter of each equivalent decimal.

12. 6.2
    a. 6.02   b. 6.20   c. 6.200

13. 31.09
    a. 31.090   b. 31.90   c. 31.9

14. 207.10
    a. 207.100   b. 207.01   c. 207.1

15. 5450.5
    a. 5455   b. 5450.50   c. 5450.05

Write each decimal in standard form.

16. four and five tenths

17. thirty-six and fifty-one hundredths

18. seventy and three hundredths

19. eight and ninety-nine thousandths

Write the value of the 4 in each number.

20. 135,402   21. 65.974   22. 4,800,000   23. 713.043

ADDITION AND SUBTRACTION

The Ton-o-Fun Toy Company makes dinosaur erasers. In the month of January, they sold 238,450 erasers. In February, they sold 232,175 erasers. How many erasers have they sold so far this year?

Find: 238,450 + 232,175

A quick estimate before you compute will help you check your answer.

Because the computed answer is close to the estimate, the answer is reasonable.

They have sold 470,625 erasers so far this year.

Estimate.

```
  200,000
+ 200,000
  400,000
```

Add. Regroup where necessary.

```
    1  1
  238,450
+ 232,175
  470,625
```

Last year, the company sold a total of 345,730 erasers in January and February. How many more erasers have they sold this year?

Find: 470,625 − 345,730

A quick estimate before you compute will help you check your answer.

Estimate.

```
  400,000
− 300,000
  100,000
```

Subtract. Regroup.

```
     6  9   15 12
  4  7  0 , 6  2 5
− 3  4  5 , 7  3 0
  1  2  4 , 8  9 5
```

They have sold 124,895 more erasers this year.

 Think

- Would you ever use addition to check subtraction? Give an example.

Other Examples

```
   2  10
  4 3 , 0 8 5
−    2 , 4 1 3
  4 0 , 6 7 2
```

```
  7 ft   4 in.
+ 5 ft   6 in.
 12 ft  10 in.
```

```
  1 1 1   1
  $167,938
+  $53,422
  $221,360
```

```
  3  12      2  11
  4  2 min  3  1 s
− 1  7 min  2  2 s
  2  5 min     9 s
```

24

Solve each problem.

1. A truck has been loaded with 80,625 erasers in crates. At the last minute, one more crate holding 6025 erasers is put on the truck. How many erasers are being shipped?

2. In 1990, the Ton-o-Fun Company earned $785,430 from dinosaur eraser sales. In 1991, they earned $787,650. In which year did they earn more money from eraser sales? How much more?

3. Did you add or subtract to solve exercises 1 and 2? How did you decide?

Write the answer.

4. $\begin{array}{r} 1753 \\ + 1611 \end{array}$

5. $\begin{array}{r} 9386 \\ - 3257 \end{array}$

6. $\begin{array}{r} 7750 \\ - 2299 \end{array}$

7. $\begin{array}{r} 43,026 \\ - 38,418 \end{array}$

8. $\begin{array}{r} 2891 \\ + 2384 \end{array}$

9. $\begin{array}{r} \$1688.39 \\ 432.78 \\ + \quad 84.22 \end{array}$

10. $\begin{array}{r} 4478 \\ - 3712 \end{array}$

11. $\begin{array}{r} 8679 \\ 1921 \\ + 4015 \end{array}$

12. $\begin{array}{r} 520,001 \\ - 417,338 \end{array}$

13. $\begin{array}{r} 12 \text{ min } 13 \text{ s} \\ + \quad 4 \text{ min } 39 \text{ s} \end{array}$

14. $41,034 - 8719$

15. $12 \text{ lb } 3 \text{ oz} + 9 \text{ lb } 4 \text{ oz}$

16. $\$1.60 - \$0.86$

Problem Solving Use the table.

17. Of the erasers made in January, 100,000 were used to fill a special order. How many erasers did that leave to fill other orders?

18. By the third week of April, 115,610 erasers had been made. How many more needed to be made to make April the most productive month so far?

Dinosaur Erasers Made at Ton-o-Fun Factory	
January	122,567
February	124,812
March	121,476

19. Did the factory make more than or less than 400,000 erasers in the three months shown?

25

ROUNDING

The actual attendance at the 1989 Super Bowl was 75,129. A newspaper reporter rounded the number to the nearest thousand.

The reporter knew that 75,129 is between 75,000 and 76,000, but is closer to 75,000. So she rounded 75,129 to 75,000.

She could also have rounded 75,129 to the greatest place. In this case, ten thousand is the greatest place.

75,129 is between 70,000 and 80,000.
75,129 is closer to 80,000.
So, it rounds to 80,000.

The headline could have rounded the attendance to 80,000. However, 75,000 is a closer estimate.

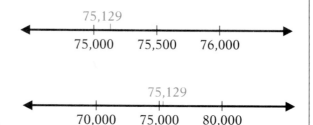

Think

• What is a quick way to determine whether you are going to round a number up or down?

Other Examples

Round each decimal to the nearest whole number.	Round each number to the nearest ten.	Round to the greatest place.
6.8 ⟶ 7	2179 ⟶ 2180	472 ⟶ 500
3.26 ⟶ 3	3442 ⟶ 3440	1158 ⟶ 1000
0.57 ⟶ 1	515 ⟶ 520	66,982 ⟶ 70,000

GUIDED PRACTICE

1. Write the missing digit.

a. The decimal 3.8 is between 3 and 4 but is closer to ▓ .

b. The decimal 7.2 is between 7 and 8 but is closer to ▓ .

Round each number to the greatest place.

2. 674   **3.** $265   **4.** 47   **5.** 27,011   **6.** 7.23   **7.** 43.92

Round each number to the nearest hundred.

8. 4235   **9.** 746   **10.** 3219   **11.** 14,809   **12.** 445   **13.** $6459

14. Do you think newspapers usually use exact numbers or rounded numbers? Why?

INDEPENDENT PRACTICE

Round each number to the greatest place.

15. $2459   **16.** 36.21   **17.** 475   **18.** 4.72

19. $144   **20.** 6271   **21.** 322   **22.** $7579

Round each number to the nearest hundred.

23. 272   **24.** 4976   **25.** 8344   **26.** 1211   **27.** 297

28. 131   **29.** 675   **30.** 4082   **31.** 1849   **32.** 1851

Write *rounded* or *exact* to describe the number in each headline.

33.

★ COUNTRY NEWS ★
County Fair Draws Crowd of 5000

34.

★ COUNTRY NEWS ★
Magician Gives 100th Show Tonight

35.

★ COUNTRY NEWS ★
200 Pound Elephant Born at Zoo

Maintain • Multiplication Facts

Write the product.

1. 5×6 **2.** 9×4 **3.** 4×7 **4.** 8×3 **5.** 3×8

6. 5×7 **7.** 6×0 **8.** 9×6 **9.** 8×9 **10.** 7×7

ADDITION AND SUBTRACTION

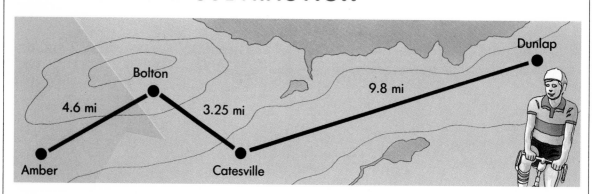

About how many miles is it from Amber to Dunlap?

There are many good ways to estimate this distance. You learned how to make a front-end estimate in earlier lessons. In this lesson, you will learn how to estimate by rounding.

● **Round each number. Then add.**

4.7 mi + 3.25 mi + 9.8 mi

↓   ↓   ↓

5 mi + 3 mi + 10 mi

Estimate: 18 miles

It is about 18 miles from Amber to Dunlap along the route shown.

> **Remember: to round a number, think about what it is close to.**

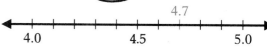

Since 4.7 is between 4 and 5 but is closer to 5, then 4.7 rounds to 5.

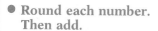 

• Make a front-end estimate of 4.7 + 3.25 + 9.8. Adjust it. Compare it to the estimate you got by rounding. What do you notice?

Both estimating by rounding and front-end estimation are useful strategies.

Other Examples

2.15 + 0.87 + 3.46
↓   ↓   ↓
2   1   3
Estimate: 6

$43.69 − $9.87
↓   ↓
$40 $10
Estimate: $30

4592 − 269
↓   ↓
4600   300
Estimate: 4300

Write the missing digit.

1. The decimal 4.9 is between 4 and 5 but is closer to ■.

2. The decimal 7.2 is between ■ and ■ but is closer to ■.

3. The decimal 3.8 is rounded to ■.

4. The decimal 5.1 is rounded to ■.

Estimate by rounding to the greatest place.

5. 6.8 + 3.2 + 5.3

6. 587 + 364

7. $8.95 − $5.27

8. Is the actual sum in exercise 6 greater than or less than 1000? How can you tell?

Write the missing digit.

9. 3.82 is between 3 and 4 but is closer to ■.

10. $5.29 is between $■ and $■ but is closer to $■.

11. 6.7 is rounded to ■.

12. $8.47 is rounded to $■.

13. 491 is rounded to ■ hundred.

14. 628 is rounded to ■ hundred.

Estimate by rounding to the greatest place.

15. 385 + 219 + 334

16. 493 − 326

17. 8.24 − 5.97

Problem Solving Use estimation to solve each problem.

18. About how much farther is it from Cole to Dixon than from Cole to Belgrade?

19. Is it more than or less than 10 miles from Belgrade to Dixon?

20. Is Belgrade farther from Ames or from Dixon?

21. Which is farther, from Cole to Belgrade and back or from Cole to Dixon?

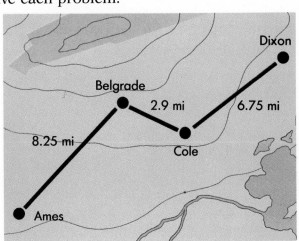

ADDING DECIMALS

Obstacle Course Results		
Run	Time in Seconds	Penalty
1	32.017	none
2	29.466	5 s

Jordan gets two turns to run the obstacle course. For every obstacle he misses, 5 seconds is added to his time as a penalty.

Think

• Is Jordan's time for the two runs, not including the penalty, greater than or less than 65 seconds? How do you know?

What is Jordan's total time for the two runs, including the penalty?

Add: 32.017 s + 29.466 s + 5 s

● Line up the numbers by place value.

$$\begin{array}{r} 32.017 \text{ s} \\ 29.466 \text{ s} \\ +\ 5.000 \text{ s} \end{array}$$ 5 = 5.000

● Add.

$$\begin{array}{r} {}^{1}\ \ {}^{1} \\ 32.017 \text{ s} \\ 29.466 \text{ s} \\ +\ 5.000 \text{ s} \\ \hline 66\ 483 \text{ s} \end{array}$$

● Write the decimal point.

$$\begin{array}{r} {}^{1}\ \ {}^{1} \\ 32.017 \text{ s} \\ 29.466 \text{ s} \\ +\ 5.000 \text{ s} \\ \hline 66.483 \text{ s} \end{array}$$

Jordan's total time for the two runs, including the penalty, is 66.483 seconds.

The addition properties for whole numbers also apply to decimals.

Zero Property   4.9 + 0 = 4.9
The sum of zero and one other addend is the other addend.

Order or Commutative Property   2.4 + 5.9 = 5.9 + 2.4
The sum stays the same when the order of addends is changed.

Grouping or Associative Property   3.6 + (1.7 + 8.3) = (3.6 + 1.7) + 8.3
The sum stays the same when the grouping of addends is changed.

Write the sum.

1. 9.04 + 3.217

2. $165.60 + $24.39

3. 7 cm + 2.5 cm

4. 27.68 + 12.004

5. 0 + 659.3

6. 45.3 + 108.7

7. 65.5 + 4.35 + 13.65

8. 9.75 kg + 4.5 kg + 12.025 kg

9. How can the associative property of addition help you add in exercise 7?

Match the exercise with an equal sum.

10. (32.49 + 7.25) + 14.75

a. 42.03 + 909.5

11. 12.338 + 71.68

b. 242.992

12. 909.5 + 42.03

c. 32.49 + (7.25 + 14.75)

13. 0 + 242.922

d. 242.992 + 242.992

e. 71.68 + 12.338

Write the sum.

14.
$$\begin{array}{r} 38.66 \\ + 52.87 \\ \hline \end{array}$$

15.
$$\begin{array}{r} 423.02 \\ + 299.18 \\ \hline \end{array}$$

16.
$$\begin{array}{r} \$219.98 \\ + \quad 47.20 \\ \hline \end{array}$$

17.
$$\begin{array}{r} 67.009 \\ + 40.992 \\ \hline \end{array}$$

18.
$$\begin{array}{r} 189.2 \\ + \quad 0.0 \\ \hline \end{array}$$

19. 12.866 + 91.4 + 78.723

20. 146.02 cm + 205.89 cm

21. $219 + $420.79

22. 347.21 + 0.098 + 927.3

23. 23.679 + 0.07 + 912.6 + 634.222

24. $16.99 + $142.25 + $189 + $34.59

Problem Solving

25. The official weight for a basketball is from 21.16 ounces to 22.93 ounces. Should the combined weight of 4 basketballs be less than 80 ounces?

26. If popcorn costs $2.75 and lemonade costs $0.95, how much will Paul pay for 2 lemonades and 1 popcorn?

27. If 3 baseballs weigh about 1 pound, about how many baseballs would it take to equal your weight?

SUBTRACTING DECIMALS

The chart shows the record speeds for different modes of transport. Comparing these speeds to something familiar, such as riding in a car at 55 miles per hour (mph), might help you to understand them better.

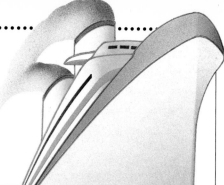

Form of Transportation	Year	Record Speed	Record Holder
Rocket-powered ice sled	1945	247.93 mph	Sammy Miller
Steamship	1952	40.98 mph	The *United States*
Bicycle	1980	58.64 mph	Dave Gryll

How much slower did the steamship travel than a car traveling at 55 miles per hour?

Subtract: 55 mph − 40.98 mph

 Think

- What do you estimate the difference will be? Explain.

● Line up the numbers by place value.

$$55.00 \text{ mph} \quad (55 = 55.00)$$
$$-\ 40.98 \text{ mph}$$

● Subtract.

$$\begin{array}{r} \overset{9}{5}\ \overset{4\ \ \cancel{10}\ 10}{\cancel{5}\ .\ \cancel{0}\ \cancel{0}} \text{ mph} \\ -\ 4\ 0\ .\ 9\ 8 \text{ mph} \\ \hline 1\ 4\ \ \ \ 0\ 2 \text{ mph} \end{array}$$

● Write the decimal point.

$$\begin{array}{r} \overset{9}{5}\ \overset{4\ \ \cancel{10}\ 10}{\cancel{5}\ .\ \cancel{0}\ \cancel{0}} \text{ mph} \\ -\ 4\ 0\ .\ 9\ 8 \text{ mph} \\ \hline 1\ 4\ .\ 0\ 2 \text{ mph} \end{array}$$

Is this reasonable?

The steamship traveled 14.02 mph slower than the car.

Other Examples

$(6 = 6.000)$

$$\begin{array}{r} \overset{9\ \ 9}{5}\ \overset{\cancel{10}\ \cancel{10}\ 10}{\cancel{6}\ .\ \cancel{0}\ \cancel{0}\ \cancel{0}} \\ -\ 2\ .\ 4\ 6\ 3 \\ \hline 3\ .\ 5\ 3\ 7 \end{array}$$

$(0.2 = 0.200)$

$$\begin{array}{r} 4\ .\ 6\ 6\ 1 \\ -\ 0\ .\ 2\ 0\ 0 \\ \hline 4\ .\ 4\ 6\ 1 \end{array}$$

$$\begin{array}{r} \overset{9}{1}\ \overset{\cancel{10}\ 13}{\cancel{0}}\ \overset{8\ \ 12}{\cancel{9}\ \cancel{2}} \\ \$\ 2\ \cancel{0}\ \cancel{3}\ .\ \cancel{9}\ \cancel{2} \\ -\ \ \ \ \ \ 7\ .\ 4\ 4 \\ \hline \$\ 1\ 9\ 6\ .\ 4\ 8 \end{array}$$

$$\begin{array}{r} \overset{12}{5}\ \overset{\cancel{13}\ 13}{\cancel{6}\ .\ \cancel{3}\ \cancel{3}} \text{ m} \\ -\ 4\ .\ 6\ 8 \text{ m} \\ \hline 1\ .\ 6\ 5 \text{ m} \end{array}$$

Write the difference.

1. 39.26
− 15.40

2. 42.00 g
− 38.77 g

3. 116.825
− 64.006

4. $87.25
− 9.99

5. $50 − $14.67

6. 792.1 − 6.87

7. Why is it important to line up the numbers by place value before computing?

INDEPENDENT PRACTICE

Write the difference.

8. 68.86
− 18.83

9. $129.43
− 65.31

10. 5.214 kg
− 0.062 kg

11. 100.100
− 33.654

12. 73.01 − 71.984

13. $225 − $29.69

14. 425.3 − 64.771

15. 62.36 − 15.09

16. 62.36 − 47.27

17. 124.213 − 10.765

18. 203 − 98.91

19. 521.2 − 495.974

20. 3869.101 − 3573.92

Problem Solving Use the chart on page 32.

21. In 1988, Rick Mears won the Indy 500 car race, traveling at an average speed of 144.809 miles per hour. Is this closer to the speed of the ice sled or the bicycle?

22. Compare the record speed for a bicycle and for a steamship. They are close. Which was faster? How much faster?

CHALLENGE • Technology

What can you do so that the following digits in the calculator display will be replaced with zero, leaving the other digits unchanged?

1. 5   **2.** 2   **3.** 9

USING STRATEGIES

The Busby Mall Bicycle Race is next Saturday. The bikers will follow a route that goes around and between the buildings of the retangular mall. This year's route is shown in the plan below.

If you get stuck, remember....

Tips for Problem Solving

on pages 448–449

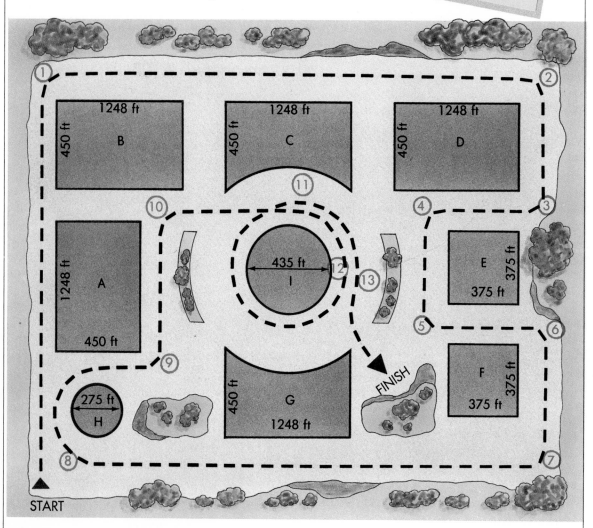

Buildings A and B are 100 feet apart. The numbers in circles show some of the turns in the race.

Work in pairs. Use estimation to help you.
Remember to show how you got your answer.

1. Estimate the distance the bikers will ride from Start to turn 1.

2. Will the bikers ride more than or less than 3000 feet from turn 1 to turn 2? Explain.

3. Is the racecourse more than a mile long? HINT: There are 5280 feet in one mile.

4. About how much farther is it from turn 2 to turn 7 than from Start to turn 1?

5. Is the distance the bikers will travel from turn 9 to turn 11 greater than or less than the distance from turn 2 to 4?

6. What might be a good way to estimate the distance from turn 7 to 8? HINT: Is it about the same as a distance you have already estimated?

7. Between turn 12 and 13, the bikers ride completely around building I. Is that distance greater than or less than 800 feet? How do you know?

8. About how long is the distance from turn 12 to 13 around building I? HINT: Use string or a piece of paper to compare the distance around building I to another distance on the plan.

9. Which turn is at the halfway point in the race— turn 2 or turn 6?

PROJECT • Problem Formulation

You may use tracing paper. Work in groups.

Copy the map of the Busby Mall. Use it to design your own route for the race. You can make your route longer than or shorter than the one shown. Use the size of the buildings to estimate the length of your race. Make up problems about your route.

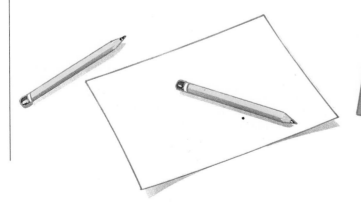

SUBTRACTION

$5.00 − $3.99

Notice that $3.99 is 1 cent less than $4.00.

You can subtract $4.00 from $5.00, which equals $1.00.

Since you subtracted 1 cent too much, add 1 cent back.

The change is $1.01.

Other Example

73 − 39

73 − 40 = 33

33 + 1 = 34

> **Notice that 39 is 1 less than 40, so compute with 40.**

> **Since you subtracted 1 too many, add 1 back.**

INDEPENDENT PRACTICE

Write the difference. Use mental math.

1. 80 cm − 39 cm   **2.** 400 mL − 99 mL   **3.** 500 m − 299 m   **4.** $5.00 − $2.99

5. $6.00 − $1.99   **6.** $3.00 − $0.99   **7.** 95 − 69   **8.** 73 − 49

9. 326 − 99   **10.** 683 − 199   **11.** 6000 − 3999   **12.** 4268 − 999

13. $8.67 − $1.99   **14.** $3.27 − $0.99   **15.** $10.00 − $3.99   **16.** $30.00 − $19.99

SECTION REVIEW

for pages 24–36

Write the letter of the correct answer.

1. The length of the Mississippi River is 2348 miles. The length of the Nile River is 4160 miles. How many miles longer is the Nile River?
   - **a.** 1822 miles
   - **b.** 6508 miles
   - **c.** 1812 miles
   - **d.** 2822 miles

2. The distance between Washington, D. C., and New Orleans is 1098 miles. Round this distance to the nearest hundred.
   - **a.** 2000 miles
   - **b.** 1100 miles
   - **c.** 1198 miles
   - **d.** 2100 miles

Write the letter of the correct answer.

3. 14.928 + 5.62 + 112.2
   - **a.** 132748
   - **b.** 16.612
   - **c.** 132.748
   - **d.** 82.348

4. 21.679 + 0.005 + 816.3 + 1.06
   - **a.** 839.044
   - **b.** 29.953
   - **c.** 114.409
   - **d.** 839,044

5. $175 + $25.62 + $1.98 + $14.99
   - **a.** $77.91
   - **b.** $217.59
   - **c.** $44.34
   - **d.** $21,759

6. 2.56 + 7 + 19.8 + 214.1
   - **a.** 243.46
   - **b.** 24,346
   - **c.** 136.81
   - **d.** 260.2

7. 36.1 − 4.829
   - **a.** 32
   - **b.** 4468
   - **c.** 32.929
   - **d.** 31.271

8. 629.2 − 6.02
   - **a.** 5690
   - **b.** 623.22
   - **c.** 623.18
   - **d.** 623.00

9. $627 − $16.29
   - **a.** $611.00
   - **b.** $610.71
   - **c.** $1002
   - **d.** $611.29

Write the answer.

10. 15 min 40 s
    + 3 min 15 s

11. 176,819
    − 9,009

12. $20,829.16
      500.16
    + 19.98

13. 135,625
    − 21,999

14. $19.98 + $16.75

15. 14 lb 19 oz − 6 lb 3 oz

16. 21,009 − 865

Round each number to the greatest place.

17. 452

18. 8.39

19. 72.8

20. $3704

Round each number to the nearest hundred.

21. 6170

22. 132

23. 2881

24. 695

CHAPTER REVIEW

Language Connection

Look at the word groups shown here. Explain why each set of words has been grouped together. Think of two other words to add to each group.

WORD GROUPS

hundredths • thousandths • decimals

mental math • front-end estimate • adjusted estimate

mph • speed • distance

Test •••••••

Write the expanded form of each number.

1. 3,000,467,001   **2.** 15,756

Write in short word form.

3. 600,204   **4.** 13,780,040

Write the standard form of each decimal.

5. eleven
thousandths

6. four and twelve
hundredths

Write in word form.

7. 5.075   **8.** 0.65

Order from greatest to least.

9. 8.517, 8.751, 7.158, 7.851   **10.** 306.1, 160, 306, 163.0

11. 46, 45.613, 44.2, 46.12   **12.** 4910, 4899, 4910.2, 4901

Write the answer.

13. 147.2
    − 138.34

14. $ 16.80
      104.96
    + 213.87

15. 916,423
    + 421,961

16.   18.6
    − 12.757

17. 157,061
    − 63,243

18. 176.112
      812.345
    +   1.761

19. 261,431
    − 176,421

20. 12,789
    + 1423

Round each number to the greatest place.

21. 551

22. $1.63

23. 6.37

24. 44

PROBLEM SOLVING

Solve each problem.

25. A plane carrying 86,000 pencils was waiting for take-off. Before it left, a crate containing 7850 pencils was put on the plane. How many pencils are being shipped altogether?

26. In 1990, the Preferred Pencil Company earned $897,975 from pencil sales. How much more money did the company need to earn to reach $900,000 in sales?

27. If hot dogs cost 84¢ each and 1 cup of fruit juice costs 49¢, how much will Matthew pay for 2 hot dogs and 1 cup of juice?

28. The actual attendance at a concert given by the rock group The Futures was 63,567. A newspaper reporter rounded the number to the nearest thousand. What number did she use?

EXCURSION
NUMERATION

THE MAYAN SYSTEM

The Maya were a group of people who lived in Central America about 1700 years ago. They developed their own language, calendar, and numeration system. They also had a numeral for zero. Over time, the Mayan culture has changed and no longer exists as it once did. However, many Mayan descendants still live in Mexico and Central America. Some of these people continue to spread the Mayan language and to practice some of the religious customs of their ancestors.

Some of the Mayan numbers:

Mayan Number	Our Number
⬯	0
•	1
▬	5

Numbers were written vertically.

So, ⬤⬤⬤ (three dots over two bars) would equal our number *13*.

• over ▬ = 6   ▬▬ = 10   •• over three bars = 17

Write the Mayan symbol for each number.

1. 3   **2.** 8   **3.** 9   **4.** 5

5. 2   **6.** 4   **7.** 19   **8.** 0

Write our number for each Mayan symbol.

9. ▬▬

10. ▬▬
    ▬▬

11.  • • •
    ▬▬
    ▬▬
    ▬▬

12.  •
    ▬▬
    ▬▬

13.  • •
    ▬▬
    ▬▬

14.  •
    ▬▬
    ▬▬
    ▬▬

15.  • • •
    ▬▬

16. ▬▬
    ▬▬
    ▬▬

17. Which number system would you rather use? Explain.

18. Copy and complete the chart. Use Mayan symbols.

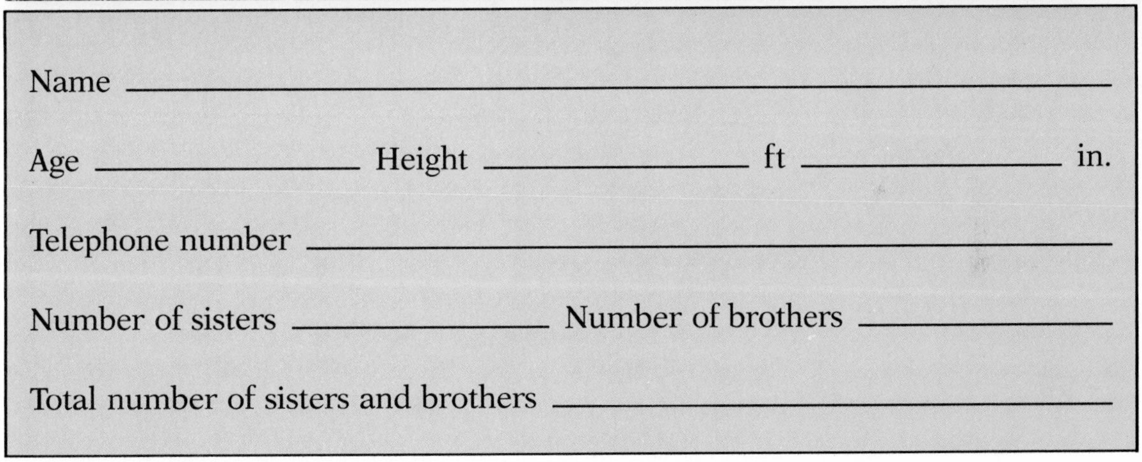

Name _____

Age _____ Height _____ ft _____ in.

Telephone number _____

Number of sisters _____ Number of brothers _____

Total number of sisters and brothers _____

19. Copy the chart in exercise 18 again. Fill in the information for a friend.

MATH LOG _____
What problems would you have if the number zero hadn't been invented?

MULTIPLICATION OF WHOLE NUMBERS

Science

Mathematics in Nature The wood lily is found in dry woods and thickets. It blooms during the summer months. As you can see, each flower has 6 clearly developed petals.

The number of flower parts can be used to classify flowers into two groups. One group has flower parts in multiples of 4 or 5. The other group has flower parts in multiples of 3. The wood lily belongs to the second group.

Classify the flowers shown on this page by counting the number of petals. You should come up with two separate groups. However, one flower may confuse you. It is actually about 100 tiny flowers in one. Which flower is it?

If you see a cut flower or a wildflower, look for petals in multiples of 3, 4, or 5. But when looking for wildflowers, watch out for a certain plant with shiny leaves in multiples of 3. It may spoil your fun.

EXPRESSIONS

The Big Shot Poster Company can use a snapshot to make a poster of just about any size. They always put a 2-inch white border at the top and bottom of the poster.

The border at the top and bottom of the poster makes the picture 4 inches shorter than the poster.

You can write a rule to show this relationship.

The height of the picture is equal to:

the poster height minus 4 inches

or

poster minus 4

or

$p - 4$

This short form, $p - 4$, is called an **expression.** The letter p stands for the height of the poster.

 Think

- Why do we use a letter instead of a number to stand for the height of the poster?

The expression $p - 4$ tells the picture height of a poster of any size. If the poster height (p) is 18 inches, then the picture height ($p - 4$) is $18 - 4$, or 14 inches.

If the poster height (p) is 30 inches, then the picture height ($p - 4$) is $30 - 4$, or 26 inches.

The chart shows the picture height for different poster sizes. You can use the same expression for any size poster.

Poster Height (p)	Picture Height ($p - 4$)
18	$18 - 4$, or 14
22	$22 - 4$, or 18
26	$26 - 4$, or 22
30	$30 - 4$, or 26
34	$34 - 4$, or 30

1. Mr. Chin has 26 students. To determine the number of students present he counts how many students are absent. If a stands for the number of absent students, which expression tells how many students are present?

   a. $a + 26$ b. $a - 26$ c. $26 - a$

2. All Hits Record Club adds a shipping charge of $4.00 to the cost of a record order. If c stands for the cost of the records, what expression tells the final price? Copy and complete the table at the right.

Cost of Records (c)	Final Price (■)
17	17 + 4, or ■
24	■, or ■
34.50	■, or ■

3. Could you have used some other letter to stand for the cost of records in exercise 2? Explain.

Write the value of each expression.

4. What is $q + 5$ if $q = 2$? If $q = 6$?

5. What is $20 - n$ if $n = 9$? If $n = 11$?

6. What is $w - 9$ if $w = 9$? If $w = 19$?

7. What is $t + \frac{1}{2}$ if $t = 6$? If $t = 12$?

Problem Solving

8. Big Shot customers receive a coupon that lets them buy any poster for $3.00 off the regular price. If r stands for the regular price, which expression tells the sales price?

   a. $r + 3$ b. $r - 3$ c. $3 - r$

9. The Big Shot Company is 15 years old. If y stands for the number of years from now, which expression tells how old Big Shot will be at that time?

   a. $15 + y$ b. $y - 15$ c. $15 - y$

10. Big Shot gives discount coupons. It prints one coupon for each customer on its mailing list plus 250 extra. If c stands for the number of mailing list customers, write an expression to tell how many coupons will be printed.

MULTIPLICATION EXPRESSIONS

The Big Shot Poster Company has a special product called Funny Fotos. It will make a snapshot three times longer than the original, but keep the width the same.

Instead of addition or subtraction, we will use multiplication in an expression to describe the Funny Fotos.

The height of a Funny Foto is equal to: three times the height of the original snapshot

or

3 × height of original

or

3 × h

a multiplication expression in which *h* stands for the height of the original snapshot

To avoid confusion with the letter *x*, multiplication can be shown by using a dot instead of ×.

3 • *h* means *3 times h*   3 • 8 means *3 times 8*   3 • *x* means *3 times x*

Big Shot decides to offer another type of Funny Foto where the width changes, but not the height. Funny Foto #2 is described in the chart at the right.

Funny Foto #2

	Width
Shapshot (*w*)	**Funny Foto (4 · *w*)**
3	4 · 3, or 12
6	4 · 6, or 24
$7\frac{1}{2}$	4 · $7\frac{1}{2}$, or 30

Think

• Will the Funny Foto #2 be tall and skinny or short and fat?

46

Write a multiplication expression to describe each situation.

1. Andrea earns 5¢ for every aluminum can she returns to the grocery store. If *c* stands for the number of cans she returns, how much will she earn?

2. CD's cost $10 each. If *n* stands for the number of CD's that Nick will buy, how much money will he spend for them?

3. In exercise 1, how much does Andrea earn if she returns 8 cans to the store? 12 cans?

4. Suppose exercise 1 had said that *x* stands for the number of cans. Would that have changed the answers you got for exercise 3? Explain.

Copy and complete each table.

5. To write feet as inches, multiply the number of feet (*f*) by 12.

6. To write weeks as days, multiply the number of weeks (*w*) by 7.

Feet (*f*)	Number of Inches (12 · *f*)
5	5 · 12, or ■
9	■, or ■
12	■, or ■

Weeks (*w*)	Number of Days (7 · *w*)
6	6 · 7, or ■
4	■, or ■
0	■, or ■

Problem Solving Write an expression to describe each situation.

7. One container of juice serves 8 children. If *j* stands for the number of containers that were used, how many children were served?

8. There are 16 ounces in one pound. If *p* stands for the number of pounds of meat needed for a recipe, how many ounces of meat are needed?

MULTIPLES AND LEAST COMMON MULTIPLE

Jesse is tiling the hallway in his restaurant. He plans to use 3-inch tiles, 4-inch tiles, and 6-inch tiles. He will lay each row with only one size tile. At what lengths will the tiles line up across all three rows?

You can solve the problem using a model like the one below.

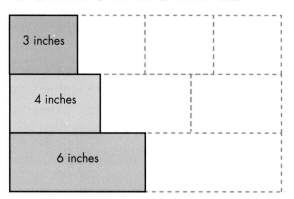

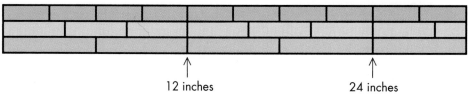

12 inches   24 inches

The tiles will line up at 12 inches and 24 inches, and so on.

You can also solve the problem using multiplication.

$1 \cdot 3 = 3$ $2 \cdot 3 = 6$ $3 \cdot 3 = 9$ $4 \cdot 3 = 12$ $5 \cdot 3 = 15$

Each product above is a **multiple** of 3.

The first five multiples of 4 and 6 are:

$1 \cdot 4 = 4$ $2 \cdot 4 = 8$ $3 \cdot 4 = 12$ $4 \cdot 4 = 16$ $5 \cdot 4 = 20$

$1 \cdot 6 = 6$ $2 \cdot 6 = 12$ $3 \cdot 6 = 18$ $4 \cdot 6 = 24$ $5 \cdot 6 = 30$

▶ The number 12 is a multiple of 3 and a multiple of 4 and 6. Therefore, 12 is a **common multiple** of 3, 4, and 6.

3: 3, 6, 9, **12**, 15, 18, 21, **24**, 27, 30, . . .
4: 4, 8, **12**, 16, 20, **24**, 28, . . .
6: 6, **12**, 18, **24**, 30, . . .

Looking at the common multiples of 3, 4, and 6, you know the tiles will line up at 12 inches and 24 inches.

▶ The smallest common multiple of a set of numbers is called the **least common multiple**.

Think

• What is the least common multiple of 3, 4, and 6?

GUIDED PRACTICE

Write two common multiples for each set of numbers.

1. 2, 5   **2.** 3, 7   **3.** 4, 5, 10   **4.** 4, 8, 16

5. What is the least common multiple for each of exercises 1–4?

INDEPENDENT PRACTICE

Write the first three common multiples.

6. 4, 9   **7.** 5, 8   **8.** 8, 20   **9.** 3, 15

10. 2, 3, 6   **11.** 3, 6, 12   **12.** 2, 5, 10   **13.** 10, 15, 30

Write the least common multiple.

14. 5, 6   **15.** 4, 9   **16.** 10, 14   **17.** 12, 30

18. 2, 4, 5   **19.** 5, 6, 10   **20.** 3, 4, 9   **21.** 2, 7, 28

Problem Solving You may use a calculator.

22. The dining room is 60 feet long. The 4-foot windows are set 4 feet apart. There are 6-foot rugs set along the wall below the windows. At what points will the edge of a window line up with the edge of a rug? HINT: Draw a sketch.

24. Jesse waters his marigolds every 4 days and his violets every 7 days. Not counting the first day, when is the first time both are watered on the same day? When is the next time?

25. Jesse needs to buy 48 candles, tablecloths, and sugar bowls. The candles come with 12 in a box, the tablecloths with 8, and the sugar bowls with 6 in a box. How many boxes of each must he buy?

23. Jesse stacks cans of beets next to cans of corn. The beet cans are 6 inches high and the corn cans are 9 inches high. The cans line up at the top of the stack, but nowhere else. What is the least number of cans of corn there can be in one stack?

MULTIPLES OF 10, 100, AND 1000

▶ Maiyani wants to make 20 bracelets.
Each bracelet has 30 beads. How many
beads will she need in all?

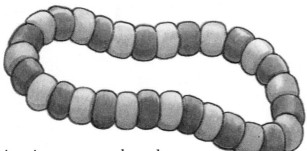

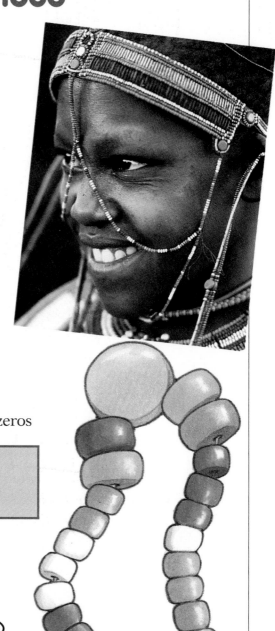

Maiyani uses mental math.

Multiply 30 by 20 mentally.

● First, multiply the nonzero digits.	● Then, put as many zeros at the end of the product as there are in both factors together.
$2 \times 3 = 6$	$20 \times 30 = 600$ ↑ ↑ ↑↑ 1 zero + 1 zero = 2 zeros

Think

≋ • How does the number of zeros differ in the
product of 20×30 and the sum of $20 + 30$?

▶ You can also use mental math to
multiply three factors.

> Look for factors like 2 and 5 that
> will make a multiple of 10.

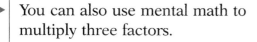

     10   20

$2 \times 9 \times 5 = 9 \times 10 = 90$ $4 \times 7 \times 5 = 7 \times 20 = 140$

Other Examples

$9 \times 100 \text{ yd} = 900 \text{ yd}$ $8 \times 1000 = 8000$

$20 \times 700 = 14,000$ $60 \times 50 = 3000$

GUIDED PRACTICE

Write the product. Use mental math.

1. 8×10

2. 7×100 m

3. 20×40

4. 30×600 kg

5. 8×50

6. 60 yd $\times 50$

7. $2 \times 7 \times 5$

8. $5 \times 8 \times 3$

9. $6 \times 2 \times 5$

10. In exercises 1–6, which products have more zeros than the total number of zeros in the two factors? Why is this so?

INDEPENDENT PRACTICE

Write the product. Use mental math.

11. 1000 yd $\times 3$

12. 8×600

13. 70×80

14. 30×900

15. 20×50

16. 50×40 m

17. $8 \times 2 \times 5$

18. $5 \times 7 \times 6$

19. $4 \times 9 \times 5$

Write the missing number. Use mental math.

20. $\blacksquare \cdot 5 = 50$

21. $20 \cdot \blacksquare = 1600$

22. $\blacksquare \cdot 40 = 16,000$

23. $1000 \cdot \blacksquare = 9000$

24. $60 \cdot \blacksquare = 1200$

25. $50 \cdot \blacksquare = 3000$

26. $\blacksquare \cdot 70 = 4200$

27. $800 \cdot \blacksquare = 5600$

28. $\blacksquare \cdot 90 = 36,000$

Problem Solving Use mental math.

29. Maiyani made one necklace every day for a week. Each necklace used 200 beads. How many beads did she use in all?

30. Maiyani has 2000 beads. Does she have enough beads to make 40 bracelets if each bracelet uses 60 beads?

MATH LOG
Many calculators cannot show the answer to $6000 \times 40,000,000$ because the product has too many digits. How would you compute this product?

ESTIMATING PRODUCTS

Jake, the zookeeper, gives the elephants a total of 78 bales of hay each day. Will 400 bales be enough to feed the elephants for 5 days?

Jake does not have paper and pencil with him to figure this out, so he estimates.

Estimate: 78 × 5

78 × 5
↓   ↓
80 × 5 = 400

> **Round to the nearest ten. Then multiply mentally.**

Since the elephants actually eat less than 80 bales of hay a day, 400 bales will be enough.

Think

- Will 650 bales of hay feed the elephants for 8 days? Explain.

Like Jake, you need to be able to estimate mentally. If you have trouble rounding mentally, you can use front-end estimation. This will not usually get you as close to the actual product as rounding, but it is easy to do mentally and does give you a rough estimate.

	Front-end	**Rounding**
Estimate: 32 × 26	32	32 30
	× 26	× 26 × 30
	Estimate: **30 × 20 = 600**	Estimate: 900

Other Examples

6 × 429   35 × 42   185 × 9

6 × 400 = 2400   40 × 40 = 1600   200 × 9 = 1800   or   185 × 10 = 1850

GUIDED PRACTICE

Write your estimate.

1. 23 × 7
2. 7 × 48
3. 445 × 3
4. 183 × 4

5. 34 × 32
6. 59 × 41
7. 27 × 65
8. 46 × 9

9. Is the actual product in exercise 1 greater than or less than 140? Explain.

INDEPENDENT PRACTICE

Write your estimate.

10. 4 × 43
11. 54 × 5
12. 66 × 7
13. 32 × 9

14. 6 × 238
15. 5 × 487
16. 178 × 9
17. 34 × 23

18. 32 × 49
19. 46 × 67
20. 25 × 16
21. 63 × 28

PROJECT • Technology

You will need a calculator. Work in pairs.

Products like 25 × 65 in which both factors end in 5 are special. Copy and complete the chart to discover a rule for making very close estimates of these products.

a. Estimate 35 × 45 in each of the four ways shown.
b. Use a calculator to find the exact product.
c. Circle the estimate that is closest to the exact product.
d. Repeat steps a–c for the last rows.
e. Which method gives the estimate closest to the exact product?
f. Does this method follow the normal rules for rounding? Explain.
g. Add the four estimates and divide your answer by 4. What do you find?

The Exact Product	Four Ways to Estimate			
	Round up ↑ ↑	Round down ↓ ↓	Round one up; one down ↓ ↑	↑ ↓
25 × 65 1625	30 × 70 2100	20 × 60 1200	20 × 70 1400	30 × 60 1800
35 × 45 1575				
55 × 75				
85 × 65				

LOGICAL REASONING

You can use the words *and, or,* and *not* to describe how numbers or objects are related.

Look at the set of figures below. Then read the statements that follow.

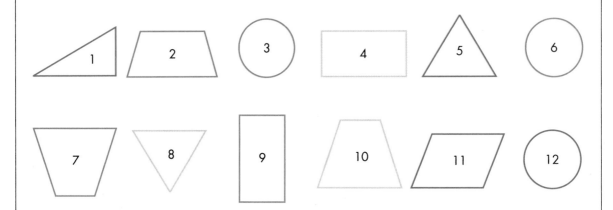

- Figures 3 and 6 are red *and* circles.

- Figures 4, 8, 9, and 10 are yellow *or* rectangles.

- Figure 11 is *not* a triangle.

Use the set of figures above to answer each question.

1. Which figures are triangles and green?

2. Which figures are not quadrilaterals?

3. Which figures are green or circles?

4. Which figures are green and not triangles?

5. Which quadrilaterals are:
   a. not red?
   b. not rectangles?

6. Which figures are:
   a. yellow or circles?
   b. yellow and circles?

7. Which figures are yellow or green but are not quadrilaterals?

8. Which pair of figures has the same shape and color?

9. Make up three questions about the set of figures. Use the words *and, or,* and *not* in your questions. Trade questions with a friend. Discuss your answers.

SECTION REVIEW

for pages 44–54

1. Daryl weighs each of his cats by holding it in his arms and standing on the bathroom scale. He weighs 96 pounds. If s stands for the number on the scale, which expression tells the weight of the cat?

   a. $s + 96$
   b. $96 - s$
   c. $s - 96$

Copy and complete the table.

2. To write hours as minutes, multiply the number of hours by 60.

hours (h)	number of minutes (60 · h)	hours (h)	number of minutes (60 · h)
2	2 × 60, or 120 min	10	■, or ■
3	■, or ■	1	■, or ■
7	■, or ■	9	■, or ■

Write the letter of the answer.

3. $4 + n$ when $n = 7$
   a. 28
   b. 8
   c. 11
   d. $4 + 7$

4. $17 - n$ when $n = 12$
   a. 5
   b. $17 - 12$
   c. 0
   d. 29

5. $5 \cdot n$ when $n = 3$
   a. 53
   b. $5 \cdot 3$
   c. 9
   d. 15

6. $9 \cdot n$ when $n = 7$
   a. 97
   b. 49
   c. 63
   d. $9 \cdot 7$

7. $7 \cdot n$ when $n = 8$
   a. 78
   b. 64
   c. $7 \cdot 8$
   d. 56

8. $5 \cdot n$ when $n = 1$
   a. 5
   b. 15
   c. 1
   d. $5 \cdot 1$

Write the letter of the least common multiple.

9. 8, 12
   a. 4
   b. 24
   c. 48
   d. 12

10. 12, 15
    a. 3
    b. 15
    c. 180
    d. 60

11. 4, 6, 8
    a. 2
    b. 48
    c. 8
    d. 24

MULTIPLYING BY 1-DIGIT NUMBERS

Jill's heartbeat goes up to 203 beats per minute while playing basketball. How many heartbeats will there be altogether if she plays for 5 minutes?

Multiply:
203 × 5

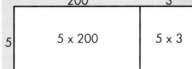

	200	3
5	5 x 200	5 x 3

Estimate:
200 × 5 = 1000

▶ Multiply by using the **distributive property** of multiplication.

$$203 \times 5 = (200 + 3) \times 5$$
$$= (200 \times 5) + (3 \times 5)$$
$$= 1000 + 15$$
$$= 1015$$

If Jill plays for 5 minutes her heart will beat 1015 times.

▶ You can also use these steps to multiply.

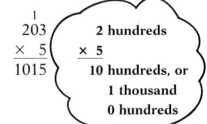

● Multiply the ones. Regroup?	● Multiply the tens. Add the tens. Regroup?	● Multiply the hundreds.

$$\begin{array}{r} 1 \\ 203 \\ \times 5 \\ \hline 5 \end{array} \qquad \begin{array}{r} 3 \\ \times 5 \\ \hline 15 \end{array}$$

$$\begin{array}{r} 1 \\ 203 \\ \times 5 \\ \hline 15 \end{array}$$

0 tens   0 tens
× 5   + 1 ten
0 tens   1 ten

$$\begin{array}{r} 1 \\ 203 \\ \times 5 \\ \hline 1015 \end{array}$$

2 hundreds
× 5
10 hundreds, or
1 thousand
0 hundreds

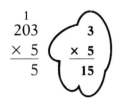

Think

• How could you use addition to check your product?

Other Examples

9 × 4 × 7 = (9 × 4) × 7
36 × 7
252

$$\begin{array}{r} 1\ 2 \\ \$4.23 \\ \times \quad 7 \\ \hline \$29.61 \end{array}$$

$$\begin{array}{r} 2 \\ 87 \text{ cm} \\ \times \ 4 \\ \hline 348 \text{ cm} \end{array}$$

GUIDED PRACTICE

Write the product.

1. 97	2. 22	3. 415	4. $1.02	5. 74 in.	6. 25 cm
× 5	× 5	× 5	× 4	× 6	× 7

7. Show how you can use the distributive property to write the product of 6 × 78.

INDEPENDENT PRACTICE

Write the product.

8. 112	9. 412	10. $1.51	11. $4.66	12. $1.21	13. 91
× 3	× 5	× 3	× 6	× 3	× 8

14. 400 m	15. 55	16. 39	17. 148	18. 225 ft	19. 736
× 4	× 2	× 7	× 9	× 4	× 8

20. 7 × 74   21. 5 × 416 km   22. 3 ft × 167   23. 6 × 75 cm

24. 200 yd × 6   25. 5 × 84   26. $3.56 × 3   27. 3 × 356

28. 7 · 2 · 4   29. 3 · 8 · 2   30. 4 · 5 · 6   31. 6 · 7 · 3

Complete.

32. 506 × 4 = (500 × ▨) + (▨ × 4)   33. 6 × 1250 = (6 × ▨) + (▨ × 50)

34. 8 × 72 = (8 × ▨) + (8 × ▨)   35. 407 × 9 = (400 × ▨) + (7 × ▨)

Problem Solving

36. An average adult human heart pumps 299 liters of blood per hour. How much blood does it pump in 7 hours?

37. Peter's pulse is 65 beats per minute when he is at rest. At that rate, how many times does it beat in 10 minutes?

38. On the average, a person's blood travels 269 kilometers per day through the different blood vessels. How far does it travel in a week?

39. Maurice collects 3 pledges of $75 each for the heart association fund drive. Judy collects $50 more than Maurice. How much does Judy collect?

MULTIPLYING BY 2-DIGIT NUMBERS

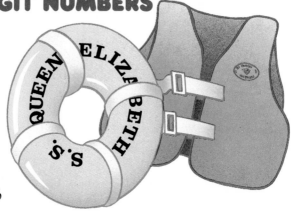

The *Queen Elizabeth* was the largest ocean liner ever built. It carried 26 lifeboats. Each lifeboat could hold 145 people. How many people could the lifeboats hold in all?

A quick estimate would be 30 × 100, or 3000.

To find the product, multiply: 145 × 26

● **Multiply the ones.**

$$\begin{array}{r} 145 \\ \times\ 26 \\ \hline 870 \end{array}$$

$$\begin{array}{r} \mathbf{145} \\ \times\ \ \mathbf{6} \\ \hline \mathbf{870} \end{array}$$

● **Multiply the tens.**

$$\begin{array}{r} 145 \\ \times\ 26 \\ \hline 870 \\ 2900 \end{array}$$

$$\begin{array}{r} \mathbf{145} \\ \times\ \mathbf{20} \\ \hline \mathbf{2900} \end{array}$$

● **Add.**

$$\begin{array}{r} 145 \\ \times\ 26 \\ \hline 870 \\ 2900 \\ \hline 3770 \end{array}$$

The lifeboats could hold 3770 people.

Think

● Would you choose to solve this problem by addition? Why or why not?

Other Examples

$$\begin{array}{r} 347 \\ \times\ \ 62 \\ \hline 694 \\ 20820 \\ \hline 21{,}514 \end{array}$$

$$\begin{array}{r} \$4.08 \\ \times\ \ \ 23 \\ \hline 1224 \\ 8160 \\ \hline \$93.84 \end{array}$$

$$\begin{array}{r} 14 \text{ in.} \\ \times\ 35 \\ \hline 70 \\ 420 \\ \hline 490 \text{ in.} \end{array}$$

$$\begin{array}{r} 140 \\ \times\ \ 67 \\ \hline 980 \\ 8400 \\ \hline 9380 \end{array}$$

$$\begin{array}{r} 87 \text{ cm} \\ \times\ \ 50 \\ \hline 4350 \text{ cm} \end{array}$$

GUIDED PRACTICE

Write the product.

1. $$\begin{array}{r} 324 \\ \times\ \ 20 \end{array}$$
2. $$\begin{array}{r} \$5.05 \\ \times\ \ \ \ 20 \end{array}$$
3. $$\begin{array}{r} 199 \text{ mm} \\ \times\ \ \ 99 \end{array}$$
4. $$\begin{array}{r} 44 \text{ ft} \\ \times\ 18 \end{array}$$
5. $$\begin{array}{r} 201 \\ \times\ \ 14 \end{array}$$
6. $$\begin{array}{r} 78 \\ \times\ 30 \end{array}$$

7. For which of these exercises could you have used mental math? Explain your method.

INDEPENDENT PRACTICE

Write the product.

8.	64	**9.**	75 km	**10.**	43	**11.**	34	**12.**	52	**13.**	93 mi
	× 32		× 40		× 65		× 22		× 14		× 60

14.	302	**15.**	$9.21	**16.**	645	**17.**	$5.34	**18.**	908	**19.**	231
	× 32		× 20		× 73		× 41		× 98		× 40

20. 13 × 84   **21.** 500 · 30   **22.** $3.61 × 44

23. 20 · 16   **24.** 17 m × 15   **25.** 692 · 36

Complete. Write >, <, or =.

26. 3 × 15 ● 4 × 10   **27.** 8 × 20 ● 4 × 40   **28.** 9 × 25 ● 8 × 30

Problem Solving

29. On one trip across the Atlantic, the *Queen Elizabeth* carried 2082 passengers and 1180 crew members. If each lifeboat held 145 people, were 26 lifeboats enough to carry everyone?

30. The ocean liner had a movie theater with 15 long rows and 10 short rows. Each long row had 20 seats, and each short row had 12 seats. How many seats in all were in the theater?

31. If the *Queen Elizabeth* traveled at an average of 625 miles per day, how many miles could the ocean liner travel in 3 weeks?

32. Write a word problem of your own. Make sure you need to multiply by a 2-digit number to solve it.

CHALLENGE • Estimation

Estimate. Write the factor from the box to complete each sentence.

29	66	58	47	24

1. 23 × ▦ = 1334   **2.** ▦ × 64 = 1856   **3.** 34 × ▦ = 2244

MAKE NOTES

You may remember that making notes can help you keep track of the information in a problem. I remember making notes to help figure out my pay.

MY PROBLEM

I work 20 hours a week at a bowling alley and get paid $5 per hour. One week, my boss asked me to work overtime. He said he would pay me an extra $2 an hour for every hour over 20 hours. I worked 28 hours that week. I wanted to know how much I had earned.

MY SOLUTION

I made notes so I wouldn't have to keep track of all the information in my head. First, I wrote down the different rates.

First 20 h:	$5 per hour
Over 20 h:	$7 per hour

Then, I wrote down how much I worked and what I wanted to find.

First 20 h:	$5 per hour
Over 20 h:	$7 per hour
Hours worked: 28	
Amount earned: ?	

My notes helped me think about the problem.

Regular time:	20 h × $5 per hour
Overtime:	8 h × $7 per hour

Can you figure out how much money I earned?

GUIDED PRACTICE

Solve the problem. Use one of the sets of notes to help you.

1. Sally is getting the supplies ready for the camping trip next month. She is bringing 3 packets of instant soup for each person. How many soup packets should Sally pack for the 7 adults and 31 children who are going?

A.
Name:	Sally
Job:	help get supplies

Event:	camping trip
Where:	Lucky Lake
When:	next month

B.
Soup:	3 packets per person
People:	7 adults
	31 children

•••••••••••••••••••

APPLICATION

Solve each problem. Making notes may help you.

2. A sign at the Silver Screen Movie Theater is made up of 15 rows of light bulbs. There are 8 bulbs in each row. In the third row 2 bulbs are burnt out, and in the fifth row 3 are burnt out. How many bulbs are working?

3. Danny's Superwash has an automatic washer that cleans 2 cars every minute. Danny notices there are 7 sports cars, 14 compact cars, and 11 station wagons lined up to be washed. How much time will it take to wash all the cars?

4. John babysits for $3 an hour during the day and evening. At 9 P.M. he begins charging an extra dollar each hour. How much will he charge to babysit from 6 P.M. to 11 P.M.?

5. Randy keeps track of the socks in the Sunville Sock Shop. On Monday morning, the shop has 60 full boxes of socks with 8 pairs in each box and 1 opened box with 5 pairs. The store sells 75 pairs of socks on Monday and the same number on Tuesday. When Randy checks on Wednesday morning, how many pairs of socks should there be?

MULTIPLYING BY 3-DIGIT NUMBERS

An adult whale shark can have as many as 311 rows of teeth. Each row can have as many as 115 tiny teeth. How many teeth is this in all?

To find the answer, multiply: 311 × 115

```
      115
   ×  311
      115   ←        1 × 115
     1150   ←       10 × 115
    34500   ←      300 × 115
   35,765
```

An adult whale shark can have as many as 35,765 teeth.

Think

- In the example above, why is it *300 times 115* instead of *3 times 115*?

One whale shark at the aquarium has 308 rows of teeth. Each row has 112 teeth. How many teeth is this in all?

To find the answer, multiply: 308 × 112

```
      112
   ×  308
      896   ←        8 × 112
        0   ←        0 × 112
    33600   ←      300 × 112
   34,496
```

> You do not need to record the zero.
> ```
>       112
>    ×  308
>       896   ←     8 × 112
>     33600   ←   300 × 112
>    34,496
> ```

This whale shark has 34,496 teeth.

Write the product.

1. 528 × 354   2. 920 × 94   3. 544 × 408   4. 218 m × 200   5. $5.06 × 221

6. How are the two problems at the right similar? How are they different?

$$\begin{array}{r} 321 \\ \times\ 146 \\ \hline 46{,}866 \end{array} \qquad \begin{array}{r} 321 \\ \times\ \ 46 \\ \hline 14{,}766 \end{array}$$

Write the product.

7. $\begin{array}{r} 298 \\ \times\ 224 \end{array}$
8. $\begin{array}{r} \$5.04 \\ \times\ \ 139 \end{array}$
9. $\begin{array}{r} 635 \\ \times\ 327 \end{array}$
10. $\begin{array}{r} \$4.36 \\ \times\ \ 341 \end{array}$
11. $\begin{array}{r} 411\ cm \\ \times\ 100 \end{array}$

12. $\begin{array}{r} 698 \\ \times\ \ 77 \end{array}$
13. $\begin{array}{r} 260 \\ \times\ 437 \end{array}$
14. $\begin{array}{r} \$1.09 \\ \times\ \ 363 \end{array}$
15. $\begin{array}{r} 447 \\ \times\ 971 \end{array}$
16. $\begin{array}{r} 607 \\ \times\ 841 \end{array}$

17. 589 × 314

18. 474 × 312

19. 274 × 828

Problem Solving

20. Tickets to the aquarium cost $3.25 per student. How much will it cost for the 123 fifth- and sixth-graders at the Park Street School to go?

21. A large blue whale can swallow 100 pounds of food at a time. If a whale swallows this much food 90 times during the day, how much does it eat in one day?

22. How much more do 10 imported goldfish cost than 10 domestic goldfish?

23. Which will cost more, 20 imported fish or 60 domestic fish?

Goldfish Prices	
Imported	$2.99 each
Domestic	$1.09 each

● **Mixed Practice**

Write the answer.

1. 145 − 76

2. 56 + 32

3. 32 + 56

4. 1225 − 606

5. 23,209 − 5976

6. 366,121 + 151,479

USING STRATEGIES

Ms. Spinner owns a record store. The graphs below show the number of records and tapes sold in her store in January, February, and March. Records sell for $7 each, and tapes sell for $6 each.

WHOLE-DOLLAR SOUNDS

OUR PRICES ARE EASY TO READ
BUT
HARD TO BEAT!

RECORDS									
Number sold	50	100	150	200	250	300	350	400	450
JAN									
FEB									
MAR									

TAPES									
Number sold	50	100	150	200	250	300	350	400	450
JAN									
FEB									
MAR									

Use the graphs to solve each exercise. Work in groups.
Remember, always show how you get your answer.

1. Did Ms. Spinner sell more records or more tapes in March?

2. Did Ms. Spinner receive more money from the sale of records or tapes in March?

Use the graphs on page 64 to solve exercises 3 and 4.

3. Did Ms. Spinner sell more records or tapes for the three-month period shown on the graphs?

4. Ms. Spinner buys the tapes and records from a warehouse. She pays $4 for a tape and $5 for a record. She then sells the tapes for $6 each and the records for $7 each.

   Selling Price − Cost = Profit
   $6 − $4 = ?
   $7 − $5 = ?

   a. How much profit does she make on each tape or record she sells?
   b. In January, were her profits from record and tape sales more than or less than $400?

5. Ms. Spinner's computer prints out charts that help her run her store. The computer printed out a row of ** instead of some numbers. Help Ms. Spinner by finding the missing numbers.

Item	Number Sold	Price	Total
poster	***	$5	$***
bag	***	$10	$***
total	100		$800

6. Ms. Spinner is getting new racks to hold the cassette tapes. She is ordering enough racks to cover a wall 10 feet wide and 8 feet tall. Will the racks hold her entire supply of 5000 tapes?

7. Ms. Spinner can spend up to $3000 on new record bins. Can she buy enough to hold her entire collection of almost 900 golden-oldie albums?

TIP TOP TAPE RACKS

Now you can have wall to wall tapes.

Each rack holds 480 tapes.

Only 4 feet high and only 2 feet wide. $399

RECORD BINS

Record Bins
Each Section
holds 40 records. $860

MULTIPLICATION

> I wonder how much 3 cans of tuna will cost. I didn't bring my calculator.

Tony doesn't need a calculator. It's easy to multiply by numbers that end in 9.

Multiply: 3 × $0.99

Notice that $0.99 is 1 cent less than $1.00.

3 × $1.00 = $3.00

But $3.00 is a little too much, since each can cost $0.99.

So, subtract 1 cent for *each* dollar.

$3.00 − $0.03 = $2.97

Three cans of tuna cost $2.97.

Other Examples

Multiply: 6 × 99	Multiply: 4 × $1.99	Multiply: 3 × 49
6 × 100 = 600	4 × $2.00 = $8.00	3 × 50 = 150
600 − 6 = 594	$8.00 − $0.04 = $7.96	150 − 3 = 147
So, 6 × 99 = 594	So, 4 × $1.99 = $7.96	So, 3 × 49 = 147

INDEPENDENT PRACTICE

Write the product. Use mental math.

1. 2 × 99
2. 4 × 99
3. 7 × 99
4. 8 × 99
5. 4 × $0.99
6. 6 × $0.99
7. 2 × 199
8. 3 × $1.99
9. 5 × $1.99
10. 2 × $0.49
11. 4 × $0.49
12. 2 × 29
13. 3 × 19
14. 4 × 19
15. 3 × 29
16. 5 × $0.19

SECTION REVIEW

for pages 56–66

Write the letter of the correct answer.

1. There are 24 students in Mrs. Glynn's class. If each student brings in $2.50 for the heart fund, how much will the class contribute?
   a. $6
   b. $60
   c. $600

2. A common dolphin weighs about 130 kilograms. A blue-nosed dolphin weighs about 650 kilograms. A blue-nosed dolphin weighs about the same as:
   a. 3 common dolphins.
   b. 4 common dolphins.
   c. 5 common dolphins.

Find each product. Write the letter of the correct answer.

3. 217×4
   a. 8428
   b. 868
   c. 848
   d. 928

4. 75×4
   a. 300
   b. 2820
   c. 280
   d. 360

5. $\$7.29 \times 7$
   a. $84.63
   b. 49.43
   c. $51.03
   d. $4914.63

6. 203×8
   a. 1604
   b. 1624
   c. 2464
   d. 16,024

7. 354×12
   a. 4248
   b. 4148
   c. 4348
   d. 9648

8. $\$4.55 \times 23$
   a. $22.75
   b. $104.65
   c. $92.55
   d. $117.85

9. $227 \text{ g} \times 5$
   a. 3555 g
   b. 1005 g
   c. 101,035 g
   d. 1135 g

10. 936×45
    a. 42,120
    b. 8424
    c. 30,790
    d. 42,220

11. 128×373
    a. 47,744
    b. 14,124
    c. 1664
    d. 98,984

12. $\$5.28 \times 750$
    a. $396.00
    b. $3960.00
    c. $3950.00
    d. $3796.00

13. 893×100
    a. 8930
    b. 89,300
    c. 893,000
    d. 80,903

14. 307×222
    a. 67,044
    b. 8214
    c. 68,154
    d. 69,464

CHAPTER REVIEW

Language Connection

A translator changes words from one language into another. You translate all the time. You read and write math problems, which use the language of numbers and symbols. But you talk about the problems in the language of words. Look at the following expression.

3×2

Can you translate that idea into words? What would you say? Look at the expressions and number sentence in the picture. How would you translate those ideas into words?

$4 \cdot X$
$1 \cdot 7 \cdot 4$
$5 \cdot 9 > 40$

Test ● ● ● ● ● ●

Write the least common multiple.

1. 2, 3

2. 3, 7, 12

3. 25, 30

4. 3, 6, 9

Write the product.

5. 402
× 22

6. 68
× 9

7. $7.75
× 15

8. 97 m
× 16

9. 347
× 102

10. 561 × 4

11. 40 × 70

12. $8.50 × 6

13. 222 × 333

Write the value of each expression.

14. What is $a + 6$ if $a = 7$?

15. What is $26 - b$ if $b = 18$?

16. What is $c - 12$ if $c = 24$?

17. What is $d + \frac{1}{2}$ if $d = 8$?

18. What is $e - 7$ if $e = 11$?

19. What is $f + 16$ if $f = 9$?

Write an expression to describe each situation.

20. Classic Classics book club adds a shipping charge of $5 to the cost of a book order. If *b* stands for the cost of the books, what expression tells the final price?

21. Books cost $2 each at the used-book store. If *p* stands for the number of books that Sandy will buy, what expression tells how much money Sandy will spend?

PROBLEM SOLVING

Solve each problem.

22. Cooper Elementary School is renting a boat to go whale watching. The trip costs $9.75 per student. This year, there are 138 students going on the trip. What is the total cost?

23. A warehouse has many cartons of yo-yos stacked along one wall. Each carton contains 145 yo-yos. How many yo-yos are there in 50 cartons?

24. Jesse plants vegetables in three rows of equal length. He places his tomato plants 5 inches apart, his beets 3 inches apart, and his cucumbers 2 inches apart. At how many inches will all three vegetables line up?

25. Maria is getting the supplies ready for a hiking trip. She plans to bring 4 packets of trail mix for each person. How many packets should Maria bring for the 6 adults and 28 children who are going?

CUMULATIVE REVIEW

Write the number in standard form.

26. three and two tenths

27. six hundredths

28. five hundred twenty-seven thousandths

29. six and eighty-four thousandths

Round each number to the nearest hundred.

30. 9553   **31.** 2143   **32.** 8808   **33.** 4660   **34.** 5419

Round each decimal to the nearest whole number.

35. 7.35   **36.** 2.82   **37.** 9.407   **38.** 5.68   **39.** 3.59

EXCURSION

USING TECHNOLOGY

LEAST COMMON MULTIPLE

How would you find the least common multiple (LCM) of a set of numbers? The simplest way is to write out the multiples of each number in the set. Then you can look for the smallest number that appears in all the lists. But writing out all those multiples can take a long time.

The program below prints out lists of multiples for you. The steps are as follows:

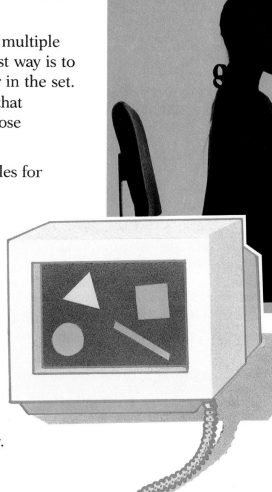

- You tell the computer how many numbers are in the set.

- You type in each number.

- You then tell the computer how many multiples you want it to list.

- The computer lists that many multiples of each number in the set for you. You can look at the lists to find the LCM.

Type the BASIC program into your computer.

```
10 REM LEAST COMMON MULTIPLE

20 PRINT "HOW MANY NUMBERS ARE IN THE SET";

30 INPUT N

35 PRINT

40 FOR X = 1 TO N

50 PRINT "WHAT IS NUMBER"; X;

60 INPUT A(X)

70 NEXT X

75 PRINT
```

```
80 PRINT "HOW MANY MULTIPLES DO YOU
WANT";
90 INPUT M
95 PRINT
100 FOR X = 1 TO N
110 PRINT A(X);" ";
120 FOR Y = 2 TO M
130 PRINT A(X) * Y;" ";
140 NEXT Y
145 PRINT:PRINT
150 NEXT X
999 END
```

Write the letter of the number of multiples you need to list
before you can find the common multiple of each set of
numbers. Use your computer program to help you.

1. 8, 12	**a.** 3	**b.** 6	**c.** 9
2. 7, 11	**a.** 3	**b.** 7	**c.** 11
3. 15, 21	**a.** 3	**b.** 7	**c.** 11
4. 2, 4, 5	**a.** 5	**b.** 10	**c.** 15
5. 6, 8, 9	**a.** 12	**b.** 15	**c.** 18

Write the LCM of each set of numbers. Use your computer
program to help you.

6. 9, 7   **7.** 9,15   **8.** 14, 18

9. 4, 6, 8   **10.** 14, 8, 7   **11.** 3, 10, 12

12. 12, 16, 18   **13.** 2, 4, 6, 8, 12   **14.** 18, 12, 16, 24

15. Would you want to use the computer program to
find the LCM of 5 and 25? Explain.

CHAPTER 3

DIVISION OF WHOLE NUMBERS

Operation Sense

Fun with Numbers Some card tricks and number tricks seem like magic. But many of these "tricks" are based on math, not magic.

When you work with numbers, sometimes you see a pattern. For example, when you multiply a number by 2, you double the number. If you divide a number by 2, your answer is one half of the number. Sometimes you can find an answer without using a pencil and paper. Solve the following riddle using mental math.

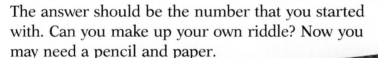

Think of a number.
Double it.
Add four.
Divide by two.
Add seven.
Multiply by eight.
Subtract twelve.
Divide by four.
Subtract fifteen.
Divide by two.
What is your answer?

The answer should be the number that you started with. Can you make up your own riddle? Now you may need a pencil and paper.

DIVISION EXPRESSIONS

▶ The Big Shot Company has a special offer. Their Funny Foto machine will take any snapshot and divide the height in half.

"Special offer! Half as much! Pay only one half the regular price. Get a Funny Foto just one half as tall as the regular size."

Think

• In the special offer, what number should the original height measure be divided by?

A division expression can be used to describe this "Half as Much" special.

The height of a Funny Foto is equal to:

the original snapshot height divided by 2

or

height of original ÷ 2

or

$h \div 2$

Another way to show division is with a fraction:

$h \div 2$ can be written $\frac{h}{2}$

If the original height (h) is 14 inches, the Funny Foto height $\left(\frac{h}{2}\right)$ is $\frac{14}{2}$, or 7 inches.

If the original height (h) is 24 inches, the Funny Foto height $\left(\frac{h}{2}\right)$ is $\frac{24}{2}$, or 12 inches.

▶ Another Funny Foto machine can take a 24-inch poster and reduce the height by any amount. You set the dial to tell the machine what number to divide by.

The letter d stands for the dial setting. The chart shows the Funny Foto height for different settings.

Dial setting (d)	Funny Foto height $\left(\frac{24}{d}\right)$
2	$\frac{24}{2}$, or 12
4	$\frac{24}{4}$, or 6
8	$\frac{24}{8}$, or 3
12	$\frac{24}{12}$, or 2

Write an expression to describe each situation.

1. A stereo is on sale for $360. The buyer can choose the number of equal payments. If *p* stands for the number of payments, what expression tells the amount of each payment?

2. To write the number of centimeters as meters, divide the number of centimeters by 100. If *l* stands for the length of a board in centimeters, what is the length in meters?

3. What would be the value of the expression in exercise 2 if *l* = 200? 500?

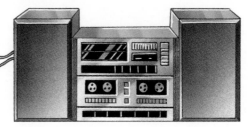

Write the value of the expression when *s* = 3; when *s* = 9.

4. $\dfrac{18}{s}$

5. $\dfrac{s}{3}$

6. $81 + s$

7. $\dfrac{81}{s}$

Copy and complete each chart.

8. To write the number of weeks as months, divide the number of weeks (*w*) by 4.

Weeks (*w*)	Number of Months $\left(\dfrac{w}{4}\right)$
16	$\dfrac{16}{4}$, or ▢
24	▢, or ▢
36	▢, or ▢

9. To write the number of feet as yards, divide the number of feet (*f*) by 3.

Feet (*f*)	Number of Yards $\left(\dfrac{f}{3}\right)$
6	$\dfrac{6}{3}$, or ▢
15	▢, or ▢
21	▢, or ▢

Problem Solving Write an expression to describe each situation.

10. The Big Shot Company offers a giant group poster for $120. If each person in the group pays an equal share, and *n* stands for the number of people, how much will each person pay?

11. The Big Shot employees work 40 hours a week. If *w* stands for the amount of money an employee earns weekly, how much money does an employee earn each hour?

QUOTIENTS WITH 1-DIGIT DIVISORS

The bicycle costs $258. You can divide this amount into 6 monthly payments. About how much will each payment be?

$258
6-month
payment plan

Estimate: $6\overline{)258}$

Choose a number close to 258 that you can mentally divide by 6. Thinking of the basic facts will help you.

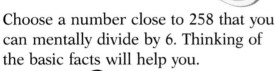

$6\overline{)258}$ $\dfrac{40}{6\overline{)240}}$

Compatible numbers are numbers that are easy to work with mentally.

The numbers 6 and 240 are **compatible numbers.**
Each monthly payment will be about $40.

Think

- What other compatible numbers can you use to estimate 258 ÷ 6?

There is usually more than one good estimate.

Estimate: $3\overline{)1684}$

$\dfrac{500}{3\overline{)1500}}$ $\dfrac{600}{3\overline{)1800}}$

To find compatible numbers, look for basic facts, like 15 ÷ 3 or 18 ÷ 3.

Both 500 and 600 are reasonable estimates.

Other Examples

Estimate: 675 ÷ 4

$400 ÷ 4 = 100$
$800 ÷ 4 = 200$

Estimate: 1763 ÷ 6

$1800 ÷ 6 = 300$

Estimate: $5\overline{)37,620}$

$\dfrac{7,000}{5\overline{)35,000}}$ $\dfrac{8,000}{5\overline{)40,000}}$

GUIDED PRACTICE

Write the compatible numbers you would use to estimate the quotient. Then write the estimate.

1. $3\overline{)137}$

2. $4\overline{)2295}$

3. $6\overline{)34,247}$

4. $236 \div 5$

5. $4736 \div 9$

6. $24,821 \div 3$

7. Explain why there can be more than one reasonable estimate for exercise 1.

INDEPENDENT PRACTICE

Choose the numbers that are compatible. Write *a, b,* or *c.*

8. $7\overline{)364}$ **a.** $7\overline{)360}$ **b.** $7\overline{)350}$ **c.** $7\overline{)300}$

9. $4381 \div 5$ **a.** $4500 \div 5$ **b.** $4400 \div 5$ **c.** $4380 \div 5$

10. $517 \div 9$ **a.** $500 \div 9$ **b.** $600 \div 9$ **c.** $540 \div 9$

11. $8\overline{)61,527}$ **a.** $8\overline{)60,000}$ **b.** $8\overline{)64,000}$ **c.** $8\overline{)62,000}$

Write your estimate.

12. $3\overline{)228}$

13. $4\overline{)936}$

14. $5\overline{)327}$

15. $6\overline{)2172}$

16. $7\overline{)3402}$

17. $2\overline{)1538}$

18. $8\overline{)43,044}$

19. $4\overline{)25,762}$

20. $232 \div 4$

21. $481 \div 3$

22. $927 \div 8$

23. $2668 \div 5$

24. $1756 \div 4$

25. $7512 \div 6$

26. $23,426 \div 7$

27. $39,501 \div 4$

Estimate the monthly payment.

28.

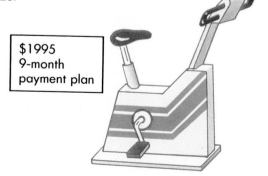

$1995
9-month
payment plan

29.

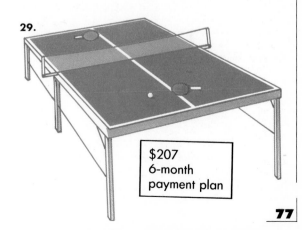

$207
6-month
payment plan

DIVIDING BY A 1-DIGIT DIVISOR

Six friends buy 229 stickers at a sidewalk sale. If they divide the stickers equally, how many will each friend get? How many stickers will be left?

Divide: 6)229

> **Estimate, using compatible numbers: 240 ÷ 6 = 40. This tells you the quotient will be in the tens. Write 2 dashes.**

$$6\overline{)2\ 2\ 9}$$

Find the tens digit. Start with your estimate.

$6 \times 40 = 240$.

Since $240 > 229$, the estimate is too high.

$6 \times 30 = 180$. This works!

The answer will be in the 30's. The tens digit is 3.

● Write the tens digit. Multiply. Subtract.

```
      3 _
6) 2 2 9
 - 1 8 0   ← 6 × 30
     4 9
```

● Write the ones digit. Multiply. Subtract. Is there a remainder?

```
      3 8  R1
6) 2 2 9
 - 1 8 0   ← 6 × 30
     4 9
   - 4 8   ← 6 × 8
       1
```

Each friend gets 38 stickers. One sticker is left.

Think

• How many more stickers do they need in order to share the extra stickers equally?

Other Examples

```
   12 R3
5)63
 - 50   ← 5 × 10
   13
 - 10   ← 5 × 2
    3
```

```
    78
4)312
 - 280   ← 4 × 70
    32
 - 32   ← 4 × 8
    0
```

GUIDED PRACTICE

Write the answer.

1. $4\overline{)39}$ **2.** $6\overline{)84}$ **3.** $3\overline{)84}$ **4.** $3\overline{)42}$

5. $75 \div 4$ **6.** $665 \div 7$ **7.** $319 \div 5$ **8.** $287 \div 7$

9. Could 7 friends divide 287 baseball cards equally? 288 baseball cards? Explain.

INDEPENDENT PRACTICE

Write the answer.

10. $5\overline{)49}$ **11.** $3\overline{)67}$ **12.** $4\overline{)56}$ **13.** $6\overline{)300}$ **14.** $3\overline{)83}$

15. $61 \div 2$ **16.** $88 \div 4$ **17.** $711 \div 9$ **18.** $206 \div 3$ **19.** $206 \div 6$

First estimate. Then compute only those answers less than 50.

20. $8\overline{)93}$ **21.** $4\overline{)372}$ **22.** $7\overline{)539}$ **23.** $2\overline{)114}$

24. $264 \div 6$ **25.** $86 \div 5$ **26.** $402 \div 6$ **27.** $555 \div 9$

Write the missing number.

28. $\blacksquare \div 4 = 10$ **29.** $36 \div \blacksquare = 6$ **30.** $72 \div \blacksquare = 8$ **31.** $72 \div \blacksquare = 9$

32. $88 \div \blacksquare = 8$ **33.** $32 \div \blacksquare = 4$ **34.** $\blacksquare \div 9 = 6$ **35.** $\blacksquare \div 11 = 8$

Problem Solving Use the drawing below. You may use a calculator.

36. Molly wants to cover this floor using only whole tiles of the same size.
  a. Which tile can she use?
  b. Which way should the tile be placed?
  c. How many tiles are needed?
  d. Can Molly buy that exact number if the tiles come in boxes of 8? Explain.

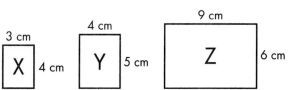

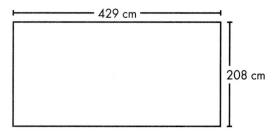

ZEROS IN THE QUOTIENT

Kurt is flying round trip from London to Berlin.
How many miles will his flight be each way?

	Berlin	Bombay	Buenos Aires	Cairo	Caracas	Chicago	London
Round Trip Distance (miles)							
Berlin							
Bombay	7810						
Buenos Aires	14,790	18,536					
Cairo	3590	5408	14,672				
Caracas	10,476	5616	6330	12,672			
Chicago	8798	16,088	11,192	3880	5000		
London	1160	8988	13,914	4386	9384	7946	

Divide: 2)1160

> **Estimate, using compatible numbers:**
> **1000 ÷ 2 = 500. This tells you the quotient**
> **will be in the hundreds. Write 3 dashes.**

$$2\overline{)1\ 1\ 6\ 0}$$ (with 3 dashes)

Find the hundreds digit. Start with your estimate.

2 × 500 = 1000; see if you can get closer.

2 × 600 = 1200; too high; use 500.

The hundreds digit is 5.

- Write the hundreds digit. Multiply. Subtract.

$$
\begin{array}{r}
5\ \_\ \_ \\
2\overline{)1\ 1\ 6\ 0} \\
-1\ 0\ 0\ 0 \quad \leftarrow 2 \times 500 \\
\hline
1\ 6\ 0
\end{array}
$$

- Write the tens digit. Multiply. Subtract.

$$
\begin{array}{r}
5\ 8\ \_ \\
2\overline{)1\ 1\ 6\ 0} \\
-1\ 0\ 0\ 0 \quad \leftarrow 2 \times 500 \\
\hline
1\ 6\ 0 \\
-1\ 6\ 0 \quad \leftarrow 2 \times 80 \\
\hline
0
\end{array}
$$

- Write the ones digit. Multiply. Subtract. Is there a remainder?

$$
\begin{array}{r}
5\ 8\ 0 \\
2\overline{)1\ 1\ 6\ 0} \\
-1\ 0\ 0\ 0 \\
\hline
1\ 6\ 0 \\
-1\ 6\ 0 \\
\hline
0
\end{array}
$$

> **There are no ones. Write a zero in the quotient.**

Think

- Why must you put zero in the quotient?

Kurt's flight will be 580 miles each way.

Write the answer.

1. $3\overline{)92}$ 2. $4\overline{)805}$ 3. $6\overline{)24,042}$ 4. $832 \div 4$

5. $7045 \div 5$ 6. $31,430 \div 7$ 7. $\dfrac{287}{7}$ 8. $\dfrac{912}{3}$

9. Why is there a zero in the quotient of exercise 4?

INDEPENDENT PRACTICE

Write the answer.

10. $2\overline{)61}$ 11. $4\overline{)323}$ 12. $3\overline{)906}$ 13. $6\overline{)5430}$

14. $4\overline{)8032}$ 15. $8\overline{)3256}$ 16. $5\overline{)35,005}$ 17. $9\overline{)86,418}$

18. $215 \div 7$ 19. $2036 \div 4$ 20. $7920 \div 9$ 21. $6328 \div 9$

22. $\dfrac{83}{4}$ 23. $\dfrac{781}{6}$ 24. $\dfrac{912}{3}$ 25. $\dfrac{300}{2}$

Problem Solving Use the chart on page 80.

26. The airline will give you a free flight if you travel 20,000 miles. How many round trips between Chicago and Caracas would it take to earn a free flight?

27. Marta is flying from Caracas to Bombay. The pilot announces they are halfway there. About how many miles have they flown?

28. Which trip is shorter, from London to Chicago to Buenos Aires, or from Berlin to Bombay to Buenos Aires? Can you tell without computing? Explain.

29. Plan a trip of your own that begins and ends in Chicago and stops in two other cities. What is the total number of miles you will fly?

CHALLENGE • Number Sense

If today is Wednesday, what day of the week will it be 75 days from now? Explain how you got your answer.

PROBLEM SOLVING
USING STRATEGIES

Solve each problem.

1. Jeff has a board 38 inches long. He cuts an inch off each end. He then cuts the board into 4 pieces of equal length. How long is each piece?

2. Jeff's desk is 38 inches tall. It has a top that is 2 inches thick, and it has 4 legs. How long is each leg?

3. Which package of tapes is the better deal? Why?

4. Which bicycle is the better deal? Why?

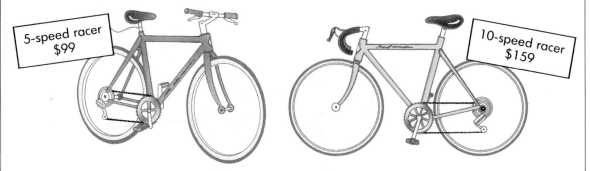

5. Pam's group is in charge of the ticket booth at the school fair from 11:15 A.M. to 1:15 P.M. One person at a time sells tickets. They agree to take equal turns.
   a. There are 3 people in Pam's group. How long will each turn be?
   b. Another student joins Pam's group before they start selling tickets. How much shorter will Pam's turn be?

6. A rectangular garden is 40 feet wide and 120 feet long. The garden is divided into 4 equal rectangular sections. What could the length and width of each section be?

7. In exercise 6, what other lengths and widths could you have and still have 4 equal sections? Write as many combinations as you can.

SECTION REVIEW

for pages 74–82

1. To write the number of weeks, divide the number of days (d) by 7. Copy and complete the chart at the right.

Days (d)	Number of Weeks ($\frac{d}{7}$)
21	$\frac{21}{7}$, or ■
28	■, or ■
42	■, or ■

Write the answer.

2. $24 \div 3$

3. $812 \div 4$

4. $410 \div 6$

5. $702 \div 9$

6. $60 \div 10$

7. $1903 \div 3$

8. $310 \div 2$

9. $64 \div 4$

Write the letter of the correct answer.

10. $365 \div 3$
    a. 121 R2
    b. 12 R12
    c. 121
    d. 1212

11. $729 \div 4$
    a. 182
    b. 18 R21
    c. 182 R1
    d. 1821

12. $943 \div 5$
    a. 1883
    b. 188
    c. 18 R83
    d. 188 R3

13. $7\overline{)713}$
    a. 101
    b. 101 R6
    c. 10 R16
    d. 1016

14. $3\overline{)9054}$
    a. 318
    b. 3018
    c. 3180
    d. 3108

15. $6\overline{)12,044}$
    a. 27 R2
    b. 207 R2
    c. 2700 R2
    d. 2007 R2

16. $\frac{2004}{4}$
    a. 501
    b. 5001
    c. 51
    d. 510

17. $\frac{9045}{9}$
    a. 105
    b. 1050
    c. 1005
    d. 15

18. $\frac{20,015}{5}$
    a. 4300
    b. 4003
    c. 403
    d. 43

Solve each problem.

19. Can 5 friends divide 162 colored beads equally?

20. If 3 friends divide 162 colored beads equally, how many will each one get?

USING THE REMAINDER

▶ Division problems often have remainders. How you use the quotient and remainder depends on the problem.

Timely Transit is reopening its Boondock branch. To celebrate, they are giving a banquet for 89 people. If each table seats 12 people, how many tables are needed?

The remainder 5 means that 5 people will not get a seat if 7 tables are used. So, 8 tables are needed.

$$\begin{array}{r} 7 \text{ R5} \\ 12\overline{)8\ 9} \\ -8\ 4 \\ \hline 5 \end{array}$$

Think

- If only 7 tables were used, how many people would get a seat?

▶ Sometimes it is necessary to use fractions and mixed numbers in your answer.

The kitchen has prepared 20 pounds of potato salad to be divided equally among the 8 tables. How many pounds will be served to each table?

The 2 in the answer tells us that each table gets 2 pounds. The remaining 4 pounds are also divided equally among the 8 tables.

$$\begin{array}{r} 2 \text{ R4} \\ 8\overline{)20} \\ -16 \\ \hline 4 \end{array}$$

Each table gets an additional $\frac{1}{2}$ pound of potato salad.

So, each table gets a total of $2\frac{1}{2}$ pounds.

$$\begin{array}{r} 2 \text{ R4} \\ 8\overline{)20} \\ -16 \\ \hline 4 \end{array} \longrightarrow 2\frac{4}{8} \longrightarrow 2\frac{1}{2}$$

Use the remainder as the *numerator* and the divisor as the *denominator*.

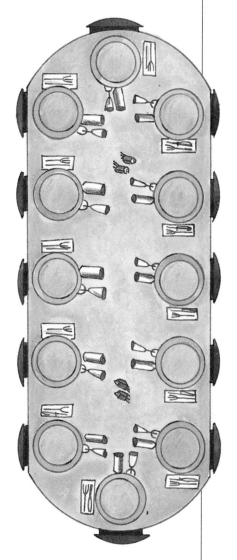

Write the answer to each exercise below.

Timely Transit is giving each of its 125 employees a clock. The clocks come in boxes of 8.

1. How many boxes of clocks must be ordered? How did the remainder help you decide?

2. After the clocks are given out, all but the last box are empty. How many clocks were used from the last box?

3. In exercise 2, is the number of clocks used from the last box more than or less than half of the box?

Problem Solving

4. Timely Transit sells souvenir train pins. The company raises $9 for each pin sold. If the goal is to raise $5000, how many pins must be sold?

5. Because the tracks need repairs, 52 employees take minivans to the work area. Each minivan seats 8 people. All but the last van are completely filled. What fraction of the last van is filled?

6. Timely Transit pays its workers $150 to clean each train car. If John cleans 14 train cars, how much money will he be paid?

7. Engineers work a total of 160 hours each month. They work both 7-hour shifts and 9-hour shifts. How many of each shift do they work?

Maintain • **Subtraction**

Write the difference.

1.	2.	3.	4.	5.
12.94	$45.97	13.26	384.97 cm	117.52
− 9.04	− $12.24	− 11.21	− 124.67 cm	− 109.23

DIVIDING BY MULTIPLES OF TEN

One North Sea oil well can produce about 2400 gallons of oil per hour. How many gallons of oil can it produce per minute?

Think

≋ • Will the number of gallons of oil that the well produces per minute be greater than or less than 2400?

Divide: 2400 ÷ 60

This problem can be done mentally.

2400 ÷ 60 = ■ asks the same question as 60 × ■ = 2400.

> **Remember the rule for multiplying mentally:**
>
> **First, multiply the non-zero digits. Then, place as many zeros at the end of the product as there are in both factors together.**

This rule can help you find the missing factor.

$$60 \times \blacksquare = 2400$$
$$60 \times 40 = 2400$$
$$\uparrow \qquad \uparrow \qquad \uparrow\uparrow$$

1 zero + 1 zero = 2 zeros

Since 60 × 40 = 2400, then 2400 ÷ 60 = 40.

The oil well can produce 40 gallons per minute.

Other Examples

350 ÷ 7	80)4000	60)42,000
7 × ■ = 350	80 × ■ = 4000	60 × ■ = 42,000
7 × 50 = 350	80 × 50 = 4000	60 × 700 = 42,000
	50	700
350 ÷ 7 = 50	80)4000	60)42,000

GUIDED PRACTICE

Write the quotient.

1. $20\overline{)80}$ **2.** $30\overline{)600}$ **3.** $40\overline{)1600}$ **4.** $6\overline{)48,000}$

5. $450 \div 90$ **6.** $2400 \div 6$ **7.** $2400 \div 60$ **8.** $2000 \div 50$

9. Exercise 8 could be written as $50 \times \blacksquare = 2000$.
How do you decide the number of zeros in your answer?

INDEPENDENT PRACTICE

Choose the correct quotient. Write *a, b,* or *c.*

10. $40\overline{)280}$ **a.** 7   **b.** 70   **c.** 700

11. $8\overline{)3200}$ **a.** 4   **b.** 40   **c.** 400

12. $35,000 \div 70$ **a.** 5   **b.** 50   **c.** 500

13. $4000 \div 50$ **a.** 8   **b.** 80   **c.** 800

Write the quotient.

14. $20\overline{)60}$ **15.** $80\overline{)320}$ **16.** $40\overline{)800}$ **17.** $6\overline{)360}$

18. $7\overline{)1400}$ **19.** $60\overline{)4200}$ **20.** $30\overline{)9000}$ **21.** $40\overline{)8000}$

22. $210 \div 3$ **23.** $240 \div 60$ **24.** $3500 \div 7$ **25.** $1800 \div 20$

26. $2000 \div 4$ **27.** $1000 \div 20$ **28.** $14,000 \div 7$ **29.** $12,000 \div 30$

Write the missing number.

30. $40 \cdot \blacksquare = 800$ **31.** $\blacksquare \cdot 20 = 600$ **32.** $20 \cdot \blacksquare = 8000$

33. $\blacksquare \cdot 60 = 18,000$ **34.** $7 \cdot \blacksquare = 2800$ **35.** $\blacksquare \cdot 20 = 1000$

Problem Solving

36. One gold mine in the Soviet Union produces about 15,000 pounds of gold in 30 days. About how many pounds of gold does it produce per day?

37. A famous oil well was opened in the Middle East in 1956. The well took only 20 hours to produce 100,000 barrels of oil. How many barrels per hour is that?

QUOTIENTS WITH 2-DIGIT DIVISORS

Mr. Todd owns a horse ranch. He feeds the horses a total of 30 bales of hay each day. About how many days will 1325 bales of hay last?

Estimate: $30\overline{)1325}$

Replace 1325 with a number that is compatible with 30. Choose a number close to 1325 that you can mentally divide by 30.

$30\overline{)1325}$ $\overset{40}{30\overline{)1200}}$

The bales of hay will last about 40 days.

• What other compatible numbers can you use to estimate $30\overline{)1325}$?

To find compatible numbers, you can change one number or both numbers.

Change one number.

$43\overline{)2000}$ $60\overline{)2568}$

$\overset{50}{40\overline{)2000}}$ $\overset{40}{60\overline{)2400}}$

Change both numbers.

$29\overline{)957}$

$\overset{30}{30\overline{)900}}$

Other Examples

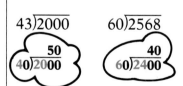

Estimate: $32\overline{)24,603}$

$\overset{800}{30\overline{)24,000}}$

Estimate: $1726 \div 61$

$1800 \div 60 = 30$

Estimate: $428 \div 19$

$400 \div 20 = 20$

GUIDED PRACTICE

Write the compatible numbers you would use to estimate the quotient. Then write the estimate.

1. $20\overline{)456}$ **2.** $54\overline{)1000}$ **3.** $43\overline{)1267}$ **4.** $18\overline{)435}$

5. $895 \div 30$ **6.** $1200 \div 29$ **7.** $350 \div 12$ **8.** $37,085 \div 72$

9. Find a reasonable estimate for exercise 7, using different compatible numbers.

INDEPENDENT PRACTICE

Choose the reasonable estimate. Write *a, b,* or *c.*

10. $4\overline{)2467}$ **a.** 6 **b.** 60 **c.** 600

11. $34\overline{)153}$ **a.** 5 **b.** 50 **c.** 500

12. $1286 \div 40$ **a.** 3 **b.** 30 **c.** 300

13. $\$3567 \div 52$ **a.** \$7 **b.** \$70 **c.** \$700

Write your estimate.

14. $6\overline{)351}$ **15.** $40\overline{)976}$ **16.** $33\overline{)465}$ **17.** $27\overline{)90,000}$

18. $544 \div 8$ **19.** $490 \div 76$ **20.** $173 \div 60$ **21.** $724 \div 22$

22. $2087 \div 70$ **23.** $2560 \div 52$ **24.** $1368 \div 31$ **25.** $28,955 \div 34$

Write your estimate of the cost.

26. one bale **27.** one bag **28.** one month

DIVIDING BY 2-DIGIT DIVISORS

Ezra owns an antique shop. At an auction, he buys a collection of 493 old wind-up toys. Ezra divides the toys into groups of 25 to sell. How many groups are there? How many toys are left over?

Divide: $25\overline{)493}$

> Estimate, using compatible numbers: 500 ÷ 25 = 20. This tells you the quotient will be in the tens. Write 2 dashes.

$$25\overline{)4\ 9\ 3}$$

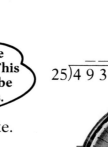

Find the tens digit. Start with your estimate.

25 × 20 = 500.
Since 500 > 493, the estimate 20 is too high.

25 × 10 = 250. This works!

The answer will be in the 10's. The tens digit is 1.

● **Write the tens digit. Multiply. Subtract.**

$$
\begin{array}{r}
1 \\
25\overline{)4\ 9\ 3} \\
-2\ 5\ 0 \quad \leftarrow 25 \times 10 \\
\hline
2\ 4\ 3
\end{array}
$$

● **Write the ones digit. Multiply. Subtract. Is there a remainder?**

$$
\begin{array}{r}
1\ 9\ \text{R}18 \\
25\overline{)4\ 9\ 3} \\
-2\ 5\ 0 \quad \leftarrow 25 \times 10 \\
\hline
2\ 4\ 3 \\
-2\ 2\ 5 \quad \leftarrow 25 \times 9 \\
\hline
1\ 8
\end{array}
$$

There are 19 groups of toys with 18 toys left over.

Think

• How many more toys would Ezra need to make 20 groups?

Other Examples

$$
\begin{array}{r}
2\ \text{R}6 \\
36\overline{)78} \\
-7\ 2 \quad \leftarrow 36 \times 2 \\
\hline
6
\end{array}
\qquad
\begin{array}{r}
5\ \text{R}10 \\
70\overline{)360} \\
-3\ 5\ 0 \quad \leftarrow 70 \times 5 \\
\hline
1\ 0
\end{array}
\qquad
\begin{array}{r}
4\ 1 \\
24\overline{)984} \\
-9\ 6\ 0 \quad \leftarrow 24 \times 40 \\
\hline
2\ 4 \\
-2\ 4 \quad \leftarrow 24 \times 1 \\
\hline
0
\end{array}
$$

GUIDED PRACTICE

Write the answer.

1. $29\overline{)72}$ 2. $40\overline{)340}$ 3. $77\overline{)301}$ 4. $14\overline{)756}$

5. $99 \div 26$ 6. $622 \div 68$ 7. $810 \div 45$ 8. $709 \div 79$

9. If a divisor is 2-digit, can you have a remainder that is 1-digit? 2-digit? 3-digit? Explain.

INDEPENDENT PRACTICE

Write the answer.

10. $24\overline{)81}$ 11. $17\overline{)86}$ 12. $33\overline{)67}$ 13. $13\overline{)62}$

14. $37\overline{)219}$ 15. $48\overline{)624}$ 16. $12\overline{)756}$ 17. $29\overline{)736}$

18. $86 \div 29$ 19. $76 \div 19$ 20. $98 \div 27$ 21. $378 \div 90$

22. $360 \div 40$ 23. $462 \div 9$ 24. $978 \div 69$ 25. $859 \div 14$

Problem Solving Use the catalog page below.

26. Mr. Chan has $300. He wants to buy president mugs. How many sets of mugs can he buy? How much money will he have left over?

27. Mrs. Chan buys two sets of baseball figures. She gives Ezra three $20 bills. How much money does she get back?

28. Mr. Elliot pays for 3 souvenir watches with $200. Is the money he receives as change enough to buy a set of baseball figures?

29. Ezra will lower the price of each souvenir watch by $4 if you buy 5 or more watches. How many watches can you buy for $300?

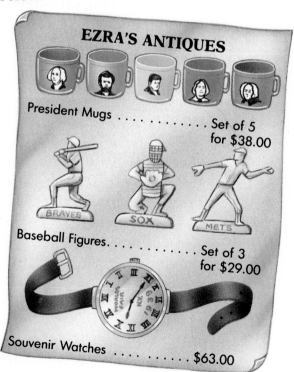

EZRA'S ANTIQUES

President Mugs . . . . Set of 5 for $38.00

Baseball Figures . . . . Set of 3 for $29.00

Souvenir Watches $63.00

DIVIDING GREATER NUMBERS

How many one-pound ingots can be made from 3587 ounces of gold? To solve this problem, use equivalent measures.

Think

- Is the number of pounds in 3587 ounces less than or greater than 3587? Explain.

Sometimes you need to divide to find equivalent measures.

$3587 \div 16$

> 16 oz and 1 lb are equivalent measures. Divide the number of ounces by 16.

Divide: $16\overline{)3587}$

> Estimate, using compatible numbers: $3000 \div 15 = 200$. This tells you the quotient will be in the hundreds. Write 3 dashes.

$16\overline{)3\ 5\ 8\ 7}$

Find the hundreds digit. Start with your estimate.

$16 \times 200 = 3200$; see if you can get closer.

$16 \times 300 = 4800$; too high; use 200.

The hundreds digit is 2.

● Write the hundreds digit. Multiply. Subtract.	● Write the tens digit. Multiply. Subtract.	● Write the ones digit. Multiply. Subtract. Is there a remainder?
$\begin{array}{r} 2\underline{\ \ \ } \\ 16\overline{)3\ 5\ 8\ 7} \\ -3\ 2\ 0\ 0 \\ \hline 3\ 8\ 7 \end{array}$ ← 16 × 200	$\begin{array}{r} 2\ 2 \\ 16\overline{)3\ 5\ 8\ 7} \\ -3\ 2\ 0\ 0 \\ \hline 3\ 8\ 7 \\ -3\ 2\ 0 \\ \hline 6\ 7 \end{array}$ ← 16 × 200 ← 16 × 20	$\begin{array}{r} 2\ 2\ 4\ \text{R3} \\ 16\overline{)3\ 5\ 8\ 7} \\ -3\ 2\ 0\ 0 \\ \hline 3\ 8\ 7 \\ -3\ 2\ 0 \\ \hline 6\ 7 \\ -6\ 4 \\ \hline 3 \end{array}$ ← 16 × 200 ← 16 × 20 ← 16 × 4

So, 224 one-pound ingots can be made from 3587 ounces of gold.

GUIDED PRACTICE

Write the answer.

1. $20\overline{)740}$
2. $51\overline{)863}$
3. $37\overline{)7591}$
4. $41\overline{)96,111}$
5. $1296 \div 36$
6. $2137 \div 52$
7. $2010 \div 25$
8. $26,663 \div 31$

Complete. Use the Table of Measures in the Data Book.

9. 272 oz = ■ lb
10. 2412 in. = ■ ft
11. 2000 min = ■ h ■ min
12. To find the missing measure at the right, would you multiply or divide? Explain.

■ oz = 5 lb

INDEPENDENT PRACTICE

Write the answer.

13. $40\overline{)690}$
14. $35\overline{)912}$
15. $86\overline{)3784}$
16. $72\overline{)6060}$

17. $30\overline{)8160}$
18. $22\overline{)6908}$
19. $17\overline{)7717}$
20. $54\overline{)8802}$

21. $599 \div 23$
22. $4083 \div 63$
23. $42\overline{)8456}$
24. $47,888 \div 29$

Write the equivalent measure. Use the Table of Measures in the Data Book.

25. Evan is 60 inches tall. How many feet is this?

26. A boat ride lasts 180 minutes. How many hours is this?

27. A football field is 100 yards long. How many feet is this?

28. A small dog weighs 288 ounces. How many pounds is this?

Problem Solving Use the Table of Measures in the Data Book.

29. Each gold coin contains 2 ounces of gold. How many pounds of gold are needed to make 4800 gold coins?

30. A miner has a bag with 2-ounce gold coins and 5-ounce gold coins. How can he give out exactly 1 pound of gold?

ORDER OF OPERATIONS

Some exercises have more than one operation. You may get different answers if you do the operations in different orders. So rules have been made for the order of the operations.

> **Order of Operations**
>
> • Do the operations in parentheses.
>
> • Then multiply or divide from left to right.
>
> • Then add or subtract from left to right.

▶ Example: $3 + 6 \times 7$

There are no parentheses.

First multiply. $3 + 6 \times 7$

Then add. $3 + 42 = 45$

▶ Example: $27 - 18 \div 3 \times 4$

There are no parentheses.

First, divide. $27 - 18 \div 3 \times 4$

Next, multiply. $27 - 6 \times 4$

Then, subtract. $27 - 24 = 3$

Think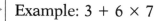

 • What answer could you get for $3 + 6 \times 7$ if you do not follow the order of operations?

• Why do you divide before you multiply in the example $27 - 18 \div 3 \times 4$?

▶ Example: $6 + 3 \times (9 - 3)$

First do the operation in parentheses. $6 + 3 \times (9 - 3)$

Next multiply. $6 + 3 \times 6$

Then add. $6 + 18 = 24$

Decide which operation you would do first. Write *add*, *subtract*, *multiply*, or *divide*.

1. $5 + 8 \times 2$
2. $5 - 8 \times 2$
3. $3 + 6 \div 2 \times 4$
4. $3 + 6 + 2 - 4$
5. $(5 + 8) \cdot 2$
6. $5 \cdot (8 - 2)$
7. $3 \times 6 \div (2 + 4)$
8. $3 \times (6 \div 2) + 4$

Write the answer.

9. $13 + 2 \times 3$
10. $4 + 6 \div 2$
11. $23 + 7 \times 6$
12. $60 \div (3 \times 5)$
13. $(42 - 3) \div 3$
14. $24 \div (6 \div 3)$

15. Do exercises 7 and 8 have the same answers? Write the answer to each.

Write the answer.

16. $14 - 7 + 8$
17. $5 \times 8 \div 4$
18. $31 + 9 + 3$
19. $20 + 3 \times 9 - 5$
20. $6 \div 3 + 9 \times 2$
21. $25 - 9 + 4 \times 3$
22. $5 + (8 - 2)$
23. $(13 + 2) \cdot 2$
24. $6 \times (5 \times 0)$
25. $(7 - 3) + 3 \times 4$
26. $7 + (3 + 3) \cdot 4$
27. $16 \div (4 \times 2) + 8$

28. Copy each number sentence. Then use parentheses to make the sentence true.

    a. $72 \div 2 \times 9 = 4$
    b. $5 \times 8 + 4 \div 2 = 30$
    c. $13 + 2 \times 2 - 6 = 24$

29. Write an exercise that has each following answer. Use at least two operations.

    a. 4
    b. 9
    c. 16

CHALLENGE • Operation Sense

Use the numbers 3, 4, 6, and 8 to make each sentence true.

1. $\blacksquare \times (\blacksquare - \blacksquare) + \blacksquare = 20$
2. $(\blacksquare - \blacksquare) \times (\blacksquare \times \blacksquare) = 120$
3. $(\blacksquare + \blacksquare) \times (\blacksquare \times \blacksquare) = 168$
4. $(\blacksquare \times \blacksquare) - (\blacksquare \times \blacksquare) = 14$

DIVISIBILITY

Suppose you divide a number by another number and the remainder is zero. Then the first number is **divisible** by the second number.

Divisibility rules can help you decide if one number is divisible by another number. The chart below shows the divisibility rules for 2, 3, 5, and 10.

In this lesson, you will discover number patterns. The patterns will help you write divisibility rules for the numbers 4, 6, and 9. You will need the recording sheet and a calculator.

A number is divisible by . . .	when . . .	Examples
2	The ones digit is an even number.	342 58 1364
3	The sum of the digits is divisible by 3.	621 2082 87
5	The ones digit is 5 or 0.	36,190 85 320
10	The ones digit is 0.	36,190 90 320

Chart A

Number	Divisible by 4?
424	yes
7,103	no
45,922	
104	
3,016	
226,934	
98,112	

Work in small groups. Complete Chart A on your recording sheet. Use a calculator.

1. Look at the numbers that are divisible by 4. Circle the number formed by the digits in the tens and ones places. What pattern do you notice? Example: 4⟨24⟩

2. Use the pattern to predict which of the following numbers will be divisible by 4. Write *yes* or *no*.
   a. 532   b. 4121
   c. 64,046   d. 739,496

3. Use a calculator to check your prediction.

Next you will look for a pattern in numbers that are divisible by the number 6.

Look at the first three entries on Chart B on your recording sheet to answer the following questions.

4. Which numbers are divisible by 2? By 3? By both 2 and 3? By 6?

5. What pattern do you notice for numbers divisible by the number 6?

6. Use the pattern to complete the chart.

7. Use a calculator to check your predictions.

Chart B

	Divisible by		
Number	2?	3?	6?
122	yes	no	no
234	yes	yes	yes
1,257	no	yes	no
71			
15,016			
28,458			
7,383			

To discover a pattern of divisibility for the number 9, complete Chart C on your recording sheet.

8. Look at the sums column. Circle the sums of the numbers that are divisible by 9. What pattern do you notice?
   Example: $1 + 0 + 8 = $ ⑨

9. Use the pattern to predict which of the following numbers will be divisible by 9. Write *yes* or *no*.
   a. 716   b. 207   c. 8244   d. 65,037

Chart C

Number	Sum of Digits	Divisible by 9?
108	$1 + 0 + 8 = 9$	yes
648	$6 + 4 + 8 = 18$	yes
249	$2 + 4 + 9 = 15$	no
53,784		
5,113		
99,873		
4,725		

SUMMING IT UP

10. Use the patterns you discovered to write divisibility rules for the numbers 4, 6, and 9.

11. Without using a calculator, write two numbers that are divisible by 4; by 6; and by 9. Explain why you chose them.

12. Discuss your divisibility rules for the numbers 4, 6, and 9 with the class.

GREATEST COMMON FACTOR

In this lesson, you will learn about factors and the greatest common factor. Work in pairs. You will need centimeter squared paper, scissors, and tape.

Using 12 square units, you can make 6 rectangles. As you can see below, the length and width of each rectangle is a whole number.

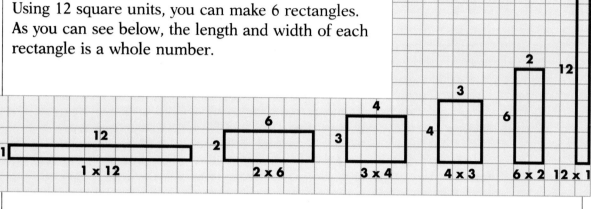

The whole numbers 1, 2, 3, 4, 6, and 12 are called the **factors** of 12.

1. Is 12 divisible by each of its factors? Explain.

Rectangles can be used to find the factor pairs of a number.

2. On squared paper, draw all the possible rectangles that have 15 square units. Use only whole numbers for the lengths and widths. Label the lengths and widths.

3. Cut out the rectangles, and tape them in order from shortest to tallest on a piece of paper.

4. Write the multiplication expression for each rectangle.

5. Write the factors of 15.

6. Use squared paper to decide whether 3 is a factor of either 11 or 21. Show your work on your paper.

7. Repeat the steps in exercise 2 for 18 square units. Cut out the rectangles.

8. Move the 1 × 18 rectangle so that it fits exactly on top of the 18 × 1 rectangle.

9. Find all the other rectangle pairs that will fit one on top of the other. Tape each pair onto your paper.

10. Write the two multiplication expressions that go with each pair.

11. Write the factors of 18.

12. How could your multiplication and division facts help you to find the factors of a number?

13. What factors are the same for 12, 15, and 18? These are called their **common factors.**

14. What is the largest number that is a factor of 12, 15, and 18? This is called the **greatest common factor** of 12, 15, and 18.

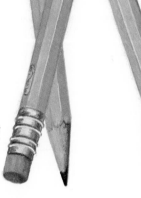

SUMMING IT UP

15. Determine if 4 is a factor of each number. Write *yes* or *no*.
    a. 32   **b.** 19   **c.** 26   **d.** 40

16. Is a number always divisible by its factors? Explain.

17. Write the factors of each number. Circle the common factors in each set.
    a. 8, 16   **b.** 12, 24   **c.** 6, 8, 18   **d.** 21, 24, 30

18. Write the greatest common factor for each set of numbers in exercise 17.

19. Discuss with your class how you can find all the factors of a number.

 • **Multiplication**

Write the product. Use mental math where you can.

1. 300 × 60   **2.** 90 × 800   **3.** 74 × 243   **4.** 594 × 361

PRIME AND COMPOSITE NUMBERS

In this lesson, you will learn about numbers that have more than two factors. You will also learn about numbers that have exactly two factors. Work in pairs. You will need the recording sheet, centimeter squared paper, a calculator, and green and yellow crayons.

Using 10 square units, you can make four different rectangles.

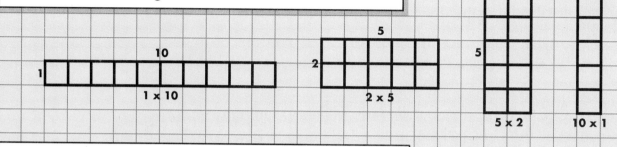

1. Which rectangles show the same factors?

2. Write the factors of the number 10.

A **composite** number has more than two factors. The number 10 is a composite number.

Using 11 square units, only two different rectangles can be made.

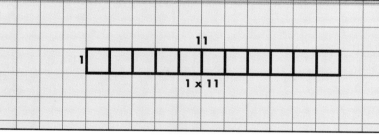

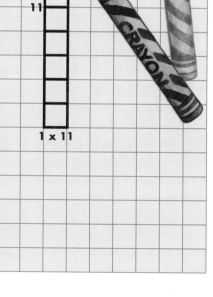

3. Write the factors of the number 11.

A **prime** number is a number greater than 1 that has exactly two factors, itself and 1. The number 11 is a prime number.

4. On your squared paper, draw all the rectangles for the number 2. Cut and tape them in section A of your recording sheet. Write the factors of the number 2.

5. Is the number 2 prime or composite?

6. On your squared paper, draw all the rectangles for the number 15. Cut and tape them in section B of your recording sheet. Write the factors of the number 15.

7. Is the number 15 prime or composite?

Use your squared paper to complete Chart A on your recording sheet.

Chart A

Number	Number of Rectangles	Factors	Prime or Composite
2	2	1, 2	prime
3	2	1, 3	prime
4	3	1, 2, 4	composite
5			
6			
7			
8			
9			
10			

SUMMING IT UP

8. How do you decide if a number is prime or composite?

9. Do you need to draw all the rectangles or write all the factors to decide if a number is prime or composite? Explain.

10. The number 263 is prime. How many numbers is it divisible by? Explain.

11. Use Chart B on your recording sheet. Identify the numbers from 11 to 50 as prime or composite. Color the prime number squares yellow and the composite number squares green. Use divisibility rules, a calculator, or any method you choose to find the factors.

Chart B

11	12	13	14	15	16	17	18	19	20
21	22	23	24	25	26	27	28	29	30
31	32	33	34	35	36	37	38	39	40
41	42	43	44	45	46	47	48	49	50

12. Look at charts A and B.
    a. Write all the even prime numbers from 2 to 50.
    b. Write all the odd composite numbers from 2 to 50.

13. Discuss your results with the class.

PRIME FACTORIZATION

A prime number is a number greater than 1 that has exactly two factors: itself and 1. The number 3 is a prime number.

1 x 3

factors : 1, 3

3 x 1

A composite number has more than two factors. The number 4 is a composite number.

1 x 4

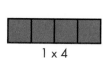

2 x 2

factors : 1, 2, 4

4 x 1

A composite number can be shown as the product of prime factors. This is called **prime factorization.** A factor tree helps you find the prime factorization of a number.

Find the prime factorization of 56. Start with 7 × 8.

```
     56
    / \
   7 × 8
```

7 is prime. Continue factoring 8.

```
     56
    / \
   7 × 8
      / / \
   7 × 2 × 4
```

2 is prime. Continue factoring 4.

```
     56
    / \
   7 × 8
      / / \
   7 × 2 × 4
     / / / \
  7 × 2 × 2 × 2
```

2 is prime. All the factors are prime. Stop.

The prime factorization of 56 is 7 × 2 × 2 × 2.

Here are other factor trees for 56:

```
      56
     / \
   4 × 14
  / \   / \
2 × 2 × 2 × 7
```

```
      56
     / \
   2 × 28
     / / \
   2 × 7 × 4
     / / / \
  2 × 7 × 2 × 2
```

 Think

- Do all the factor trees for 56 show the same prime factorization? Explain.

- How can a factor tree help you decide if a number is prime or composite?

GUIDED PRACTICE

Copy and complete each factor tree.

1.
$$18$$
$$2 \times 9$$
$$2 \times \blacksquare \times \blacksquare$$

2.
$$20$$
$$5 \times 4$$
$$\blacksquare \times \blacksquare \times \blacksquare$$

3.
$$36$$
$$4 \times \blacksquare$$
$$\blacksquare \times \blacksquare \times \blacksquare \times \blacksquare$$

Write the prime factorization. Use a factor tree.

4. 27   5. 40   6. 50   7. 48   8. 84

9. Lee began factoring 40 with 2×20. Alice began factoring 40 with 5×8. Will Lee and Alice get the same prime factorization? Explain.

INDEPENDENT PRACTICE

Write the letter of the prime factorization for each number.

10. 12   a. 4×3 b. $2 \times 2 \times 3 \times 3$ c. $2 \times 2 \times 3$

11. 42   a. $7 \times 2 \times 3$ b. $6 \times 7 \times 1$ c. $2 \times 2 \times 7$

12. 28   a. $7 \times 3 \times 2$ b. $2 \times 2 \times 7$ c. $2 \times 2 \times 7 \times 1$

13. 36   a. $2 \times 2 \times 2 \times 3$ b. $2 \times 2 \times 3 \times 3$ c. $2 \times 3 \times 3 \times 3$

14. 120   a. $2 \times 2 \times 5 \times 2 \times 3$ b. $4 \times 5 \times 2 \times 3$ c. $2 \times 2 \times 2 \times 2 \times 5$

Write *prime* or *composite* for each number. If the number is composite, give its prime factorization using a factor tree.

15. 16   16. 33   17. 54   18. 47   19. 64

20. 75   21. 19   22. 46   23. 53   24. 100

 MATH LOG

How does learning about factors help you understand divisibility?

CALCULATOR OR MENTAL MATH

A calculator is a useful tool for computing quickly. But do you always need it? Sometimes, using mental math to solve a problem is quicker than using a calculator.

Questions to consider.

• Can I quickly compute in my head?

• Will entering the problem into a calculator take too much time?

....

INDEPENDENT PRACTICE

Solve each problem. Write whether you used a calculator or mental math.

1. 20×3
2. $\$26.16 + \$39.29$
3. $60 \div 6$
4. $500 - 36$
5. $5 + 50 + 5 + 5 + 50$
6. 30×10
7. $0.17 + 2.58$
8. $200 - 99$
9. $702 \div 26$
10. $7000 - 5000$
11. $2 \times 7 \times 5$
12. $335 \times 62 \times 0 \times 8$
13. $32{,}458 + 54{,}397$
14. 36×47
15. 3×60.99
16. $74{,}005 + 20 + 10$

Problem Solving Use the Almanac section of your Data Book if you need to.

17. What is the difference between the seating capacity of Fenway Park and Wrigley Field?

18. Due to rain, the Cleveland Indians game scheduled for 7:00 didn't begin until 8:10. How long was the start of the game delayed?

19. If the Kansas City Royals Stadium had been filled to capacity at each of the home games in 1988, what would the total attendance have been?

20. Write two word problems.
   a. one mental math problem
   b. one calculator problem

SECTION REVIEW

for pages 84–104

1. The Littleton Soccer Team paid $119 for team shirts. There are 17 players. How much did each player pay?

Write the letter of the correct answer.

2. 2400 ÷ 40
   a. 600
   b. 40
   c. 60
   d. 591

3. 35)$1200
   a. 34 R10
   b. 340 R10
   c. 3400 R10
   d. 34

4. 1858 ÷ 18
   a. 13 R4
   b. 1003 R4
   c. 103
   d. 103 R4

Write the letter of the greatest common factor.

5. 12, 4
   a. 12
   b. 24
   c. 4
   d. 2

6. 14, 42
   a. 7
   b. 42
   c. 28
   d. 14

7. 15, 35
   a. 105
   b. 5
   c. 35
   d. 3

8. 12, 15, 18
   a. 6
   b. 3
   c. 18
   d. 45

Write the letter of the prime factorization.

9. 18
   a. 3 × 3 × 3
   b. 3 × 3 × 3 × 2
   c. 3 × 3 × 4
   d. 3 × 3 × 2

10. 30
    a. 2 × 3 × 5 × 2
    b. 2 × 2 × 5
    c. 2 × 3 × 5
    d. 2 × 15

11. 52
    a. 2 × 2 × 13
    b. 2 × 2 × 1 × 3
    c. 4 × 13
    d. 2 × 26

Solve the problem.

12. The Oak Hill School is planning a trip to the wildlife park. There will be 378 people going. Each bus can seat 45 people.
    a. How many buses are needed?
    b. How many empty seats will there be?
    c. If the same number of people go on each bus, how many people will be on each one?

CHAPTER REVIEW

Language Connection

When you give a definition of a word, you have to choose your words carefully. All of the vocabulary words shown here have something to do with division or dividing numbers. Think about how each word is related to division or dividing. Define each word, using *divide* in your definition.

VOCABULARY WORDS

compatible numbers   greatest common factor
common factors   composite number
prime number   prime factorization

Test ● ● ● ● ● ● ●

Write the value of each expression when $m = 9$.

1. $\frac{36}{m}$

2. $m + 92$

3. $\frac{72}{m}$

4. $\frac{m}{9}$

Write the greatest common factor for the set of numbers.

5. 10, 18

6. 3, 9

7. 12, 30

8. 18, 36, 54

Write the answer.

9. $3600 \div 6$

10. $5641 \div 9$

11. $79 \div 21$

12. $647 \div 41$

13. $550 \div 4$

14. $856 \div 6$

15. $8924 \div 16$

16. $190 \div 33$

17. $2\overline{)5639}$

18. $3\overline{)789}$

19. $72\overline{)777}$

20. $31\overline{)1896}$

Write the prime factorization for each number.

21. 18

22. 20

23. 37

24. 28

PROBLEM SOLVING

Solve each problem.

25. The Berman family is driving from Millers Falls to Lamesa, a distance of 1700 miles. They are halfway there. How many miles has the Berman family traveled?

26. Ellen and her 3 friends take turns selling tickets at the school fair from 12:30 P.M. to 3:30 P.M. If they agree to take equal turns, how long will each turn be?

27. The students in Ms. Wu's class are selling school jackets. They earn $15 for each jacket they sell. If the goal is to raise $1000, how many jackets must they sell?

28. One fifth-grade class decorated 194 magnets to sell at a school bazaar. They plan to package them in groups of 4. How many complete packages will they make?

CUMULATIVE REVIEW

Write the answer.

29.
$$\begin{array}{r} 34.91 \\ + 6.97 \\ \hline \end{array}$$

30.
$$\begin{array}{r} 42.603 \\ + 51.584 \\ \hline \end{array}$$

31.
$$\begin{array}{r} 239.42 \\ - 78.96 \\ \hline \end{array}$$

32.
$$\begin{array}{r} 47 \\ - 31.49 \\ \hline \end{array}$$

Write the least common multiple.

33. 3, 5, 10

34. 2, 17

35. 6, 9, 12

36. 3, 14

Write the value of each expression.

37. What is $y + 5$ if $y = 9$?

38. What is $x - 12$ if $x = 19$?

EXCURSION
CRITICAL THINKING

DECISION MAKING

If you were choosing a job to earn extra money, you might have to make several decisions first. Here are a few considerations.

What is the job?

How long will the job take?

Will you be paid by the hour or by the job?

Can you walk to the job or will you need a ride?

Will you have time for your homework and chores?

Brenda wants to earn extra money by washing and waxing cars in her neighborhood. She is deciding whether to charge $5.00 an hour or $6.00 per car. She is also thinking about charging $11.00 for neighbors that have two cars.

Before Brenda decides on her prices, she has to think about the following.

• She estimates that she can wash and wax a car in an hour. But to do an outstanding job she would need an hour and a half.

• She will wash each car in the owner's driveway. She will have to travel from house to house.

• She will be able to wash more cars if she works quickly. But she will probably get more customers if she takes the time to do an outstanding job.

• If she works on more than one car at the same house, she will save travel time.

What other factors should Brenda consider? Add
those factors to the list. Now make a decision.
Should Brenda be paid by the hour or by the car?
Should she offer a special rate to families with more
than one car? Explain your reasons for each answer.

You Decide

Suppose you have been offered two jobs for
Saturday afternoon. You need to decide which job
to choose.

- Ms. Hewitt, who lives across the
  street, has asked you to clean out
  her attic. It is a large attic, and Ms.
  Hewitt says it's "full of all kinds of
  junk." She has offered to pay you
  $15 to do the job.

- Mr. Driver has asked you to rake the
  autumn leaves in his yard. There are
  many rocks and broken branches
  scattered about. He has offered to
  pay you $3.00 an hour. It would take
  you fifteen minutes to ride your
  bike to Mr. Driver's house.

Before you decide, make a list of things you need to
consider. Use your list to help you choose the job
that would be best for you. Explain how you made
your decision. Share your reasoning with the class.

COLLECTING, ORGANIZING, AND USING DATA

Connections

Social Studies

Using Weather Data Weather people have an interesting job. They spend much of their time studying maps and data. They use these data to forecast the weather. It is not an easy job. There are many things to think about—air pressure, temperature, and wind.

Fortunately, there are weather computers. These computers receive weather data from around the world. Computers allow weather people to update a forecast in just minutes. A summary of weather data is used to make daily weather maps. Some maps are shown during television weather reports. Other maps are printed in daily newspapers.

Look at a weather map for your part of the country. Use the map to predict your weather for the next three days. Write down your forecast and trade with a partner. After three days, compare your predictions. Who made the more accurate forecast?

COLLECTING AND ORGANIZING DATA

These are the three basic types of fingerprints.

Did you know that no two people in the world have the same fingerprints? Police detectives use fingerprints to help them solve crimes.

Kevin and Taran wondered which type of thumbprint was the most common in their class. They decided to get a thumbprint from each student to find out.

Kevin recorded the results using a data table.

Thumbprint Type	Tally	Total	Fraction of the Class
Arch Thumbprint	||||	4	$\frac{4}{24}$
Loop Thumbprint	卌 卌 ||	12	$\frac{12}{24}$
Whorl Thumbprint	卌 |||	8	$\frac{8}{24}$

Taran recorded the results using a pictograph.

Thumbprint Type	
Arch Thumbprint	👍 👍 👍 👍
Loop Thumbprint	👍 👍 👍 👍 👍 👍 👍 👍 👍 👍 👍 👍
Whorl Thumbprint	👍 👍 👍 👍 👍 👍 👍 👍

Work with a partner to answer each question. You will need tape.

1. Do both the table and the pictograph show the same information? Explain.

2. Why do you think Kevin made a tally section in his table?

3. What do you think the number 24 stands for in the "Fraction of the Class" section of Kevin's table?

4. Which type of thumbprint do half the students in Kevin and Taran's class have?

5. With your partner, find the most common type of thumbprint in your class. Get one thumbprint from each of your classmates. Record your data in a pictograph and a data table.

   a. Rub dark pencil lead (graphite) on a piece of paper.

   b. Rub a student's thumb in the graphite. Make sure you rub more than just the end of the thumb.

   c. Stick a piece of clear tape on the part of the thumb that was rubbed in the graphite.

   d. Remove the tape, and place it next to the correct thumbprint type in the pictograph.

   e. Make a tally mark for the thumbprint type in the data table.

   f. Continue with the rest of the students in your class. When finished, total the tallies and complete the data table.

....
SUMMING IT UP

6. The pictograph uses pictures to show information and the data table uses numbers. Which do you like better? Why?

7. What was the most common type of thumbprint in your class?

8. Did your class have the same results as Kevin and Taran's class? Explain.

9. How do you think fingerprints help police detectives solve crimes?

MEAN AND RANGE

What is the mean height of the cheerleading team? **Mean** is another name for "average."

58 in.   59 in.   60 in.

To find the mean:

1. Find the sum of the three cheerleaders' heights.
   58 in. + 59 in. + 60 in. = 177 in.

2. Divide by the number of cheerleaders.
   177 in. ÷ 3 = 59 in.

The mean height of the three cheerleaders is 59 inches.

The **range** is the difference between the greatest number and the least number in a set.

The tallest cheerleader is 60 inches. The shortest cheerleader is 58 inches.

tallest − shortest = the range

60 in. − 58 in. = 2 in.

The cheerleaders have a 2-inch range in height.

Think

- What is the range with the new team member?

We added another person to our team.

55 in.   58 in.   59 in.   60 in.

Find the mean height of the 4-person team.

55 in. + 58 in. + 59 in. + 60 in. = 232 in.

232 in. ÷ 4 = 58 in.

The team's mean height is now 58 inches.

GUIDED PRACTICE

Write the range and the mean for each. You may use a calculator.

1.

8 oz
16 oz
4 oz
64 oz

2.
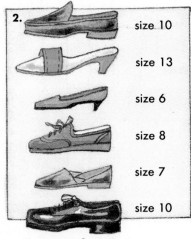
size 10
size 13
size 6
size 8
size 7
size 10

3.
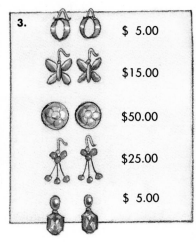
$ 5.00
$15.00
$50.00
$25.00
$ 5.00

4. Add a 12-ounce mug to the set of cups in exercise 1. Does it change the range? Explain.

INDEPENDENT PRACTICE

Write the range and the mean for each. You may use a calculator.

5.

$2.50 $0.95
$1.75 $3.00

50 inches   60 inches   50 inches   60 inches
7.

6.

400 pages
200 pages
175 pages
425 pages
150 pages

8.
1 cup
16 cups
4 cups

9. 187, 115, 163, 156, 179

10. 12, 19, 15, 26, 18, 14, 22

Maintain • **Division**

Write the answer.

1. 7)10,752
2. 30)11,359
3. 9)576
4. 64)576

5. 18,208 ÷ 82
6. 7904 ÷ 13
7. 15,000 ÷ 2
8. 31,689 ÷ 59

MEDIAN

The cheerleading team had a mean height of 58 inches.

Then they added Torrence, who is 72 inches tall.

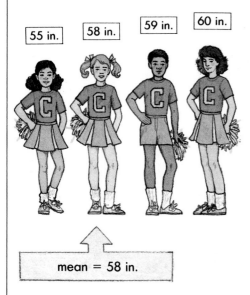

55 in. 58 in. 59 in. 60 in.

mean = 58 in.

72 in.

55 in. 58 in. 59 in. 60 in.

Torrence

The new mean = 61 in.

Does the new mean of 61 inches really describe the height of the cheerleading team?

Think

- How many of the cheerleaders are shorter than 61 inches? Taller than 61 inches?

All but one cheerleader are shorter than the mean. So, the mean doesn't really describe the team's height anymore.

If there is an unusually large or small number in a group of numbers, the *middle* number may describe the group better. The middle number, when the numbers are ordered from least to greatest, is called the **median.**

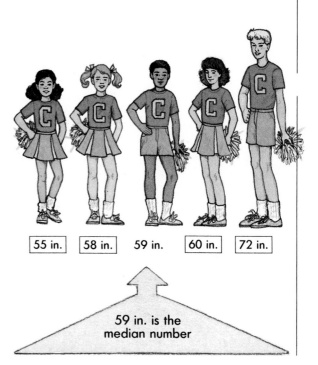

55 in. 58 in. 59 in. 60 in. 72 in.

59 in. is the median number

GUIDED PRACTICE

Order the numbers from least to greatest. Write the
median, mean, and range.

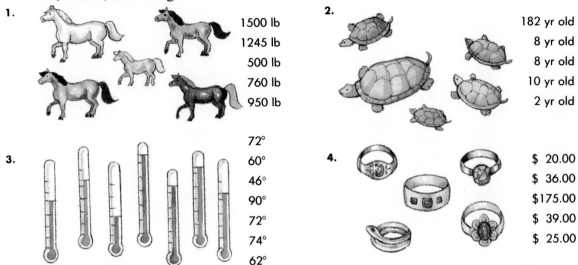

1.
1500 lb
1245 lb
500 lb
760 lb
950 lb

2.
182 yr old
8 yr old
8 yr old
10 yr old
2 yr old

3.
72°
60°
46°
90°
72°
74°
62°

4.
$ 20.00
$ 36.00
$175.00
$ 39.00
$ 25.00

5. In which exercises does the median describe the
group better than the mean? Explain.

INDEPENDENT PRACTICE

Problem Solving Mount Atwood School had a fitness day.
The results are shown in the table below. Write the mean,
median, and range.

	Kate	Ann	Jo	Fred	Dan	Mean	Median	Range
6. Push-ups	13	20	15	7	65			
7. Sit-ups	15	20	15	19	31			
8. Chin-ups	1	16	16	16	16			
9. Long Jump	68 in.	94 in.	68 in.	90 in.	130 in.			
10. 1-mile run	25 min	8 min	8 min	10 min	9 min			

MATH LOG
Do you think the median is always useful
to describe a set of numbers? Explain.

USING MATH SENSE

I wonder how long the movie is?

It starts every hour and 15 minutes. And theaters allow time for people to leave and new people to come in.

Planetarium Movie
Stargazing

10:00 A.M.	3:00 P.M.
11:15 A.M.	4:15 P.M.
12:30 P.M.	5:30 P.M.
1:45 P.M.	

So, we can tell that the movie is less than 1 hour and 15 minutes long.

Think

• Why can't you tell exactly how long the movie is?

Solve each problem.

1. Barbara has played in 4 basketball games this season. She has scored an average of 5 points per game. In each of her first 3 games she scored fewer than 5 points. What can you tell about the number of points she scored in the last game?

2. Juan has scored an average of 10 points per game. He has played 4 games this season. What can you tell about the total number of points he has scored this season?

3. In the table, the high temperature for Tuesday is missing. If the range for the week is 7°F, what can you tell about the high temperature on Tuesday?

Sunville Daily High Temperatures for the Week (°F)						
Sun	Mon	Tues	Wed	Thu	Fri	Sat
55°	52°		59°	56°	54°	59°

4. Suppose the median daily high temperature for the week was 56°F. What can you tell about the temperature high on Tuesday?

5. Suppose the mean daily high temperature for the week was also 56°F. What can you now tell about the high on Tuesday?

SECTION REVIEW

for pages 112–118

Write the mean and the range for each set of data.

1. Enrollment at West Elementary School for the last 5 years

463	486	490	468	483

2. Ted's math test scores

98	93	93	89	95	96

Use the chart to answer each question below.

Temperatures for the Week—Chicago							
High	42°F	40°F	45°F	37°F	39°F	54°F	38°F
Low	32°F	28°F	33°F	25°F	12°F	36°F	27°F

3. What is the median high temperature for the week? The median low temperature?

4. What is the range of high temperatures? Of low temperatures?

Use the chart to answer each question below.

R. Perry	GAME						
	1	**2**	**3**	**4**	**5**	**6**	**7**
Points	10	12	14	26	13	12	11
Rebounds	3	7	8	5	6	8	5

5. What was the mean number of points scored by R. Perry for the seven games? The median number of points?

6. What is the range for the number of rebounds R. Perry had for the seven games?

7. How many points can R. Perry score in his next game and not change his mean number of points per game?

8. If R. Perry gets 10 rebounds in the next game, will that change the range? Will the range change if he gets 6 rebounds?

READING GRAPHS

The bar graph shows that about 700 million people speak Chinese. To find out about how many people speak Russian you need to estimate.

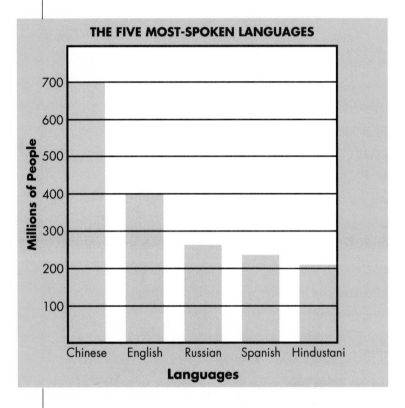

THE FIVE MOST-SPOKEN LANGUAGES

Millions of People

700 · 600 · 500 · 400 · 300 · 200 · 100

Chinese · English · Russian · Spanish · Hindustani

Languages

Think about the halfway points to help you estimate. You know that 250 is halfway between 200 and 300, and that 275 is halfway between 250 and 300.

A reasonable estimate is 270 million people.

Think

• What other number would be a reasonable estimate of the number of people who speak Russian?

• Explain how you can use halfway points to estimate how many people speak Spanish.

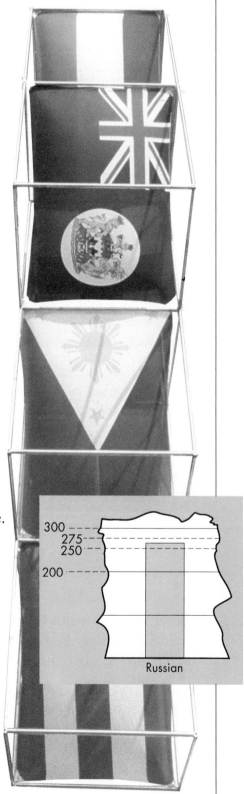

Russian

Write the answer. Use estimation.

1. About how many books were sold in 1985? 1987? 1989?

2. In which year were about 475 books sold? About 225 books?

3. In which years were fewer than 250 books sold?

4. Explain how you would estimate the number of books sold in 1986.

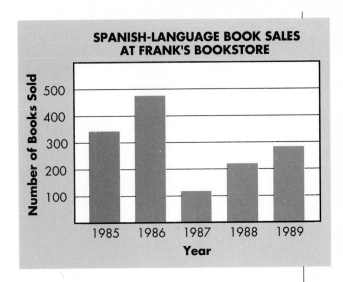

SPANISH-LANGUAGE BOOK SALES AT FRANK'S BOOKSTORE

INDEPENDENT PRACTICE

Write the answer. Use estimation.

5. In which years did City College have more than 425 students enrolled in foreign language classes?

6. About how many students were enrolled in foreign language classes in 1987? In 1988? In 1989? In 1990?

7. Were more than 550 students ever enrolled in foreign language classes in one year?

8. Were there fewer than 250 students enrolled in foreign language classes in any one year?

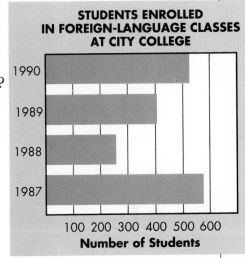

STUDENTS ENROLLED IN FOREIGN-LANGUAGE CLASSES AT CITY COLLEGE

PROJECT • Graphing Data

The data to the right show how many City College students have visited foreign countries.

• Work in pairs. Make a bar graph to show these data.

• Label the bottom line of the graph with 100, 200, 300, 400, and 500.

• Use estimation to help you draw the bars.

FOREIGN TRAVEL	
Country Visited	Number of Students
China	250
England	276
Israel	191
Spain	325
France	215
Canada	420
Mexico	342

LINE GRAPHS

Year	Attendance
1986	150
1987	250
1988	200
1989	160
1990	125

The table shows the attendance at the Fillmore High School homecoming games for 5 years.

A line graph can make it easier to see the change in attendance from year to year.

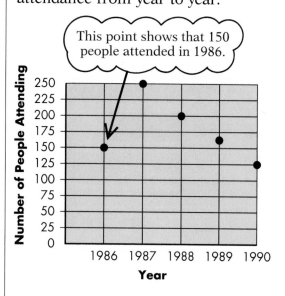

This point shows that 150 people attended in 1986.

This part of the line shows that the attendance went up from 1986 to 1987.

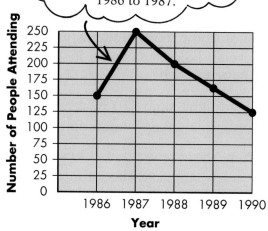

Each piece of data is shown by a point on the grid.

The points are then connected.

Notice how the graph is labeled. The attendance is listed on the **vertical axis**. The years are listed on the **horizontal axis**.

Vertical Axis

Horizontal Axis

Think

• What does the graph tell you about the attendance in the years after 1987?

Use the graph to answer each question.

1. In which year did Fillmore have its largest team?

2. Between which two years did the number of players increase the most? Decrease the most?

3. Use squared paper. Make a line graph that shows the temperature at the five Fillmore High School homecoming games.

4. Use the chart at the right. Why do you think only 125 people came to the homecoming game in 1990?

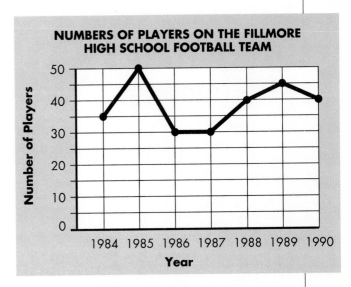

NUMBERS OF PLAYERS ON THE FILLMORE HIGH SCHOOL FOOTBALL TEAM

Temperature (°F)	45°	65°	60°	50°	20°
Year	1986	1987	1988	1989	1990

5. Use squared paper. Make a line graph that shows the number of wins the Fillmore football team had.

Year	1986	1987	1988	1989	1990
Wins	4	2	7	6	9

Use the graph you made to answer each question.

6. Between which two years was there the greatest increase in the number of wins? The greatest decrease?

7. Write *a, b,* or *c.* The graph shows that the number of wins has generally:
   a. been increasing.
   b. remained the same.
   c. been decreasing.

INTERPRETING GRAPHS

A **double-line graph** allows you to compare two sets of data. Often two colors are used to show the two sets of data.

This double-line graph shows the average daily temperatures for Denver, Colorado, and San Antonio, Texas.

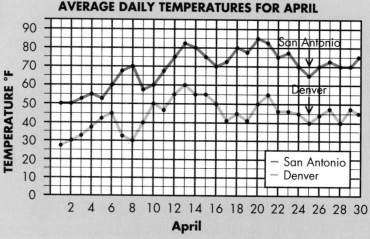

AVERAGE DAILY TEMPERATURES FOR APRIL

TEMPERATURE °F / April

— San Antonio
— Denver

From the graph, you can see that on April 20 the average temperature for San Antonio was about 85°F, and the average temperature for Denver was about 50°F.

A **double-bar graph** also allows you to compare two sets of data. This graph compares the average temperatures of Denver and San Antonio for three days in April.

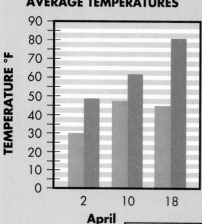

AVERAGE TEMPERATURES

TEMPERATURE °F / April

— San Antonio
— Denver

Think

• Which graph shows the difference in average temperature of the two cities on April 2 more clearly?

• Which graph shows the change in average temperature through the month of April for each city more clearly?

124

GUIDED PRACTICE

Use one of the graphs on page 124 to answer each question. Tell which graph you used.

1. In San Antonio, which were the hottest and coldest days?

2. Which city was warmer on April 2, San Antonio or Denver?

3. On which day was there the greater average temperature difference between Denver and San Antonio, April 2 or April 18?

4. How do changes in San Antonio's temperature compare to changes in Denver's temperature?

INDEPENDENT PRACTICE

Use the graph to answer each question below.

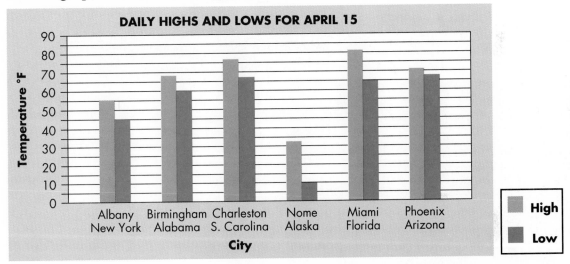

DAILY HIGHS AND LOWS FOR APRIL 15

5. How many cities are shown on the graph?

6. Which cities had low temperatures below 55°F?

7. Which cities had high temperatures above 65°F?

8. Which city had the largest range in temperatures?

9. Which city had the smallest range in daily temperatures?

10. List the cities in order from the warmest location to the coldest location.

11. What was the mean temperature for Albany, New York, on April 15? HINT: The mean temperature is the average of the high and low temperatures.

12. How does the high temperature for Nome, Alaska, compare to the low temperatures of the other cities?

CIRCLE GRAPHS

Circle graphs show all the parts of a whole. The circle graph at the right shows the colors of all the horses at the Circle F Dude Ranch.

Think

- What is the total number of horses at the Circle F Dude Ranch?

- Why is the section for brown horses twice as big as the section for black horses?

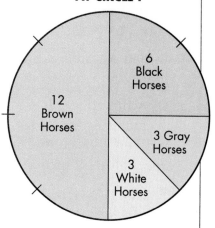

COLORS OF HORSES AT CIRCLE F

You can write the same information using fractions.

This means that $\frac{1}{4}$ of the horses at Circle F are black.

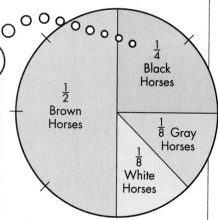

COLORS OF HORSES AT CIRCLE F

The ranch owns 24 saddles. There are two different types of saddles, English style and western style.

Think

- What fraction of the saddles are English style?

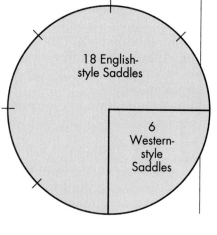

TYPES OF SADDLES AT CIRCLE F

Use tracing paper and the circle pattern.

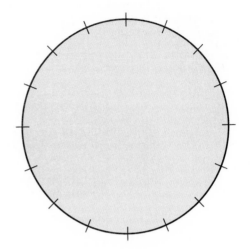

1. Make a circle graph for the horse feed recipe below.

Horse Feed Recipe	
$\frac{1}{2}$ oats	$\frac{1}{4}$ corn
$\frac{1}{8}$ molasses	$\frac{1}{8}$ oil

2. Make a circle graph for a 16-quart batch of horse feed made with: 8 quarts of oats, 4 quarts of corn, 2 quarts of molasses, and 2 quarts of oil.

3. Are both recipes the same? Explain.

INDEPENDENT PRACTICE

Problem Solving Use the graph below. Use tracing paper and the circle pattern if you need to.

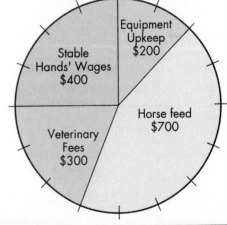

4. How much money is used to pay stable hands?

5. What fraction of the stable budget is spent on:
   a. stable hands' wages?
   b. equipment upkeep?

6. Is the amount of money spent on horse feed more than or less than half the monthly budget?

7. Make a circle graph that shows the money spent on veterinary fees.
   a. What fraction of the total bill was for Old Sue's medicine?
   b. Which horse was more expensive to keep in June, Bucky or Old Sue? Explain.

MONTHLY STABLE BUDGET ($1600 PER MONTH)

Equipment Upkeep $200

Stable Hands' Wages $400

Horse feed $700

Veterinary Fees $300

Jake's Veterinary	Bill for June
$150.00	Medicine for Old Sue
$ 75.00	Vitamins for Old Sue
$ 75.00	New Shoes for Bucky
$300.00	Total due

NOT ENOUGH INFORMATION

I bought 6 boxes of paper cups. Will that be enough for 200 people to each have a cup?

I don't know. I need to know how many cups there are in each box.

Think

- Why is the number of cups in each box important?

- How could John and Sue find that information?

Work in groups to solve each problem. If there is not enough information, tell what you need to know.

1. Joan's phone rang at 6:00 P.M. Cathleen was calling from New York City. What time was it in New York?

2. Mr. Mirez had $14.86 left after he bought food for $21.79 and gas for $11.75. Did he have more than $50 before he bought food and gas?

3. The coach chose players for all 8 teams. The 6 players who were not chosen served as substitutes. How many players were there?

4. Bill scored 12 points in the first quarter of the basketball game. Then he scored a total of 20 points in the next 3 quarters. What is the average number of points he scored each quarter?

5. Ian wants to mail a ball that is 16 inches in diameter. Will it fit in a box 2 feet long and 2 feet wide?

6. The theater holds 750 people. Each of the 5 shows during the week was sold out. The manager wants to know how much money the theater took in that week.

7. The *Detective Data* television show is on Tuesday night. Samantha wants to videotape it. The show is 2 hours long. What time should she start taping?

8. In Mr. Chu's class, half the students like comedy shows the best, 8 students like cartoons the best, and the other 4 students like adventure shows the best. How many students are in Mr. Chu's class?

9. Ellen played 6 spelling games. Her scores in the first 3 games were 90, 70, and 80. Was her average for the 6 games greater than or less than 75?

10. It took Daniel 1 hour to get to the fair. He arrived at 6:15. It took Michelle 45 minutes, but she arrived 20 minutes later. Who rode farther?

11. Orlando has some five-dollar bills and some quarters. He wants to buy a game that costs $10.50. Does he have enough money?

12. Jack has $7.00. He receives $2.50 for his allowance each week. When will he have enough money to buy the video game Zany Corners?

USING ESTIMATION

Every year thousands of books are published in the United States on many different topics. The table shows how many books were published in 5 different categories.

Number of Books Published in One Year in the United States	
Category	**Number of Books**
Art	1280
History	2250
Fiction	5647
Young Readers	3794
Travel	496

Solve each problem. Use estimation. Explain how you got your answers.

1. Were more than 12,000 books published in all 5 categories?

2. Were there more books published in the categories of history and art combined or in the category of fiction?

3. About how many more fiction books were published than history books?

4. Suppose the United States continues to publish 496 travel books each year.

   a. About how many travel books will be published during 5 years?

   b. Will this number be greater than or less than the number of fiction books published in one year?

5. Suppose that you read one book a week.

   a. Would it take more than 10 years to read all of the fiction books published in one year?

   b. About how many years would it take?

   c. About how many years would it take to read all of the travel books?

SECTION REVIEW

for pages 120–130

Solve each problem. Use the graphs at the right.

1. Did the number of students on the honor roll at Belmont Middle School increase or decrease from December to January? From January to February?

2. For which two months did the number of students on the honor roll remain unchanged?

3. Would you describe the number of students on the honor roll from February to June as:
   a. increasing?
   b. decreasing?
   c. unchanged?

4. Which student had the greatest range in test scores?

5. Which students had science scores above 80?

6. How many students had higher math scores than science scores?

7. What fraction of the students prefer aerobic-style athletic shoes? Basketball-style athletic shoes?

8. If there are 24 students in Mr. Johnson's class, how many prefer basketball-style athletic shoes?

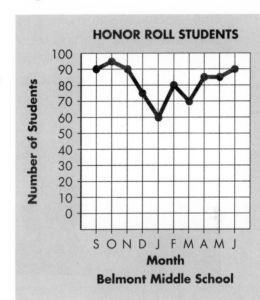

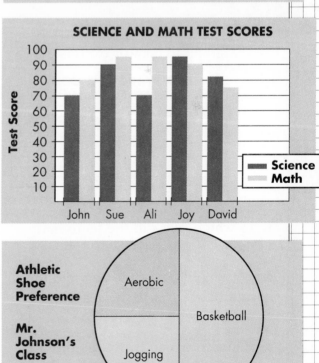

CHAPTER REVIEW

Language Connection

Good speakers can make a point by using just a few words. How few words can you use to make a point about each word group shown here? The words in each group are alike in some way. Tell how they are similar, using just one or two sentences.

WORD GROUPS

mean • median • range

bar graph • line graph • double-line graph • circle graph

"But wait! There's more...."

Test ●●●●●●

Use the graph to answer exercises 1–3.

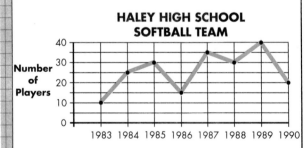

HALEY HIGH SCHOOL SOFTBALL TEAM

Number of Players

40 30 20 10 0

1983 1984 1985 1986 1987 1988 1989 1990

1. In which year did the team have the most players?

2. Between which two years did the number of players increase the most?

3. Between which two years did the number of players decrease the most?

Use the graph to answer exercises 4–6.

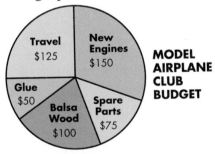

MODEL AIRPLANE CLUB BUDGET

Travel $125

New Engines $150

Glue $50

Balsa Wood $100

Spare Parts $75

4. What is the total budget of the Model Airplane Club?

5. What fraction of the budget is spent on balsa wood?

6. What is one quarter of the budget spent on?

Use the graph to answer exercises 7–10.

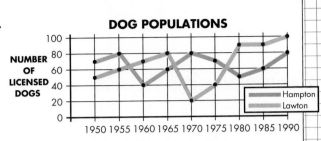

DOG POPULATIONS

7. Lawton had its highest dog population in which year?

8. Which town had the largest range in dog population?

9. How many more dogs did Hampton have than Lawton in 1970?

10. How many more dogs did Hampton have in 1955 than in 1985?

PROBLEM SOLVING

Solve each problem.

11. Larry wants to find the average age of his cousins. Their ages are 12, 10, 15, 11, 21, 10, 13, 9, 13, and 6. What is the mean age?

12. Shawna wants to find the range of her puppies' weights. Their weights (in pounds) are 5, 8, 11, 4, 9, 12. What is the range in weight?

13. Nancy and her friends want to find the average of their science test scores. The scores are 87, 97, 82, 91, 83. How much greater is the mean than the median?

14. Taro watched TV weather reports and recorded the following wind speeds (in mph): 12, 6, 30, 10, 15, 17, 22, 8, 3. What was the median wind speed?

CUMULATIVE REVIEW

Write the answer.

15. $23\overline{)6046}$

16. $21\overline{)8274}$

17. $14\overline{)988}$

18. $62\overline{)18,900}$

19. 304×7

20. $\$5.12 \times 26$

21. 987×520

Write the prime factorization for each number.

22. 111

23. 16

24. 25

25. 17

EXCURSION
NUMERATION

NUMBERS LESS THAN ZERO

Numbers can be used to describe a situation. For example, the top of the Statue of Liberty is 325 feet above sea level (⁺325). The diver is 325 feet below sea level (⁻325). The football player had a gain of 20 yards (⁺20) and then a loss of 5 yards (⁻5).

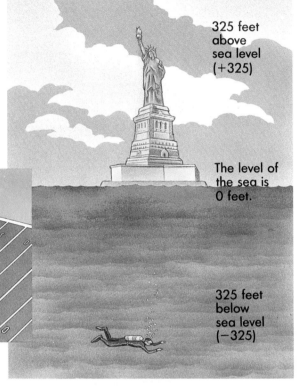

325 feet above sea level (+325)

The level of the sea is 0 feet.

325 feet below sea level (−325)

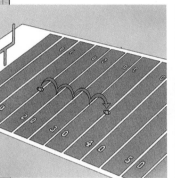

a *gain* of 20 yd (+20)

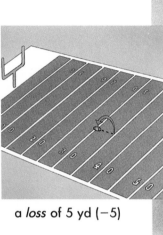

a *loss* of 5 yd (−5)

Numbers that show a *gain* or *increase* are written with a positive sign (⁺) in front. These numbers are greater than zero and are called **positive numbers.**

Numbers that show a *loss* or *decrease* are written with a negative sign (⁻) in front. These numbers are called **negative numbers.**

Look at the changes in temperature. At sundown it was 8 degrees above zero (⁺8). By 9:00 P.M. the temperature had dropped 11 degrees to 3 degrees below zero (⁻3).

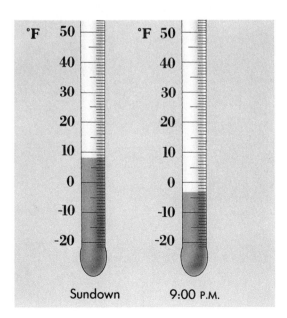

Write a positive or negative number to describe each situation.

1. a decrease of $7
2. a gain of 11 points
3. a loss of 25 pounds
4. a gain of 2 yards
5. a $6 raise
6. 3000 feet below sea level

7. If a person lost 4 pounds one week and 2 pounds the next week, what number would describe the total loss?

Write a positive or negative number to describe each situation.

8. a gain of 2 pounds
9. a decrease of $19
10. a gain of 5 points
11. 82° above zero
12. an increase of $37
13. 1000 feet below sea level
14. a rise of 16 feet
15. 5° below zero
16. 4° drop in temperature

17. Draw a number line from ⁻10 to 10. Use the number line to find the missing numbers in the path. Begin at the box with the ⁺2.

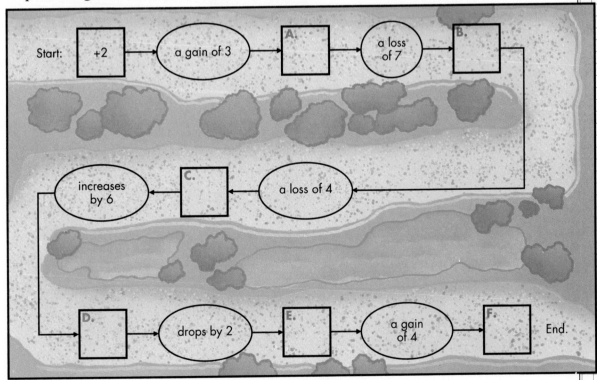

MEASUREMENT AND GEOMETRY

Connections

Art

Making a Quilt Did you know that math skills are used in making quilts? Geometry and measurement skills are used to arrange small pieces of cloth into one large design.

Quilters may use a pencil and paper to sketch their designs. When the design is finished, it will form a pattern. Each piece of fabric is cut to fit the pattern. When the pieces are sewn together, the quilt will look just like the original design.

Perhaps members of your class would like to make a quilt. Some people will have design ideas. Others can begin to collect scraps of cloth. Each member of the class can help in some way.

Once the design is finished, you can cut the cloth into pieces to fit the design. Ask an adult to help you sew the pieces together. When your quilt is finished, it should match your design. No one in the world will have a quilt exactly like yours.

MEASUREMENT SENSE

How many ways can you measure this fish? You can measure its length or its weight. You may even count its stripes.

When you measure, it is important to know what measurement information you need and what tools you need to find that information.

Suppose you wanted to set up a new aquarium. Here are some measurement questions you may need to ask yourself.

• Will the aquarium fit on the shelf?

• How much water is needed?

• How warm should the water be?

• What size fish belong in the tank?

Here are some of the tools you might use to make these measurements.

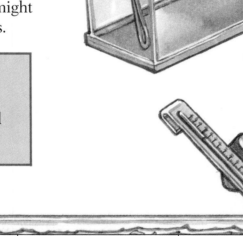

Think

• What unit of measure would you use to measure the length of the tank? What tool would be most useful?

Other Examples

Question	Measure	Unit to Use	Instrument to Use
How warm is the water?	temperature	degrees Celsius degrees Fahrenheit	thermometer
How much water is needed?	capacity	liters gallons	measuring cup

GUIDED PRACTICE

Write what measurement information you might need for the items pictured.

1.

2.

3. What unit would you use to measure the items above?

INDEPENDENT PRACTICE

Set up a chart like the one on page 138.

4. Write at least ten measurement questions from the ocean scene to complete the chart. Include at least one temperature, weight, capacity, and quantity measure.

Maintain • **Organizing Data**

Order the numbers from least to greatest. Write the median, mean, and range.

1. plant height: 3 inches, 6 inches, 4 inches, 4 inches, 3 inches

2. daily noon temperature (°F): 59°, 62°, 67°, 62°, 58°, 83°, 64°

3. fish food cost: $2.50, $2.70, $2.25, $2.70, $2.40

Measurement Lab

How long is the goldfish below? You could estimate the length or you could measure. Which unit of measure would you choose?

The customary unit for measuring the length of small objects is the inch. Use a ruler to measure the fish to the nearest inch.

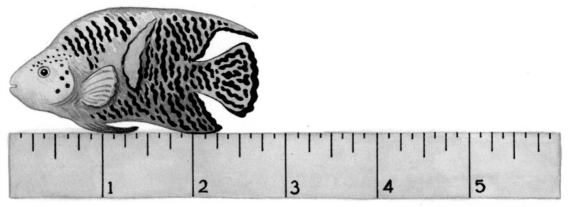

As you can see, the fish is close to 3 inches long.

Your ruler also has marks for $\frac{1}{2}$ inch, $\frac{1}{4}$ inch, and $\frac{1}{8}$ inch.

Think

- How many $\frac{1}{8}$-inches are in one inch? How do you know?

What is the length of the fish to the nearest $\frac{1}{2}$ inch? $\frac{1}{4}$ inch? $\frac{1}{8}$ inch?

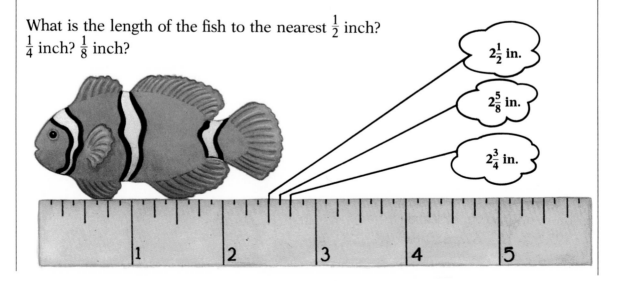

$2\frac{1}{2}$ in.

$2\frac{5}{8}$ in.

$2\frac{3}{4}$ in.

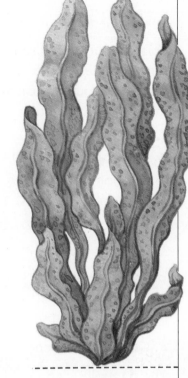

GUIDED PRACTICE

1. Estimate the height of the aquarium plant.

2. Measure the height of the aquarium plant to the nearest:

   a. inch.　　b. $\frac{1}{2}$ inch.　　c. $\frac{1}{4}$ inch.　　d. $\frac{1}{8}$ inch.

3. Which two answers in exercise 2 are the same? Explain why.

INDEPENDENT PRACTICE

Estimate the length of each fish to the nearest inch and then measure.

4.

5.

Measure the length of each fish to the nearest $\frac{1}{2}$ inch.

6.

7.

8.

Measure each object to the nearest $\frac{1}{4}$ inch and $\frac{1}{8}$ inch.

9.

10.

11.

Measure to the nearest $\frac{1}{8}$ inch:

12. your left shoe.　13. your right shoe.　14. your left foot.　15. your right foot.

16. Are your shoes the same length? Are your feet?

MATH LOG

Give an example of when you can use an estimate.
Give an example of when you need to measure.

LENGTH

You cannot always measure an object directly. Sometimes you have to estimate. You can use a measure you know to estimate other measures.

Mr. Mar is about 6 feet tall.
The flagpole looks about 3 times as tall as Mr. Mar.

▶ Betty uses what she knows about Mr. Mar's height to estimate the height of her school's flagpole.

3×6 feet $= 18$ feet

The flagpole is about 18 feet tall.

Think

≢ • About how tall is the building?

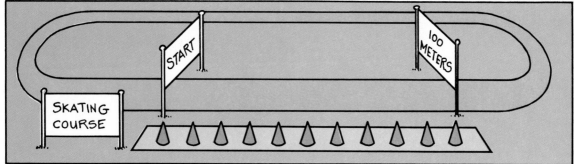

SKATING COURSE

START

100 METERS

▶ About how far apart are the cones on the roller skating course?

You can estimate that the roller skating course is about 100 meters long. There are 10 spaces separating the cones.

100 meters $\div$ 10 $=$ 10 meters

Each space is about 10 meters long, so the cones are about 10 meters apart.

GUIDED PRACTICE

1. About how long is the entire track in the picture on page 142?

2. When do you think an exact answer would be necessary for exercise 1? When would an estimate be close enough?

....

INDEPENDENT PRACTICE

Use what you know to estimate each measure.

3. About how wide is the wall?

4. About how wide is the desktop?

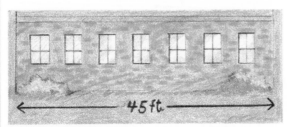

5. About how wide is each window?

6. The square patch is about how many centimeters wide?

....

PROJECT • Critical Thinking

You will need a customary or metric ruler. Work in pairs.

• Estimate the length of an object in the classroom. Record your estimate. Then use the ruler to measure the actual length of the object. Compare it with your estimate.

• Estimate, then measure four other objects in your classroom.

WORK BACKWARD

Sometimes you can solve a problem by starting from the end and working backward.

One time, we worked backward to help solve a problem in our craft store.

OUR PROBLEM We had a long piece of special trim. We needed to know how long the piece had been before it was cut. We knew:

Andy sold half of it.   Rachel sold 18 inches from the remaining half.   A 30-inch piece was left.

OUR SOLUTION First, we wrote down what had happened.

Original piece   Andy sold half.   Rachel sold 18 in.   Piece left

? in. ────(÷ 2)──────────────(− 18 in.)──→ 30 in.

Next, we worked backward. We figured out how long the piece was before Rachel sold 18 inches of it.

Length before   Rachel sold 18 in.   Piece left
Rachel sold 18 in.

48 in. ←──────(+ 18)────── 30 in.

Then, we figured out how long the piece was before Andy sold half of it.

Original   Andy sold   Length before   Rachel sold 18 in.   Piece left
piece   half.   Rachel sold 18 in.

96 in. ←──(× 2)── 48 in. ←──(+ 18)── 30 in.

So, the original piece was 96 inches long. We checked our answer by working forward.

96 in. ──(÷ 2)──→ 48 in. ──(− 18)──→ 30 in.

Continue the steps for working backward. Solve the problem.

1. Art bought 3 magazines and then a book at the bookstore. He knows he spent a total of $17 and the book cost $9.50. Each magazine cost the same amount, but Art can't remember the price. How much did each magazine cost?

Amount spent on magazines	Bought 1 book	Amount spent on book and magazines
? ←	−$9.50	$17

....
APPLICATION

Work in pairs. Continue the steps for working backward. Solve each problem.

2. Jeff saw this ad for the XQ-99 antenna. What was the original price?

Price before $15 taken off	$15 taken off	Price now
? ←	+$15	$59.50

> **OUR LOWEST PRICE EVER**
>
> XQ-99 Antenna:
>
> Two months ago: We lowered the original price by $50!
>
> Last month: We cut the price in half!
>
> This month: We're taking off another $15. The XQ-99 is yours now at the incredibly low price of $59.50

3. Diane was planning a treasure hunt. She buried the prize. Then she started walking, keeping track of her course. She stopped and marked an X. Complete her directions for the treasure hunters.

Directions to Treasure
Start at the X
Walk 20 feet west
Walk

I started at the Treasure.
I walked 10 feet east.
I walked 15 feet south.
I walked 20 feet east.
I marked an X.

PREFIXES IN MATHEMATICS

As you know, prefixes are letters that can be added to the beginning of a root word. Sometimes prefixes are used to describe geometric shapes. If you know the meanings of the prefixes, you can figure out the number of sides in a polygon. For example, the prefix *penta-* means "five." Therefore a **pentagon** is a polygon that has 5 sides. The table below shows the meaning of several prefixes.

A polygon is a closed figure formed by line segments.

tri-	quad-	penta-	hexa-	hepta-	octa-	nona-	deca-
3	4	5	6	7	8	9	10

Use the table to answer each question.

1. How many sides would you expect to find?
   a. octagon
   b. decagon
   c. hexagon

2. How many sides do you expect to find in a quadrilateral?

Use one of the prefixes in the table to write a word for each definition.

3. a 6-sided polygon
4. a 10-sided polygon
5. a 7-sided polygon

Write the name of each polygon. Choose the name from the box below.

| nonagon | hexagon | decagon |
| octagon | pentagon | heptagon |

6.

7.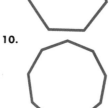

8.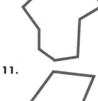

9.

10.

11.

SECTION REVIEW

for pages 138–146

Choose the correct tool to measure. Write *a, b,* or *c.*

1. the weight of a dog
   a. measuring cup
   b. scale
   c. clock

2. the baking soda for a recipe
   a. ruler
   b. measuring spoon
   c. clock

3. the width of a window
   a. ruler
   b. measuring cup
   c. scale

4. the detergent for the dishwasher
   a. ruler
   b. clock
   c. measuring spoon

Choose the correct unit to measure. Write *a, b,* or *c.*

5. the weight of a dog
   a. degree
   b. tablespoon
   c. pound

6. the baking soda for a recipe
   a. foot
   b. tablespoon
   c. degree

7. the width of a window
   a. foot
   b. degree
   c. pound

8. the detergent for the dishwasher
   a. foot
   b. minute
   c. tablespoon

Use the picture below. Choose the correct measure. Write *a, b,* or *c.*

9. to the nearest $\frac{1}{4}$ inch
   a. 4 inches
   b. $4\frac{1}{4}$ inches
   c. $4\frac{2}{4}$ inches

10. to the nearest $\frac{1}{8}$ inch
    a. 4 inches
    b. $4\frac{2}{8}$ inches
    c. $4\frac{3}{8}$ inches

POLYGONS

In this lesson, you will discover the difference between regular and irregular polygons. Work in pairs. You will need tracing paper and pipe cleaners or craft sticks.

You see polygons every day. A **polygon** is a closed figure that is formed by line segments. Most polygons are named for the number of sides they have.

1. Locate each of the following polygons in the picture:

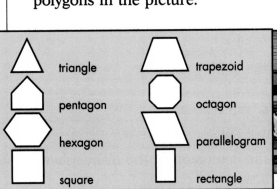

triangle
pentagon
hexagon
square
trapezoid
octagon
parallelogram
rectangle

2. The figures shown at the right are not polygons. Why?

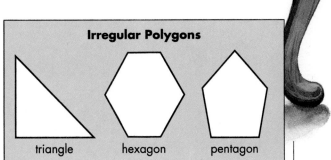

Polygons may be classified into two groups: regular polygons and irregular polygons.

Regular Polygons	Irregular Polygons
triangle hexagon pentagon	triangle hexagon pentagon

3. Put a piece of tracing paper over the regular hexagon. Trace along one side with a pencil. Measure each other side against this line. What do you notice?

4. Do the same with each of the other regular polygons. What do you notice about the length of the sides of regular polygons?

5. Now put a piece of tracing paper over one angle of the regular hexagon. Trace the angle. Measure the other angles against this angle. What do you notice?

6. Repeat this procedure with each of the other regular polygons. What do you notice about the measure of the angles of regular polygons?

7. Follow steps 3–6 again, but this time, use the irregular polygons shown. List any figures that have:
   a. all sides congruent.
   b. all angles congruent.
   c. all sides congruent and all angles congruent.

8. Is it possible to form a hexagon whose sides are congruent, but whose angles are *not* congruent? Try it. Use pipe cleaners or craft sticks.

Remember, *congruent* means "equal in measure."

SUMMING IT UP

9. What two requirements must be met for a polygon to be regular?

10. Is the square at the right a regular or irregular polygon? Why?

CHALLENGE • Geometry

You will need the tangram sheet and scissors. Arrange the seven pieces to form a square.

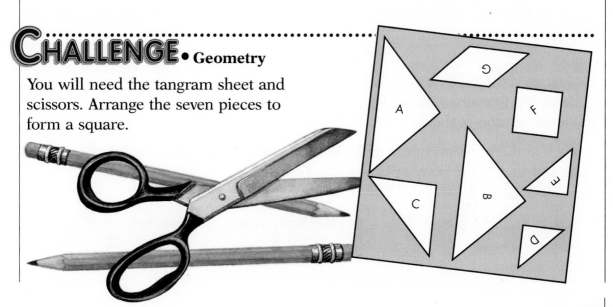

DIAGONALS IN POLYGONS

In this lesson, you will discover patterns in the number of diagonals in polygons. Work in small groups. You will need the recording sheet.

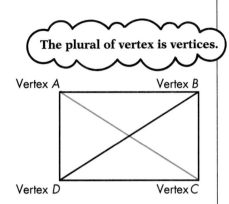

The plural of vertex is vertices.

A **diagonal** is a line segment that joins two vertices of a polygon but is not a side of the polygon. In the quadrilateral at the right, segment *AC* is a diagonal. Segment *AB* is not.

Vertex A   Vertex B

Vertex D   Vertex C

1. What is the other diagonal in the quadrilateral?

2. Why does a triangle have no diagonals?

Look at the pentagon and heptagon on the recording sheet.

3. Choose one vertex in each polygon. Draw as many diagonals as you can from that one vertex. Complete the second and third columns in the table on the recording sheet.

Polygon	Number of sides	Number of diagonals from one vertex	Total number of diagonals	
Quadrilateral	4	1	2	
Pentagon				
Hexagon	6	3	9	
Heptagon				

4. Next, find the total number of diagonals that can be drawn in each of the polygons. Complete the fourth column of the table.

5. Look at the numbers in the table. What pattern do you find in the number of sides and the number of diagonals from one vertex?

Polygon	Number of sides	Number of diagonals from one vertex	Total number of diagonals	
Quadrilateral	4	1	2	

6. Find the product of the number of sides and the number of diagonals from one vertex. Write this in the last column.

Polygon	Number of sides	Number of diagonals from one vertex	Total number of diagonals	
Quadrilateral	4	1	2	4

7. Compare the total number of diagonals with the product in the last column. What pattern do you notice?

Polygon	Number of sides	Number of diagonals from one vertex	Total number of diagonals	
Quadrilateral	4	1	2	4

You can use the patterns in the table to predict the number of diagonals in other figures.

8. Predict how many diagonals can be drawn from one vertex of:
   a. an octagon.   **b.** a nonagon.

9. Predict how many total diagonals can be drawn in:
   a. an octagon.   **b.** a nonagon.

10. Check your predictions by drawing diagonals in the octagon and nonagon on the recording sheet.

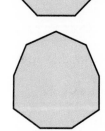

SUMMING IT UP

11. Write a rule for the number of diagonals that can be drawn from one vertex of a polygon.

12. Write a rule for the total number of diagonals that can be drawn in one polygon.

13. Look at the decagon at the right.
Use the rules you wrote to find:
   a. the number of diagonals from one vertex.
   b. the total number of diagonals.

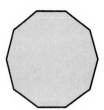

14. Discuss your rules with the class.

PERIMETER

Tonya warms up for her tennis match by jogging around the outer lines of the court. How far does she run each time?

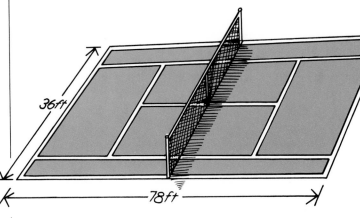

To solve this problem you need to find the distance around the tennis court. The **perimeter** is the distance around the court.

To find the perimeter, add the measures of the four sides.

78 ft + 36 ft + 78 ft + 36 ft = 228 ft

Tonya runs 228 feet each time she runs around the court.

Think

- If Tonya runs outside the lines of the tennis court, does she run more than or less than 228 feet? Explain.

Other Examples

This pentagon is a regular polygon. All the sides have the same length and all the angles have the same measure.

15.2 cm

15.2 cm + 15.2 cm + 15.2 cm + 15.2 cm + 15.2 cm = 76 cm

The perimeter of the pentagon is 76 centimeters.

Write the perimeter of each polygon.

1.

3 ft

4 ft   2 ft

2.

7.3 cm   7.3 cm

8.2 cm   8.2 cm

6.6 cm

3.

14 in.

$5\frac{1}{4}$ in.

4. If a polygon is regular, how many side lengths do you need to know to determine the perimeter? Explain.

Write the perimeter.

5. Rectangle: length = 24.2 mm
width = 11.5 mm

6. Square: side = 2.2 m

7. Basketball court: length = 90 ft
width = 54 ft

8. Regular octagon:
side = 36 in.

Problem Solving Use the information given on page 152 if you need to.

9. Tonya's tennis court is getting a new fence. It will be 10 feet away from the court all around. How many feet of fencing will be needed?

10. Tonya changes the shape of a piece of paper by cutting off squares. Does the perimeter change as the shape changes?

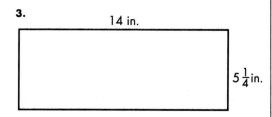

fence

10 ft

10 ft

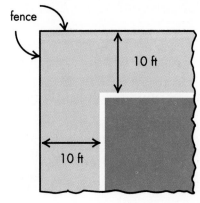

28 cm

21 cm

24 cm   4 cm

4 cm

21 cm   17 cm

28 cm

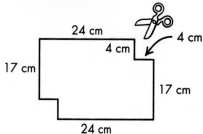

24 cm   4 cm

4 cm

17 cm   17 cm

24 cm

PERIMETER AND POLYGONS

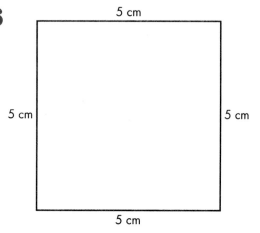

5 cm

5 cm

5 cm

5 cm

In this lesson, you will discover rules to help you find the perimeter of regular and irregular polygons. You will need the recording sheet and a centimeter ruler.

Remember, a regular polygon has congruent sides and congruent angles. A square is a regular polygon.

The perimeter of the square at the right is 20 centimeters. The perimeter can be found with the addition sentence:

5 cm + 5 cm + 5 cm + 5 cm = 20 cm

1. How can you write the addition sentence above as a multiplication sentence? Record your answer in Chart A on the recording sheet.

2. Use the figures and your ruler to complete Chart A on the recording sheet.

3. Look at Chart A. What is the least amount of information you need to find the perimeter of a regular polygon? Write *a*, *b*, or *c*.

   a. number of sides and length of one side

   b. number of sides and length of every side

   c. measure of one angle and length of one side

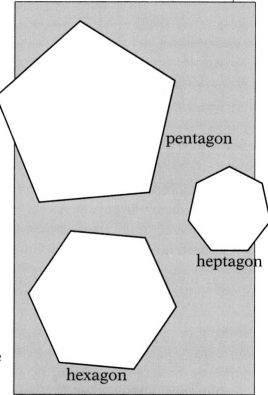

pentagon

heptagon

hexagon

Chart A

Regular Figure	Addition Expression	Multiplication Expression	Perimeter (cm)
square	5 cm + 5 cm + 5 cm + 5 cm		20 cm
pentagon			
hexagon			
heptagon			

4. Write a rule for using multiplication to find the perimeter of a regular polygon.

5. Use your rule to write a multiplication sentence for the perimeter of each regular polygon.

   a. a decagon with one side measuring 9 centimeters

   b. an octagon with one side measuring 4 centimeters

6. The rectangle at the right is not a regular polygon. Why?

7. Measure the rectangle and complete the first row in Chart B on the recording sheet.

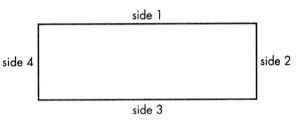

8. Measure the cover of your book and the top of your desk. Find and measure three other rectangular objects in your classroom. Complete Chart B.

9. Look at Chart B. What do you notice about the lengths of the sides in a rectangle?

10. Do you need to know the measure of all four sides of a rectangle to find the perimeter? Explain.

11. Write a rule for finding the perimeter of a rectangle.

Chart B

Object	Length of Side(cm)				Perimeter (cm)
	1	2	3	4	
Rectangle					
Book					
Desk					

12. Use your rule to find the perimeter of each rectangle.
    a. width 5 in., length 6 in.
    b. length 3 ft, width 2 ft

SUMMING IT UP

13. How can multiplication help you find the perimeter of a figure?

14. Discuss with the class your rules for finding:
    a. the perimeter of a regular polygon.
    b. the perimeter of a rectangle.

CIRCUMFERENCE

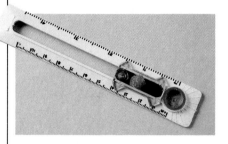

In this lesson, you will work in pairs to discover how some circle measures are related. You will need the recording sheet, a compass, a centimeter ruler, paper, and string.

Three circle measurements are shown and described below.

The **radius** is the distance from the center of the circle to any point on the circle.

The **diameter** is the distance from any point on the circle, through the center, to another point on the circle.

The **circumference** is the distance around the circle.

To draw a circle using a compass:

Draw a dot. Place the center of the red circle of the compass over it.

Set the compass to the radius you want.

Move the compass in a circle around the dot.

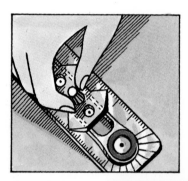

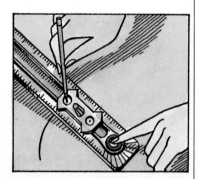

1. Use each radius measure given in the table to draw a circle on your recording sheet. Mark the center of each circle with a dot. Label the circles 1 through 4.

2. Measure the radius at 3 different points on each circle. Does the radius change?

Circle	Radius (cm)	Diameter (cm)	Circumference (cm)
1	2		
2	3		
3	4		
4	5		

3. Using your centimeter ruler, measure the diameter of each circle. Record each measure in the table on your recording sheet.

4. Measure the diameter of each circle, using 3 different sets of points (remember to go through the center point each time). Does the diameter change?

5. Compare the lengths of the radius and the diameter of each circle. How many times as great as the radius is the diameter? Why is this so?

6. Use the string to measure the circumference of each circle. Measure the string length with your centimeter ruler. Record each measure.

7. Compare the measures of the diameter and circumference of each circle. About how many times greater is the circumference than the diameter?

8. Use your findings to predict the diameter and circumference of a circle with a radius of 6 centimeters.

9. Draw the circle described in exercise 8. Measure it to check your prediction. Was your prediction correct?

SUMMING IT UP

10. Write a rule about the relationship you see in the table between:

   a. the diameter and the radius of a circle.

   b. the circumference and the diameter of a circle.

11. Draw four more circles on another piece of paper. Do your rules work for these circles also?

12. Discuss your rules with the class.

Elapsed Time

Jim wants to know how much time he will spend traveling by train between Newton and Ashton.

Here is part of the train schedule he uses. He plans to take the 10:40 train from Newton.

To Ashton	
Newton	10:40
Fleetwood	11:02
Short Isle	11:25
Wilburn	11:53
North Glen	**12:25**
Ashton	**1:15**
P.M. in darker print	

To Newton	
Ashton	**12:00**
North Glen	—
Wilburn	—
Short Isle	**1:28**
Fleetwood	—
Newton	**2:13**
P.M. in darker print	

Think
- How are A.M. and P.M. indicated on this schedule?

To find how much time Jim will spend traveling, first find the time it takes to travel each way.

From 10:40 A.M. to 12:40 P.M. = 2 hours

From 12:40 P.M. to 1:15 P.M. = 35 minutes

The train ride to Ashton takes 2 hours and 35 minutes.

The next day, Jim plans to take the 12 noon train home from Ashton. This train arrives in Newton at 2:13 P.M.

The train to Newton takes 2 hours and 13 minutes.

To find Jim's total travel time, add:

Train to Ashton	2 h 35 min
Train to Newton	+ 2 h 13 min
	4 h 48 min

Jim will spend 4 hours and 48 minutes traveling between Newton and Ashton.

How much longer will the train ride to Ashton take than the train ride to Newton?

Subtract.

	2 h 35 min
	− 2 h 13 min
	22 min

The train ride to Ashton will take 22 minutes longer.

Write how much time will pass.

1. from 6:15 A.M. to 11:25 A.M.

2. from 4:15 P.M. to 7:23 P.M.

3. from 3:00 A.M. to 6:25 P.M.

4. from 5:20 P.M. to 9:20 A.M.

Write the answer.

5.
```
  12 h 7 min
−  5 h 3 min
```

6.
```
  12 h 57 min
−  3 h  1 min
```

7.
```
  17 min 37 s
+ 41 min 11 s
```

8. Explain whether you would use "5:20 P.M." or "5 hours 20 minutes" to describe the length of time between two events.

[ID]P:0505159-1

Write how much time will pass.

9. from 8:40 A.M to 11:42 A.M.

10. from 10:16 A.M. to 2:45 P.M.

11. from 6:00 P.M to 9:23 P.M.

12. from 11:50 P.M. to 1:05 A.M.

Write the answer.

13.
```
  18 h 7 min
+  5 h 5 min
```

14.
```
  22 h 29 min
+ 17 h 12 min
```

15.
```
  57 h 43 min
−  3 h 26 min
```

16.
```
  12 min 42 s
− 10 min 12 s
```

17.
```
  8 min 47 s
− 3 min 29 s
```

18.
```
  49 min 25 s
+  7 min 13 s
```

Problem Solving Use the train schedule on page 158.

19. On the route to Newton from Ashton, which is shorter, the trip from Ashton to Short Isle, or Short Isle to Newton?

20. On the train route to Ashton, is the ride from Short Isle to Wilburn closer to half an hour or an hour?

21. How long is the train ride from Fleetwood to North Glen? From Fleetwood to Ashton?

22. Write your own word problem using the information given in the train schedule.

WORK BACKWARD

When you work backward to solve a problem, make sure you undo each step in reverse order.

Mr. Simms lives in Rosedale and works in Mill City. His home is a 30-minute drive from the Rosedale Station. The train ride to Rosedale takes $1\frac{1}{2}$ hours. His office is a 15-minute walk from the Mill City Station. Mr. Simms wants to know the latest he can leave the office and still be home by 6:15 P.M.

Rapid-Way Transit Westbound Train to Rosedale				
Station	**Train Departs (P.M.)**			
Mill City	3:30	4:00	4:30	5:00

Look at choices A and B for working backward that have been started below.

Latest time train can leave Mill City	Train ride from Mill City to Rosedale	Latest time to arrive at station	Drive home from station	Latest time to arrive home
A. ? ←	$- 1\frac{1}{2}$ hr	5:45 ←	$- 30$ min	6:15
B. ? ←	$+ 1\frac{1}{2}$ hr	6:45 ←	$+ 30$ min	6:15

Think

- How are the two ways alike? Different?

- Which way will help you solve the problem?

Finish working backward to solve the problem.

Work forward to check your answer.

Read the problem. Complete one of the two choices for
working backward to solve it.

1. Michelle was doing number tricks. She said,
   "Pick a number. First, multiply it by 4. Second,
   add 8. Third, take half of your answer. Tell me
   what you end up with." Jerry said he ended up
   with 56. What number did he pick?

Number before 2nd step	Undo 2nd step	Number before 3rd step	Undo 3rd step	Number at end
A. ? ←	-8	14 ←	$\div 4$	56
B. ? ←	-8	112 ←	$\times 2$	56

·················
APPLICATION

Work in pairs to solve each problem. Work backward or use
other strategies.

2. Jo found these directions to
   school. Where is the starting point
   for the directions?

Walk 3 blocks east.
Walk 2 blocks north.
Walk 2 blocks east.
Walk 4 blocks north
to school.

SCHOOL

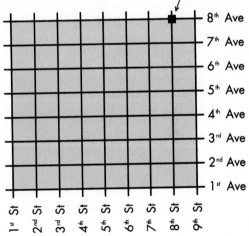

3. Kyle started the day with a big
   stack of baseball cards. He gave a
   dozen cards to Abe. Then he took
   the rest and made 2 equal stacks.
   He gave one of the stacks to
   Lewis. Later, Kyle got 5 cards
   from Alicia. He counted his cards
   and found that he had 52. How
   many did he have at the start?

4. Mr. Carlson wants to have a
   booklet printed by October 15th. It
   will take 4 weeks to write it, 3
   weeks to get it ready for printing,
   and 2 weeks to print it. When does
   the writing need to begin?

TIME ZONES

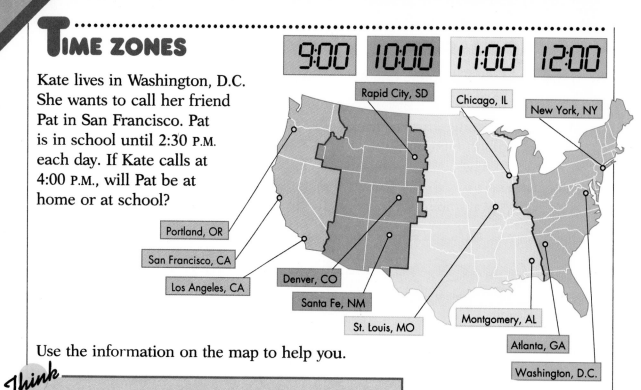

9:00 10:00 11:00 12:00

Rapid City, SD

Chicago, IL

New York, NY

Portland, OR

San Francisco, CA

Los Angeles, CA

Denver, CO

Santa Fe, NM

St. Louis, MO

Montgomery, AL

Atlanta, GA

Washington, D.C.

Kate lives in Washington, D.C. She wants to call her friend Pat in San Francisco. Pat is in school until 2:30 P.M. each day. If Kate calls at 4:00 P.M., will Pat be at home or at school?

Use the information on the map to help you.

Think

- What happens to the time when you cross time zones from east to west?

Since San Francisco is 3 time zones to the west, count backward 3 hours to find the time in San Francisco:

1 hr   1 hr   1 hr

4:00 P.M., 3:00 P.M., 2:00 P.M., 1:00 P.M.

It will be 1:00 P.M. in San Francisco, so Pat will still be in school.

If Pat returns Kate's call at 4:00 P.M. San Francisco time, what time will Kate receive the call in Washington, D.C.?

Think

- Compared with San Francisco time, is it always earlier or later in Washington, D.C.?

Kate will receive Pat's call at 7:00 P.M.

GUIDED PRACTICE

Use the map on page 162 if you need help. Write the time in St. Louis when it is:

1. 6:00 A.M. in New York.

2. 7:15 P.M. in Portland.

3. 10:23 P.M. in Rapid City.

4. 11:55 A.M. in Atlanta.

5. How can a 5-hour flight leave the East Coast at 1:00 P.M. and arrive on the West Coast at 3:00 P.M.?

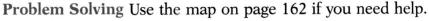

INDEPENDENT PRACTICE

Copy and complete. What time is it in the other three cities?

	Atlanta	Chicago	Santa Fe	Los Angeles
6.	5:30 P.M.			
7.		3:15 A.M.		
8.			10:00 P.M.	
9.				noon

Problem Solving Use the map on page 162 if you need help.

10. Ana Ramirez lives in Denver. She would like to call her sister in Atlanta to wish her a happy birthday. Ana's sister was born at 2:37 P.M. When should Ana call if she wants to reach her sister at 2:37 P.M., Atlanta time?

11. Roger flies from Montgomery, Alabama, to Anchorage, Alaska. How should Roger reset his watch to have the correct time in Alaska? To find the time in Anchorage, Alaska, use the Atlas section of the Data Book.

12. The Portland Trailblazer game will be broadcast live from New York at 8:00 P.M. tonight. Emma lives in California. Will she see the game begin at 5:00 P.M. or 11:00 P.M.?

USING A CALENDAR

Tomorrow, June 16, is Pimone's birthday. Her parents read about a special air fare for students. They plan to surprise Pimone with a trip next month from New York City to San Francisco to visit her grandparents. She will depart for San Francisco on July 6 and return on July 27.

Work in groups to solve each problem.

1. Pimone's mom gets a flight schedule. She looks at the calendar for June and July. If she buys Pimone's ticket on June 16, can she purchase the ticket at the discount fare?

June

Sunday	Monday	Tuesday	Wednesday	Thursday	Friday	Saturday
			1	2	3	4
5	6	7	8	9	10	11
12	13	14	15	16	17	18
19	20	21	22	23	24	25
26	27	28	29	30		

July

Sunday	Monday	Tuesday	Wednesday	Thursday	Friday	Saturday
					1	2
3	4	5	6	7	8	9
10	11	12	13	14	15	16
17	18	19	20	21	22	23
24	25	26	27	28	29	30
31						

LOW LOW PRICE!
ROUND TRIP TO SAN FRANCISCO
ONLY $699 FOR STUDENTS!
(To qualify for this *low, low rate*, you must buy your ticket at least 2 weeks before departure time and stay more than one weekend.)

Pimone's Flight

JULY 6

DEPARTURE NEW YORK	ARRIVAL SAN FRANCISCO
8:15 am	11:15 am
10:35 am	1:35 pm
2:05 pm	5:05 pm
5:30 pm	8:30 pm

JULY 27

DEPARTURE SAN FRANCISCO	ARRIVAL NEW YORK
8:15 am	4:15 pm
11:40 am	7:40 pm
2:35 pm	10:35 pm
5:50 pm	1:50 am

2. Pimone's parents also plan to visit San Francisco. They will leave exactly one week after Pimone's departure. What date is that?

3. If Pimone's parents stay for one week, on what date will they leave San Francisco?

4. Pimone's cousin Lena is also a student. She may be able to go with Pimone, but she won't know until June 23. Can Lena buy the ticket on June 23 and still qualify for the discount?

5. Pimone's grandparents want Pimone to stay a week longer. If she remains an extra week, will she get back to New York City in time for her friend's birthday on August 4?

Solve each problem. Use the Atlas section of your Data Book if you need to.

6. Pimone's mom wants Pimone to call home as soon as she arrives in San Francisco. What time will it be in New York when Pimone arrives in San Francisco?

7. How long is the flight from New York City to San Francisco?

8. How long is the flight from San Francisco to New York City?

TEMPERATURE

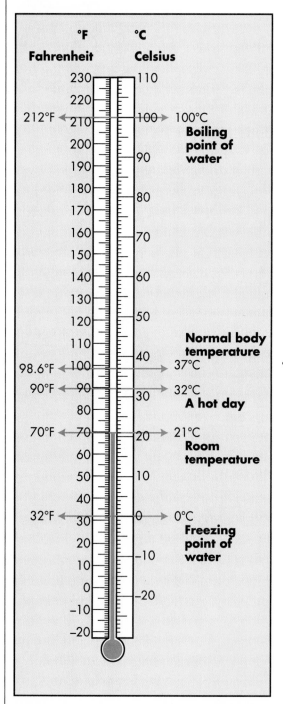

°F Fahrenheit	°C Celsius	
230	110	
220		
212°F → 210	100 → 100°C	
200		**Boiling point of water**
190	90	
180	80	
170		
160	70	
150		
140	60	
130		
120	50	
110		**Normal body temperature**
98.6°F → 100	40 → 37°C	
90°F → 90	32°C	
80	30	**A hot day**
70°F → 70	20 → 21°C	**Room temperature**
60		
50	10	
40		
32°F → 30	0 → 0°C	**Freezing point of water**
20		
10	−10	
0		
−10	−20	
−20		

Two types of scales are used to measure temperature.

One scale measures the temperature in degrees **Fahrenheit** (°F). This scale is often used in the United States to report the temperature.

The other scale measures the temperature in degrees **Celsius** (°C). This scale is mostly used in other countries to report the temperature. It is also used in this country.

When you measure the temperature of ice water, a Fahrenheit thermometer will read 32°F. A Celsius thermometer will read 0°C.

Think

- Which scale has the greater range of numbers?

Both thermometers show temperatures below zero. Degrees below zero are written with a minus (−) sign.

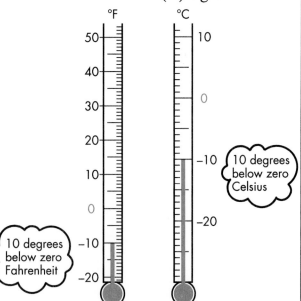

10 degrees below zero Fahrenheit

10 degrees below zero Celsius

GUIDED PRACTICE

Solve each problem.

1. Copy the graph. Record each thermometer reading on the graph. Connect the points.

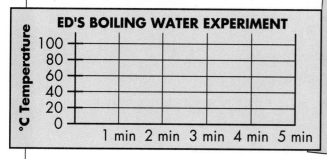

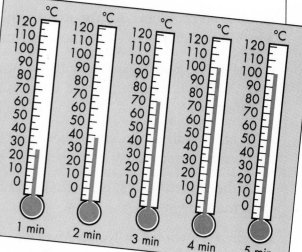

Write the letter of the more reasonable temperature.

2. a glass of juice.
   a. 15°C   **b.** 50°C

3. a hot bath
   a. 220°F   **b.** 85°F

4. melted butter
   a. 30°F   **b.** 98°F

5. What would each temperature have been in exercise 1 if Ed had used a Fahrenheit thermometer? Use the thermometer on page 166.

INDEPENDENT PRACTICE

Problem Solving. Use the picture below.

6. List the temperatures from warmest to coldest.

7. What would each temperature be if it were measured with a Fahrenheit thermometer? Use the thermometer on page 166.

USING MATH SENSE

Solve each problem. Use the temperature graph and map of
South America in the Almanac and Atlas sections of your Data Book.

1. In La Paz, Bolivia, is it usually warmer in January
   or July? What is the average temperature
   difference?

2. In how many of the cities shown on the graph is
   it warmer in January than in July?

3. In the United States, is it usually warmer in
   January or in July?

4. When it's winter in North America, what season
   do you think it is in South America?

5. In which of the cities on the graph is it warmer
   in July than in January?

6. Do you think that city is north or south of the
   equator? Why do you think so?

7. Use the map of South America to check your
   answer to exercise 6.

8. Which of the cities on the graph is closest to the
   equator? Farthest from the equator?

9. Find the average temperature difference between
   January and July for each of the two cities in
   exercise 8. What do you notice?

SECTION REVIEW

for pages 148–168

Find the perimeter. Write the letter of the correct answer.

1. a. 340 yd
   b. 170 yd
   c. 120 yd
   d. 220 yd

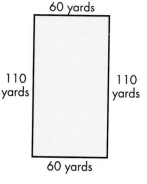

60 yards

110 yards   110 yards

60 yards

2. a. 12 cm
   b. 5 cm
   c. 2 cm
   d. 10 cm

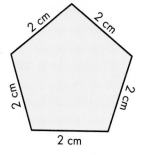

2 cm   2 cm

2 cm   2 cm

2 cm

3. Square: side = 2 ft
   a. 6 ft
   b. 8 ft
   c. 16 ft
   d. 4 ft

4. Rectangle: length = 4 in.
   width = 3 in.
   a. 14 in.
   b. 144 in.
   c. 7 in.
   d. 10 in.

Write the letter that tells how much time will pass.

5. from 1:10 P.M to 4:40 P.M.
   a. 3:30
   b. 5 h 50 min
   c. 5 h 40 min
   d. 3 h 30 min

6. from 5:05 A.M. to 8:05 A.M.
   a. 3 h 45 min
   b. 3 h
   c. 13 h 10 min
   d. 3:00

Write the answer.

7.   5 h 19 min
   + 7 h 15 min

8.   15 h 35 min
   − 6 h 20 min

9.   21 min 30 s
   + 20 min 25 s

Use the drawing of the pentagon at the right.

10. What is the greatest number of diagonals that can be drawn from one vertex?

11. What is the total number of diagonals that can be drawn in the pentagon?

CHAPTER REVIEW

Language Connection

Group your vocabulary words into three categories: polygons, circles, and temperature. Explain your grouping. Use the glossary if you need help. Some words may be placed in more than one group.

VOCABULARY WORDS

Celsius	diagonal	perimeter
circumference	diameter	radius
congruent	Fahrenheit	measure
degrees	pentagon	diagonal
sides	compass	thermometer

Test ....

Use a ruler to measure each object to the nearest inch or fraction of an inch, as shown.

1. $\frac{1}{4}$ inch

2. $\frac{1}{2}$ inch

3. inch

4. $\frac{1}{8}$ inch

Write the perimeter of each polygon.

5. 4 cm 4 cm 6 cm

6. 6 in. 3 in. 6 in.

7. 2 ft 2 ft 2 ft 2 ft 2 ft

8. 7 in. 7 in. 7 in. 7 in.

Write the answer.

9.   23 min 12 s
   + 30 min 18 s

10.   61 h 12 min
    − 53 h 11 min

Write how much time will pass.

11. from 9:10 A.M. to 12:10 P.M.

12. from 10:15 A.M. to 11:45 P.M.

PROBLEM SOLVING

U.S. Standard Time Zones			
9:00 A.M.	10:00 A.M.	11:00 A.M.	12:00 P.M.
Portland	Phoenix	Chicago	Atlanta

Use the time zone table if you need to.

13. Nathaniel flies from Atlanta, Georgia, to Portland, Oregon. He arrives in Portland at 2:00 A.M., Atlanta time. To what time should Nathaniel reset his watch to have the correct time in Portland?

14. The Bradshaw's are building a rectangular pen for their goats. It will be 65 feet long and 32 feet wide. What will be the perimeter of the pen?

15. Abbey lives $1\frac{1}{2}$ miles from school. She leaves her school at 2:15 P.M. She walks and arrives home at 2:50 P.M.. How long does it take Abbey to walk home?

16. Eli lives in Phoenix, Arizona. He wants to call his sister in Chicago, Illinois. When should Eli call if he wants to reach his sister at 6:00 P.M., Chicago time?

CUMULATIVE REVIEW

Write the answer.

17. $3\overline{)4557}$ **18.** $19\overline{)2694}$ **19.** $43\overline{)12,169}$ **20.** $27\overline{)2631}$

Use the line graph to answer exercises 21–23.

21. In which year did the greatest number of people sell crafts at the fair?

22. The same number of people sold crafts in which two years?

23. Between which two years did the number of people increase the most?

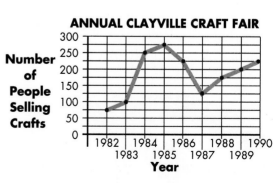

ANNUAL CLAYVILLE CRAFT FAIR

EXCURSION

CRITICAL THINKING

VENN DIAGRAMS

Venn diagrams are drawings that show relationships among sets of objects. Read each statement below. Then look at how the Venn diagram at the right shows that information.

All asps are snakes.

In this Venn diagram, notice that the blue circle is completely inside the red circle. The blue area represents the asps. The red area represents all types of snakes.

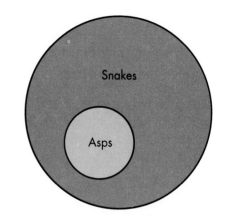

Some fiction books are paperbacks.

Notice that the two circles overlap. The purple area represents all the paperback books that are fiction books.

Which color represents fiction books that are not paperbacks?

Which color represents paperbacks that are nonfiction?

No artichokes are bananas.

Here the two circles are completely separate. This shows that there is no object that is in both sets. No bananas are artichokes, and no artichokes are bananas.

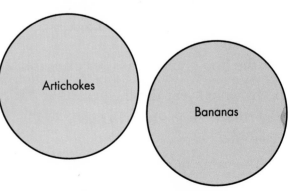

Use the Venn diagram. Write *true* or *false*.

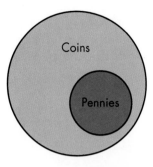
Coins
Pennies

1. All pennies are coins.

2. Some coins are pennies.

3. No coins are pennies.

Use the Venn diagram. Write *all, some,* or *no.*

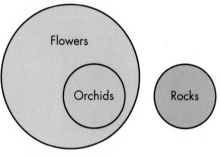
Flowers
Orchids
Rocks

4. ___ flowers are orchids.

5. ___ rocks are flowers.

6. ___ orchids are flowers.

Use the information to draw a Venn diagram.

7. Some parakeets are blue birds.
Some blue birds are parakeets.

8. All whales are mammals. Some
mammals are whales.

9. Write a sentence to describe the
information in this Venn diagram.

Clams   Freshwater
Animals

Look at this Venn diagram. What is
represented by each of the labeled areas?

10. Area A

11. Area B

12. Area C

13. Area D

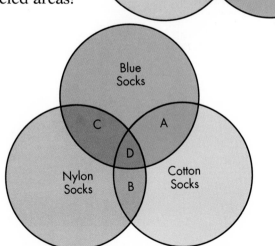
Blue
Socks
C   A
D
Nylon   Cotton
Socks B Socks

CHAPTER 6

MULTIPLICATION OF DECIMALS

Health

Reaction Time When someone tosses a ball to you, how do you react? You probably raise your hands to catch it. Think of how quickly this happens. First, you see the ball. Then, your brain processes the information. Finally, you react by raising your hands. This all happens in just a fraction of a second. The amount of time it takes to react is called reaction time.

Try the following activity to test your reaction time. Work with a partner.

- Have your partner hold a ruler at the top end. You hold your thumb and forefinger apart at the bottom, but do not touch the ruler.

- Your partner will drop the ruler with no warning. Your job is to react by catching the ruler between your forefinger and thumb.

- The distance the ruler drops is shown by where you catch the ruler. Use the chart to find your reaction time.

Try the activity five times. Does your reaction time change? Is it possible to improve your reaction time?

10 cm drop = 0.14 seconds

DISTANCE DROPPED	REACTION TIME
5 centimeters	0.10 second
10 centimeters	0.14 second
15 centimeters	0.17 second
20 centimeters	0.20 second
25 centimeters	0.23 second
30 centimeters	0.25 second

MULTIPLICATION OF DECIMALS

In this lesson, you will explore multiplying whole numbers and decimals. You will need squared paper. Work in small groups.

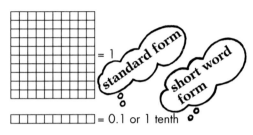

= 1   *standard form*   *short word form*

▶ The 10 x 10 squared-paper area model at the right can be used to show decimals.

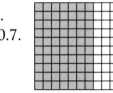 = 0.1 or 1 tenth

□ = 0.01 or 1 hundredth

The picture at the right shows 7 tenths. It can be written as either 7 tenths or 0.7. Look at some other examples:

4 tenths, or 0.4

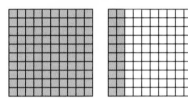

12 tenths, or 1.2

1. Write each number in standard form.
- **a.** 1 tenth
- **b.** 3 tenths
- **c.** 8 tenths
- **d.** 23 tenths
- **e.** 15 tenths
- **f.** 59 tenths

▶ You can use the picture to help you multiply a whole number by a decimal.

Multiply: 3 × 0.6

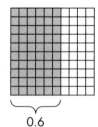 

0.6

The entire shaded area is the product of 3 × 0.6.

The picture has 18 tenths shaded.

3 × 6 tenths = 18 tenths

3 × 0.6 = 1.8

Copy and complete each multiplication sentence below. Use the model.

2. 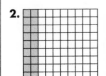   **3.**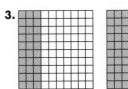

4×2 tenths = ▓ tenths

$4 \times 0.2 = ▓$

3 tenths $\times 2 = ▓$ tenths

$0.3 \times 2 = ▓$

4. How could knowing your whole number facts help you find the products in exercises 2 and 3?

Write each product. Use squared paper to make a model if you need to.

5. 12×1 tenth
12×0.1

6. 4 tenths $\times 9$
0.4×9

7. 4×3 tenths
4×0.3

8. 8 tenths $\times 7$
0.8×7

9. 2 tenths $\times 7$
0.2×7

10. 5 tenths $\times 3$
0.5×3

11. 9×6 tenths
9×0.6

12. 6×9 tenths
6×0.9

13. How many decimal places are there in each of the decimal factors above? In each product?

. . . .

SUMMING IT UP

14. How is the product of 6×0.4 similar to the product of 6×4? How is it different?

15. What do you notice about the number of decimal places in the product when there is one decimal place in the factors?

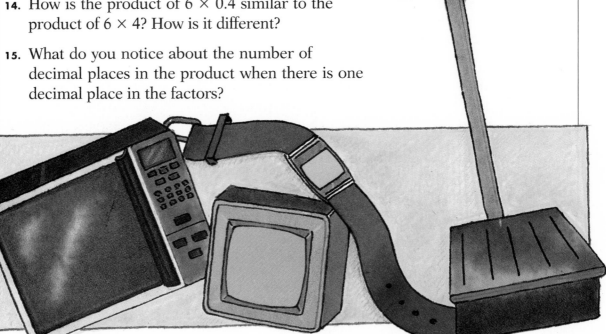

MULTIPLYING BY 10, 100, AND 1000

You can use mental math to multiply decimals by 10, 100, and 1000. Look for patterns in the multiplication sentences below to help you discover the mental math rule.

Use a calculator to complete each multiplication sentence. Write the completed sentence.

1. 64.208 × 10 = ▦
64.208 × 100 = ▦
64.208 × 1000 = ▦

2. 3.57 × 10 = ▦
3.57 × 100 = ▦
3.57 × 1000 = ▦

3. 0.8 × 10 = ▦
0.8 × 100 = ▦
0.8 × 1000 = ▦

4. What patterns do you notice?

5. In exercise 3, what happens to the place value of the digit 8 when you multiply by 10? By 100? By 1000?

Predict the product. Use the patterns to help you. Write your predictions.

6. 5.346 × 10
5.346 × 100
5.346 × 1000

7. 23.8 × 10
23.8 × 100
23.8 × 1000

8. 0.05 × 10
0.05 × 100
0.05 × 1000

Use a calculator to check your predictions.

Use the patterns to write the product.

9. 6.85 × 100

10. 2.3 × 10

11. 0.1 × 10

12. 47.21 × 1000

13. 19.4 × 10

14. 0.723 × 1000

15. 152.39 × 10

16. 0.9 × 1000

17. 0.89 × 1000

18. 0.06 × 100

19. 5.804 × 100

20. 0.005 × 10

SUMMING IT UP

21. Write a rule that you can use to mentally multiply a decimal by 10, 100, and 1000.

22. Explain how to find 5.3 × 1000 using your rule.

23. Explain how to find 42 × 100 using your rule.
HINT: 42 = 42.0

24. Test your rule. Choose one factor from box A. Use it to multiply each of the factors in box B. Write each sentence. Discuss your rule with the class.

A		
10	100	
	1000	

	B	
63.2	0.2	4.04
0.018	90	68
537	0.001	228.79

Maintain • **Measurement**

Write the perimeter of each polygon.

1.

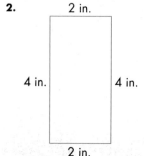
6 cm, 6 cm, 6 cm, 6 cm, 6 cm, 6 cm

2.

2 in.
4 in.   4 in.
2 in.

3.

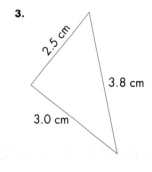
2.5 cm, 3.8 cm, 3.0 cm

4.

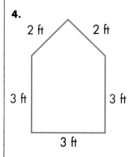
2 ft, 2 ft, 3 ft, 3 ft, 3 ft

5.

4.1 cm
4.1 cm   4.1 cm
4.1 cm

6.

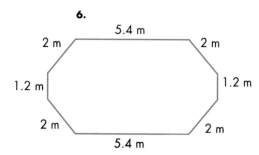
2 m, 5.4 m, 2 m, 1.2 m, 1.2 m, 2 m, 5.4 m, 2 m

PRODUCTS

TUBES OF PAINT
$4.47 EACH

Can Lisa buy 4 tubes of paint with $23?

You can answer this question by estimating. First, make a quick estimate using only the dollar amount.

4 × $4.47   (4 × $4 = $16)

Since $4.47 is greater than $4, the actual product is greater than $16.

Four tubes of paint cost more than $16. But do they cost as much as $23?

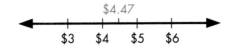

$4.47

$3 $4 $5 $6

4 × $4.47   (4 × $5 = $20)

Since $4.47 is less than $5, you know that 4 tubes of paint will cost less than $20.

You can say your estimate is "between" two numbers. You know that 4 tubes of paint will cost between $16 and $20. So, Lisa can buy 4 tubes of paint with $23.

 Think
═ • Can Lisa buy 8 tubes of paint with $30?
   Explain.

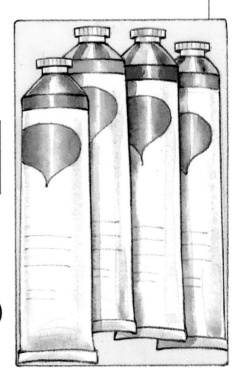

Other Examples

Estimate: 5 × 7.6

(5 × 7 = 35)   (5 × 8 = 40)   Since 7.6 is between 7 and 8, then 5 × 7.6 is between 5 × 7 and 5 × 8.

"Between 35 and 40" is a good estimate.

Write the missing number.

1. 5 × $2.67 Estimate: between $10 and $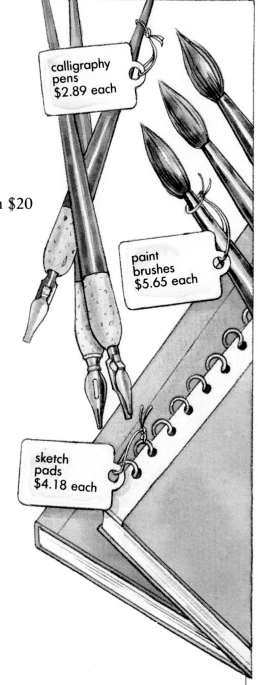

2. 4 × $3.35 Estimate: between $███ and $16

3. 7 × $2.79 Estimate: between $███ and $███

4. 3 × 5.8 Estimate: between ███ and ███

5. Look at exercise 1. Can you buy 5 caps with $20 if each cap costs $2.67? Explain.

INDEPENDENT PRACTICE

Write the missing number.

6. 5 × $3.78 Estimate: between $15 and $███

7. 6 × $7.42 Estimate: between $███ and $48

8. 3 × $2.59 Estimate: between $███ and $███

9. 4 × 2.8 Estimate: between ███ and ███

10. 6 × 3.52 Estimate: between ███ and ███

Problem Solving Estimate.

11. Can you buy 2 pens with $6?

12. Can you buy 5 sketch pads with $20?

13. Can you buy 6 paintbrushes with $25?

14. Can you buy 8 pens with $30?

15. Can you buy 3 sketch pads with $15?

calligraphy pens
$2.89 each

paint brushes
$5.65 each

sketch pads
$4.18 each

Maintain • Adding Decimals

Group the following numbers into 3 sets. Each set must have 3 numbers and a sum of 9.3.

1.4	1.2	2.1	2.6	4.6
3.5	4.6	2.9	5	

DECIMALS AND WHOLE NUMBERS

Mac is painting 3 rooms. The rooms are all the same size. If each room needs 4.5 liters of paint, how much paint will he need in all?

Multiply: 3 × 4.5 L

$(3 \times 4 = 12)$ $(3 \times 5 = 15)$

Estimate: 3 × 4.5

Mac needs between 12 and 15 liters of paint.

This problem could be solved using squared paper.

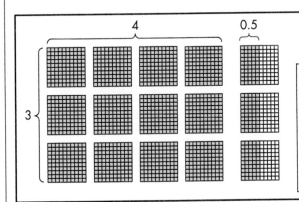

$$
\begin{array}{r}
4.5 \text{ L} \\
\times\ 3 \\
\hline
1.5 \quad \leftarrow 3 \times 0.5 \\
12 \quad \leftarrow 3 \times 4 \\
\hline
13.5 \text{ L}
\end{array}
$$

> 13.5 is reasonable. It is between 12 and 15.

Here is a shorter way to multiply.

● Multiply as you would with whole numbers.

$$
\begin{array}{r}
4.5 \text{ L} \\
\times\ 3 \\
\hline
135 \text{ L}
\end{array}
$$

● Write the decimal point.

$$
\begin{array}{r}
4.5 \text{ L} \\
\times\ 3 \\
\hline
13.5 \text{ L}
\end{array}
$$

> 45 tenths × 3 = 135 tenths

Mac will need 13.5 liters of paint in all.

Think

- What is the total number of decimal places in the factors of 4.5 × 3 = 13.5? What is the total number of decimal places in the product?

Write the product. Use squared paper if you need help.

1. 7 × 2.5

2. 1.7 × 6

3. 2 × 25.4

4.　　5.1
　　× 9

5.　　6.8
　　× 7

6.　　35.1
　　× 2

7.　　29.6
　　× 6

8. Which way of multiplying do you like better, using squared paper or the shorter method? Explain.

Write the product. Use squared paper if you need help.

9.　　22.4
　　× 3

10.　　3.7
　　× 4

11.　　31.4
　　× 6

12.　　41.5
　　× 5

13. 17.3 × 5

14. 6 × 6.4

15. 8.2 × 9

16. 2 × 54.5

Write only those products greater than 25.

17.　　4.7
　　× 6

18.　　4.9
　　× 2

19.　　2.8
　　× 4

20.　　7.6
　　× 4

21. 22.8 × 6

22. 5.5 × 2

23. 6.3 × 8

24. 18.9 × 7

Problem Solving

25. Mac knows that a large can of paint holds about 3.8 liters. He needs 13.5 liters to paint the three rooms.
    a. How many cans should he buy?
    b. Will he have more than 2 liters left over?

26. Mac earns $7.75 each hour he paints. If he works 8 hours, will he earn more than or less than $50? Explain.

ZEROS IN THE PRODUCT

Alicia's clock uses about 0.02 kilowatt-hours of electricity a day. About how many kilowatt-hours (kWh) of electricity does the clock use in 4 days?

Multiply: 4 × 0.02

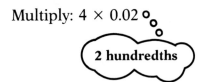

2 hundredths

● Multiply as you would with whole numbers.

$$\begin{array}{r} 0.02 \text{ kWh} \\ \times\ 4 \\ \hline 8 \text{ kWh} \end{array}$$

You may write a zero in the ones place for products less than 1.

● Write the decimal point.

$$\begin{array}{r} 0.02 \text{ kWh} \\ \times\ 4 \\ \hline 0.08 \text{ kWh} \end{array}$$

Write a zero to show the correct number of decimal places.

2 hundredths × 4 = 8 hundredths

The clock uses about 0.08 kilowatt-hours of electricity in 4 days.

Think

- Why would it have been incorrect to write the zero to the right of the 8; that is, to write 0.80?

- What is the total number of decimal places in the factors of 4 × 0.02 = 0.08? In the product of 4 × 0.02 = 0.08?

Properties for multiplying whole numbers also apply to multiplying decimals.

Property	Example
Associative	(6 × 5) × 2.35 = 6 × (5 × 2.35)
Commutative	7 × 0.007 = 0.007 × 7
Distributive	4 × 8.2 = (4 × 8) + (4 × 0.2)
Multiplying by 1	6.5 × 1 = 6.5
Multiplying by Zero	0.123 × 0 = 0

Write the product.

1.   0.09
   ×   3

2.   0.001
   ×   3

3.   0.023
   ×   5

4.   1.007
   ×   2

5. 3.004 × 2

6. 20.086 × 2

7. 3.001 × 11

8. 15 × 0.001

9. Show how to solve exercise 7 using the distributive property.

Write the product.

10.   2.03
   ×   3

11.   0.05
   ×   6

12.   0.111
   ×   5

13.   2.03
   ×   9

14. 0.006 × 0

15. 34.002 × 3

16. 3.75 × 50

17. 1 × 0.42

Match the exercise with an equal product. Write the letter of the correct answer.

18. 3.13 × 4   a. 29.14

19. 5 × 8.06   b. (5 × 8) × 0.06

20. 5 × (8 × 0.06)   c. 5 × 0

21. 29.14 × 1   d. (5 × 8) + (5 × 0.06)

22. 5 × 8.06 × 0   e. 4 × 3.13

Problem Solving

23. Suzanne's refrigerator uses about 1.5 kilowatt-hours of electricity a day.
   a. About how much electricity does it use in 10 days?
   b. It costs 12¢ for each kilowatt-hour of electricity. About how much does it cost to run the refrigerator for a week?

USING STRATEGIES

Your health depends in part on eating the proper foods. Charts like the ones below and on the next page can help you choose what to eat.

If you get stuck, remember...
Tips for Problem Solving
on page 448

Partial List of Recommended Daily Requirements

Age	Weight (pounds)	Height (inches)	Calories	Protein (g)	Iron (mg)	Calcium (mg)
Boys (9–12)	72	55	2400	60	15	1000
Girls (9–12)	72	55	2200	55	15	1100

Work in groups. Use the charts to solve each problem.

1. About how much protein do 10-year-old girls need each day? How much different are the protein needs of 10-year-old boys and girls?

Food	Approximate measure		Calories	Protein (g)	Iron (mg)	Calcium (mg)
Peaches	1 cup	257 g	200	1	52	11
Raisins	$\frac{1}{2}$ cup	80 g	230	2	2.8	50
Strawberries	1 cup	227 g	242	1	1.3	50

2. Which has more calories, $\frac{1}{2}$ cup of raisins or 2 cups of peaches?

3. Which has more calories, 100 grams of raisins or 100 grams of strawberries?

4. How much iron is in 3 cups of strawberries?

	Item	Approximate Measure		Calories	Protein (g)	Calcium (mg)	Iron (mg)
Meal A	Fried Chicken	3 oz	85 g	185	23	10	1.4
	Carrots	1 cup	150 g	45	1	38	0.9
	Biscuit	1	38 g	130	3	61	0.7
	Margarine	1 tbsp	14 g	100	trace	3	0
	Custard	1 cup	248 g	285	13	278	1
Meal B	Swordfish	1 steak	100 g	180	27	20	1.1
	Onions	1 cup	210 g	80	2	67	1
	Peas	1 cup	100 g	68	5	19	1.8
	Noodles	$\frac{1}{2}$ cup	80 g	100	3.5	8	0.5
	Milk	1 glass	244 g	165	8	285	0.5

5. Look at the two meals listed above.
   a. Which has more grams of food?
   b. Which has more calories?
   c. Which has more protein?

6. How would substituting 1 cup of peaches for the custard in meal A change the total calories? The total iron?

PROJECT • Science

The General Information section of your Data Book contains a more complete listing of foods. Use it and the charts on these two pages to plan one breakfast, one lunch, and one dinner. You need to:

• Keep the total number of calories between 2000 and 2500.

• Be sure to meet the recommended daily requirements for iron and calcium for your age group.

List the foods and approximate measures of the foods for each meal. Write the total number of calories and milligrams of iron and calcium.

ESTIMATE OR EXACT

An estimate tells you about how much. Many times an estimate is all you need to know. Other times you need an exact answer. These questions can help you decide whether you should estimate or get an exact answer.

Questions to consider:

- Is "about how much" all I need to know?

- Is an estimate enough to solve the problem?

- Is paper and pencil or a calculator not available?

- Is it impossible to get an exact answer?

- Am I just checking whether an answer is reasonable?

Think

- Would you estimate or compute the exact number of people in the United States? Why?

INDEPENDENT PRACTICE

Solve each problem. Write whether you estimated or computed the exact answer.

1.

$4.19

Is $10 enough to buy 3 pairs of socks?

2.

$4.79 a yard

About how much will 3 yards of material cost?

3.

I run 2.4 miles each day

How many miles will he run in 1 week?

4.

5.35 × 7.8

Is the answer displayed on the calculator reasonable?

SECTION REVIEW

for pages 176–188

Solve each problem.

1. Sally earns $6.50 an hour shoveling
   snow. She shovels one driveway for
   2 hours and another driveway for
   1 hour. How much does she earn?

2. Mr. Perez drives a total of 9.7 kilometers
   each day, traveling to and from work.
   Does he drive more than or less
   than 50 kilometers to and
   from work in 5 days?

Write the letter of the correct answer.

3. 4×0.7
   a. 28
   b. 2.8
   c. 0.28
   d. 280

4. 9×0.05
   a. 0.45
   b. 45
   c. 4.5
   d. 450

5. 5.5×7
   a. 3.85
   b. 385
   c. 38.5
   d. 35.5

6. 9×7.8
   a. 702
   b. 0.702
   c. 63.2
   d. 70.2

7. 100×0.96
   a. 9.6
   b. 0.0096
   c. 0.96
   d. 96.0

8. 0.025×3
   a. 0.705
   b. 0.075
   c. 0.75
   d. 750

9. 3×1.08
   a. 0.324
   b. 3.24
   c. 324
   d. 3.024

10. 0×67.4
    a. 6.74
    b. 674
    c. 0
    d. 67.4

11. 0.004×8
    a. 0.036
    b. 0.032
    c. 32
    d. 0.302

12. 8×0.008
    a. 0.064
    b. 0.604
    c. 6.4
    d. 0.004

13. 3×1.6
    a. 48
    b. 4.8
    c. 0.48
    d. 0.048

14. 0.002×5
    a. 1.0
    b. 1.0
    c. 0.1
    d. 0.01

PLACING THE DECIMAL POINT

There is another way to decide where to place the decimal point in a product. Look for patterns in the multiplication sentences below to help you discover the rule.

Work in pairs. You will need the recording sheet and a calculator.

1. Copy and complete Chart A on your recording sheet. Use a calculator to find the product.

Chart A

Multiplication Sentence	Number of Decimal Places in the Factors	in the Product
4.2 × 3 = 12.6	1	1
42 × 0.3		
6.11 × 8		
6 × 0.7		
1.2 × 8.8 = 10.56	2	2
4.6 × 7.52		

2. What pattern do you notice between the number of decimal places in the factors and the number of decimal places in the product?

Predict the number of decimal places in the product. Use the pattern to help you. Write your prediction.

3. 6.8 × 3
   0.68 × 3
   0.068 × 3

4. 5.4 × 72
   5.4 × 7.2
   5.4 × 0.72

5. 9.3 × 4.6
   0.93 × 4.6
   9.3 × 0.46

6. Use a calculator to find each product in exercises 3–5. Check your predictions.

SUMMING IT UP

7. Use your pattern to write a rule for placing the decimal point in a product.

8. Use your rule to write each multiplication problem under the correct heading in Chart B on your recording sheet. Then write each product.

| 7.2 × 9 | 5.8 × 0.8 | 6.7 × 4.2 | 6.4 × 3 | 6.8 × 5.3 | 5 × 0.09 |
| 4.4 × 3.3 | 3 × 5.2 | 0.5 × 0.23 | 8 × 0.4 | 8.1 × 0.29 | 9 × 0.02 |

Chart B

Number of Decimal Places in Product		
1 Decimal Place	**2 Decimal Places**	**3 Decimal Places**
7.2 × 9 = 64.8		

9. The product of 1.5 × 1.2 is 1.80. How does the calculator show the product? Explain.

10. Explain how you could use your rule to place the decimal point in the product of 1.1 × 0.7.

11. Discuss your rule with the class.

PROJECT • Number Sense

You will need four sets of cards with each set numbered 0 to 9. You can play with two to six players.

a. The four sets of cards are shuffled together and placed face down.

b. Each player draws a diagram as shown at the right.

c. First player takes a card. Each player records that number in one of the four boxes. The card is returned to the bottom of the deck. Players take turns choosing a card. Continue until all four boxes are filled. You cannot change a number once it is written in a box.

d. Multiply. The player with the lowest product gets 1 point.

e. Repeat steps *b* through *d*. The first player to reach 5 points wins.

MULTIPLYING DECIMALS

Greg is buying cold cuts for a party. Greg orders 1.5 pounds of American cheese. How much will the cheese cost?

Prices per pound
American Cheese $3.69
Bologna $1.98
Ham $3.89
Roast Beef $4.99
Swiss Cheese $3.65
Turkey $4.98

1 pound costs $3.69

So, 1.5 pounds costs 1.5 × $3.69.

> **number of pounds × price per pound = total price**

● Multiply as you would with whole numbers.

$$\begin{array}{r} \$3.69 \\ \times\ 1.5 \\ \hline 1845 \\ 3690 \\ \hline \$5535 \end{array}$$

● Write the decimal point.

$$\begin{array}{r} \$3.69 \leftarrow 2 \text{ decimal places} \\ \times\ 1.5 \leftarrow 1 \text{ decimal place} \\ \hline 1845 \\ 3690 \\ \hline \$5.535 \leftarrow 3 \text{ decimal places} \end{array}$$

> The number of decimal places in the product equals the total number of decimal places in the factors.

The amount $5.535 is rounded to the nearest cent. $5.535 ⟶ $5.54

Greg will pay $5.54 for 1.5 pounds of American cheese.

Think

- Why does it make sense to round $5.535?

- A calculator displays the product of 0.75 × 4 as 3. Is the calculator broken? Explain.

Other Examples

$$\begin{array}{r} \$1.03 \\ \times\ 5 \\ \hline \$5.15 \end{array}$$

$$\begin{array}{r} 2.4 \\ \times\ 0.12 \\ \hline 48 \\ 240 \\ \hline 0.288 \end{array}$$

$$\begin{array}{r} 0.32 \\ \times\ 0.3 \\ \hline 0.096 \end{array}$$

GUIDED PRACTICE

Write the product. Round dollar amounts to the nearest cent.

1. 2.1
   × 3.3

2. $4.03
   × 10

3. 317
   × 0.01

4. $2.45
   × 0.5

5. 3.12 × 1.5

6. $0.59 × 0.4

7. 4.4 × 0.02

8. 4.32 × 0.7

9. What do you notice about the size of the product when one of the factors is a decimal less than 1?

INDEPENDENT PRACTICE

Write the product. Round dollar amounts to the nearest cent.

10. $4.75
    × 1.2

11. $2.15
    × 100

12. 4.51
    × 0.6

13. 0.21
    × 0.3

14. 3.75 × 42

15. $0.45 × 1.25

16. 7.66 × 1.5

17. $4.63 × 1000

18. 0.23 × 1.6

19. 5.2 × $1.68

20. 213.7 × 5.4

21. 0.16 × 0.4

Problem Solving Use the chart on page 192.

22. Greg is thinking of buying 2.5 pounds of roast beef. How much will it cost?

23. Is $10 enough to buy 0.25 pound of Swiss cheese, 1.5 pounds of roast beef, and 0.75 pound of bologna? Why or why not?

24. Greg bought equal amounts of bologna and turkey. He spent $10.44. How many pounds of each did he buy?

25. Write your own word problem using the information given in the chart.

MATH LOG

What rule would you write to help somebody multiply with decimals?

People often combine strategies to solve a problem.

SALE TODAY!

One time, we made a plan and made a list to help sell T-shirts.

$2.00

$8.00

$6.00

$4.00

OUR PROBLEM

We had 4 different styles of T-shirts for sale. We wanted to make this sign:

We wanted to know if the sign would be false advertising.

OUR SOLUTION

First we made a plan:

Then we followed our plan.

We circled the combinations that cost less than $10.

We saw that only 2 of the 6 combinations cost less than $10. So, the sign would be false advertising. We changed the sign to read: "Most combinations $10 or less." Do you see why that worked?

BUY TWO!
CHOOSE 2 SHIRTS,
2 DIFFERENT STYLES
Most combinations under $10.00

1. List all the different combinations.
2. See how many combinations cost less than $10.00 and how many cost more.
3. See if more than half of the combinations cost less than $10.00.

$2 + $4
$2 + $6 $4 + $6
$2 + $8 $4 + $8 $6 + $8

GUIDED PRACTICE

Solve the problem.

1. Alan is buying an apple and a pear. The total comes to 57¢. Alan has 1 quarter, 6 dimes, 4 nickels, and 5 pennies. He wants to pay for the fruit with the exact amount and use as many coins as he can. What coins should he give the clerk?

....

APPLICATION

Work in groups to solve each problem.

2. The map shows how Anne walks to school. How many other routes can she take that are the same distance?

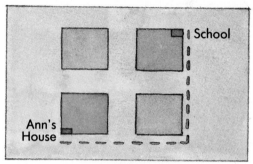

3. The game Spin 9 is played with a spinner like the one shown at the right. You spin 3 times. If your total score is 9, you win. How many sets of three numbers are winners? HINT: 1,4,4 and 4,1,4 count as the same set.

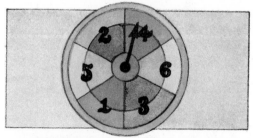

4. The Rainbow Band has 3 members— Angie, Buzz, and Chilli. They each want to wear a different-colored costume for their next concert. They can choose from red, orange, green, and violet. They agree that orange and violet won't look good on the stage together. Also, Angie won't wear green and Buzz won't wear orange. What are the different color combinations they might wear?

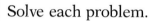
USING STRATEGIES

Mr. Ramon is buying square tiles for the playroom floor. The tiles are 0.25 meter long.

If you get stuck, remember....
Tips for Problem Solving
on pages 448–449

Solve each problem.

1. Will 10 tiles fit side by side across the length (4.5 meters) of the floor? Will 20 fit? What number of tiles will fit exactly?

2. Will 10 tiles fit side by side along the width of the floor? Will 20 fit? What number of tiles will fit exactly?

3. How many tiles are needed to cover the playroom floor?

4. Mr. Ramon will buy 12 boxes of tiles. Each box contains 2 dozen tiles. How many extra tiles will he get?

4.5 meters

3.75 meters

MILES OF TILE
Kid-Proof Tiles
41.⁹⁵ per box

TILE STYLE
Kid-Proof Tiles
Special
For every box you buy at the regular price of $60, you can buy another box at half price.

LYLES TYLES
Kid-proof tiles
SALE
3 boxes $149.99

5. At which store do the 12 boxes of tiles cost the least? How can you tell without computing the price of 12 boxes at each store?

SECTION REVIEW

for pages 190–196

Write the product.

1. 0.07×0.7 **2.** 0.081×0.84 **3.** 0.408×0.6 **4.** 0.012×3

5. 0.6×10 **6.** 0.019×0.137 **7.** 0.31×0.2 **8.** 0.064×5.4

Write the letter of the correct product. Round dollar amounts to the nearest cent.

9. 3.6×2.3
  a. 82.8
  b. 8.28
  c. 828
  d. 5.88

10. 7.9×8.21
  a. 64.859
  b. 648.59
  c. 6485.9
  d. 20.26

11. 9.43×6.3
  a. 594.09
  b. 59.40
  c. 59.409
  d. 16.31

12. 73×5.7
  a. 41.61
  b. 4.161
  c. 14.61
  d. 416.1

13. $\$4.62 \times 100$
  a. $462.00
  b. $46.20
  c. 462.00
  d. $4620.00

14. 2.3×0.1
  a. 2.3
  b. 0.23
  c. 0.023
  d. 23

15. $\$0.27 \times 1.8$
  a. $0.5
  b. $0.48
  c. $0.49
  d. 0.48

16. $\$3.87 \times 0.9$
  a. 3.48
  b. $3.5
  c. $3.48
  d. $3.47

17. 528.8×7.1
  a. 3754.48
  b. 37,544.8
  c. 375.448
  d. 37.5448

18. $\$7.85 \times 3.9$
  a. $30.61
  b. $30.6
  c. 30.62
  d. $30.62

Solve each problem.

19. Jason wants 1.75 pounds of each type of mix. He has $25. Is that enough money?

20. Cindy scoops out 1.5 pounds of the Special Mix. How much will it cost?

CHAPTER REVIEW

Language Connection

You know many words that begin with *multi-*, such as *multiply*, *multiple*, and *multiplication*. The word part *multi* is from the Latin word *multus*, which means "much" or "many." Try to guess what each word below means. Check the meanings in a dictionary. Then write each word in a sentence.

multicolored   multifamily
multilevel   multipurpose
multinational   multivitamin

See the Multitalented Bobo!!

Test ●●●●●●●

Write the product.

1. 4.3 × 2	**2.** 26.4 × 0.07	**3.** 0.16 × 0.5	**4.** 1.23 × 0.4
5. 7.8 × 9	**6.** $3.57 × 1000	**7.** 4.193 × 4	**8.** 3.5 × 0.03

9. 0.02 × 3   **10.** 9.2 × 5   **11.** 3.031 × 3   **12.** 6.2 × 7

13. 0.109 × 10   **14.** 0.15 × 2.3   **15.** 0.26 × 4   **16.** 8.3 × 8

17. 1.10 × 0.8	**18.** 0.056 × 4	**19.** 3.6 × 6	**20.** $2.42 × 100

Write the product. Round each product to the nearest cent.

21. $3.45 × 6	**22.** $7.31 × 0.3	**23.** $2.08 × 0.4	**24.** $9.26 × 0.50

| 25. | $4.30
× 10 | 26. | $6.21
× 100 | 27. | $1.53
× 6 | 28. | $2.34
× 9 |

29. $8.67 × 0.3   **30.** $5.13 × 5   **31.** $1.27 × 1.2   **32.** $4.13 × 1000

PROBLEM SOLVING

Solve each problem.

33. Beth lives 1.4 miles from the playground. On Monday, Wednesday, and Friday of each week, Beth walks to the playground and back. What is the total distance that Beth walks to the playground and back each week?

34. Ben earns $6.50 an hour mowing lawns. Ben mows Mr. Johnson's lawn from 9:00 A.M.–11:00 A.M. How much money does Ben earn for mowing the lawn?

35. Shada sells T-shirts for $8.50 each. If 7 people each buy a T-shirt, how much money will Shada receive?

36. One box of raisins weighs 3.75 ounces. What is the weight of 20 boxes?

CUMULATIVE REVIEW

37. Find the mean, median, and range of the data.

Temperatures (F): 43°, 46°, 48°, 35°, 38°

Write the answer.

38.   42 h 34 min
  − 17 h 12 min

39.   8 min 38 s
  − 4 min 29 s

Use the graph to answer each question.

40. What fraction of Jenna's earnings is spent on movies and music?

41. Jenna spends more than half her earnings on what two items?

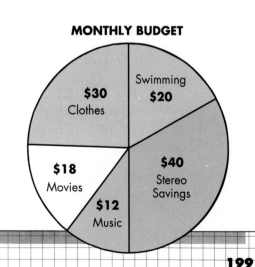

MONTHLY BUDGET

$30 Clothes
Swimming $20
$18 Movies
$12 Music
$40 Stereo Savings

EXCURSION

CONSUMER MATH

SAVINGS ACCOUNTS

A common type of savings account is a passbook account. You receive a passbook when you open your account. When you deposit money or receive interest, the amount is added to your balance. When you make a withdrawal, the amount is subtracted from your balance. Every change in your account is recorded in your passbook.

THE WESTWOOD BANK

ACCOUNT NUMBER 75437071

AN ACCOUNT WITH William Butler

No deposit can be made or money withdrawn without presentation of this book.

DATE			INTEREST	WITHDRAWALS	DEPOSITS	BALANCE
April	2	–			3 2 0 00	3 2 0 00
May	14	–			1 2 5 00	4 4 5 00
June	6	–		7 5 00		3 7 0 00
June	30	–	7 40			3 7 7 40
July	8	–		1 4 0 00		2 3 7 40
Aug.	3	–		1 3 5 75		? ? ? ??

Use the passbook shown above to solve each problem.

1. On what day did William have the greatest amount of money in his savings account?

2. If William had deposited $165.50 instead of $125.00 on May 14, what would his balance on that day have been?

3. If William were to withdraw $135.75 from his account on August 3, what would his new balance be?

Record the amounts missing in Deidre's passbook.

THE WESTWOOD BANK

ACCOUNT NUMBER 75437142

AN ACCOUNT WITH Deidre Gagnon

No deposit can be made or money withdrawn without presentation of this book.

	DATE			INTEREST			WITHDRAWALS			DEPOSITS			BALANCE		
	Jan.	2	–							6	24	35	6	24	35
	Jan.	16	–								82	75	7	07	10
4.	Mar.	31	–	1	9	87							▨▨▨		▨
	May	5	–								72	50	7	99	47
5.	June	5	–					36	20				▨▨▨		▨
	July	6	–							2	37	48	1 0	00	75
6.	Aug.	5	–				▨▨▨		▨				9	04	27
7.	Sept.	14	–					96	48				▨▨▨		▨
8.	Oct.	21	–							▨▨▨		▨	8	61	06

 Make up a passbook page like the one shown above. Record the following entries. Compute each balance. You may use a calculator.

9. January 15, deposit, $96

10. March 13, deposit, $86.50

11. April 12, withdrawal, $22

12. May 30, withdrawal, $126.37

13. June 30, interest, $1.56

14. July 28, deposit, $67.40

15. August 20, deposit, $48

16. Add two more entries to the passbook to bring the ending balance to $137.12.

CHAPTER 7

DIVISION OF DECIMALS

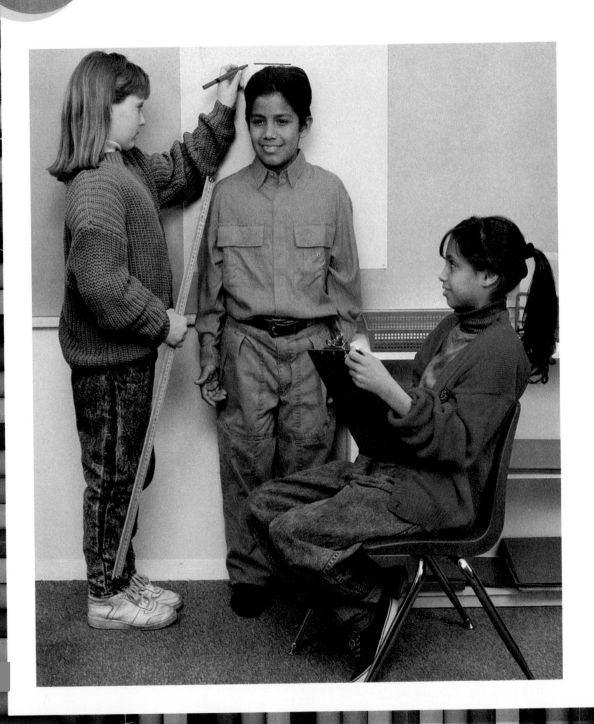

Statistics

How Tall? Mrs. Snell's class is working on graphs and tables. They collect data on many topics. They write their data in a table like the one below.

Yesterday's assignment was to compare the heights of fifth graders. The class split into groups and used a meter stick to measure each person's height. Then they wrote their data in a table.

One group's data appears below. Find the average height in centimeters.

Work in small groups. Make a table like the one below. Use a meter stick to measure each person's height to the nearest centimeter. What is the average height of the students in your group?

Name	Height (cm)
Roland	145
Enriqué	152
Carol	155
Sylvia	115
Akeem	140
Susan	130
Average Height	

DIVIDING BY A WHOLE NUMBER

Sean's orchard is 2.2 acres in size. In half the orchard he grows MacIntosh apples and in the other half he grows Red Delicious apples. How many acres are used to grow each type of apple?

Work in pairs. You will need quarter-inch squared paper.

Remember:

- One small square represents one hundredth of the whole square: $\frac{1}{100} = 0.01$.

- One column of 10 hundredths is one tenth of the whole square. So, $\frac{10}{100} = \frac{1}{10} = 0.1$ or 0.10.

- One 10 × 10 square represents one, or a whole. So 1 = 10 tenths, or 100 hundredths.

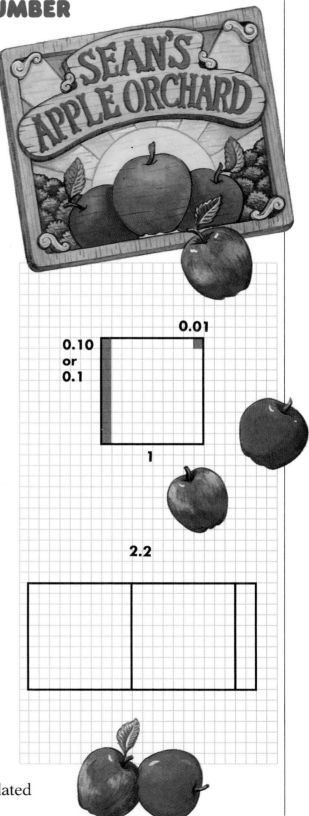

To find how many acres are used for each type of apple, divide 2.2 by 2.

Read 2.2 as "two and two tenths." Since 2 = 20 tenths, 2.2 = 22 tenths. On squared paper, divide 22 tenths into 2 equal parts.

1. How many equal parts are there?

2. How many tenths are in each part?

3. What decimal represents each part?

4. How many acres are used to grow each type of apple?

Check your quotient by thinking of the related multiplication sentence 2 × 1.1 = 2.2.

▶ Now divide 3.6 by 4.

Read 3.6 as "three and six tenths."
Since 3 is 30 tenths, 3.6 is 36 tenths. On
your paper, divide 36 tenths into 4
equal parts.

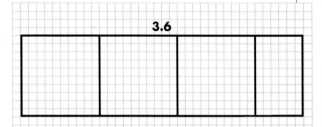
3.6

5. How many tenths are in each part?

6. What decimal represents each part?

7. Write a division sentence to describe
   dividing 36 tenths into 4 equal parts.

8. Use the related multiplication sentence
   $4 \times 0.9 = \blacksquare$ to check the quotient.

Divide: $2.2 \div 4$

Since 2 = 200 hundredths, 2.2 = 220 hundredths.
On your paper, divide 220 hundredths into 4 equal
parts.

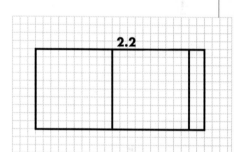
2.2

9. How many hundredths are in each part?

10. What decimal represents each part?

11. Write a division sentence to describe dividing
    220 hundredths into 4 equal parts.

12. Use the related multiplication sentence
    $4 \times 0.55 = \blacksquare$ to check the quotient.

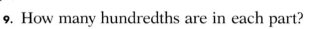

SUMMING IT UP

Use a model to find the quotient.

13. $1.6 \div 2$ 14. $2.8 \div 7$ 15. $1.8 \div 3$ 16. $3.2 \div 4$ 17. $2.4 \div 6$

18. $2.4 \div 5$ 19. $3.3 \div 6$ 20. $1.5 \div 6$ 21. $3.8 \div 4$ 22. $2.2 \div 5$

23. How is $2.1 \div 3$ similar to $21 \div 3$?
    How is it different?

24. How does knowing whole number
    division help you to find decimal
    quotients?

MATH LOG

Write a story problem and a division sentence to
describe dividing 6.4 into 8 equal parts.

DIVIDING BY 10, 100, AND 1000

This picture shows how to divide 2.3 by 10 using squared paper.

There is an easier way to divide decimals by 10, 100, and 1000. You can use mental math. Looking for patterns in the division sentences below can help you discover the mental math rule.

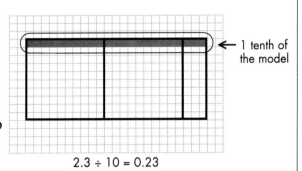

← 1 tenth of the model

$2.3 \div 10 = 0.23$

Work in groups. You will need a calculator.

Use a calculator to complete the division sentence. Write the completed sentence.

1. $794.25 \div 10 = \blacksquare$
   $794.25 \div 100 = \blacksquare$
   $794.25 \div 1000 = \blacksquare$

2. $53.2 \div 10 = \blacksquare$
   $53.2 \div 100 = \blacksquare$
   $53.2 \div 1000 = \blacksquare$

3. $227 \div 10 = \blacksquare$
   $227 \div 100 = \blacksquare$
   $227 \div 1000 = \blacksquare$

4. What patterns do you notice?

5. What happens to the place value of the digit 4 in exercise 1?

6. What happens to the decimal point of a number when you divide by 10? By 100? By 1000?

Use the patterns to help you predict the quotient. Write your predictions.

7. a. $19.45 \div 10$
   b. $19.45 \div 100$
   c. $19.45 \div 1000$

8. a. $1.07 \div 10$
   b. $1.07 \div 100$
   c. $1.07 \div 1000$

9. a. $967.12 \div 10$
   b. $967.12 \div 100$
   c. $967.12 \div 1000$

10. a. $148 \div 10$
    b. $148 \div 100$
    c. $148 \div 1000$

11. $124.7 \div 10$

12. $96.5 \div 100$

13. $841.27 \div 1000$

14. $567.8 \div 100$

15. $1.6 \div 100$

16. $3.64 \div 100$

17. $24.83 \div 1000$

18. $3.57 \div 1000$

19. $34.8 \div 10$

20. $8651 \div 10$

21. $9203 \div 1000$

22. $803 \div 100$

23. $14.24 \div 10$

24. $6.2 \div 10$

25. $727 \div 100$

26. $908 \div 100$

Use a calculator to check your predictions.

SUMMING IT UP

27. Write a rule that you can use to mentally divide a decimal by 10, 100, and 1000.

28. Explain how to find 8.3 ÷ 100 using your rule.

29. Explain how to find 37 ÷ 10.

30. How is your rule similar to the rule for multiplying a decimal by 10, 100, and 1000? How is it different?

Write the answer. Use your mental math rules.

31. 2.8 ÷ 10

32. 2.8 × 10

33. 34.895 × 100

34. 32.5 ÷ 100

35. 4.37 ÷ 100

36. 4.671 × 1000

37. 0.43 × 10

38. 52 ÷ 10

39. 3.46 × 1000

40. 0.13 × 100

41. 0.13 ÷ 10

42. 0.13 ÷ 100

43. 0.13 ÷ 1000

44. 6.9 × 100

45. 0.08 × 10

PROJECT • Game

Play this game in small groups.

a. Each group will need one deck of 18 cards (two cards of each: 11.1, 22.2, 33.3, 44.4, 55.5, 66.6, 77.7, 88.8, 99.9).

b. Shuffle the cards. Place the deck face down.

c. Take turns. Choose a card. Divide the number on the card by 10, 100, or 1000. Write the quotient on your paper.

d. Each player takes four turns.

e. Add your four quotients.

f. The player with the sum closest to 10 wins.

· SCORE CARD ·

1st turn   6.66
2nd turn   0.777
3rd turn   2.200
4th turn   0.0999
Total   9.7369

a good score. Very close to 10!

EQUIVALENT METRIC MEASURES

Alex is moving his desk. The top of the desk is 115 centimeters long. Will it fit in a crate 1.3 meters long?

Equivalent Measures of Length
1 centimeter (cm) = 10 millimeters (mm)
1 meter (m) = 1000 millimeters (mm)
1 meter (m) = 100 centimeters (cm)
1 kilometer (km) = 1000 meters (m)

To compare measurements, write them in the same unit.

▶ You can multiply to write a larger unit as a smaller one. Write 1.3 meters as centimeters:

> Centimeters are a smaller unit than meters, so your answer will have more centimeters than you had meters.

$$1.3 \text{ m} = \blacksquare \text{ cm}$$

Since 1 m = 100 cm

Then 1.3 m = (1.3 × 100) cm

So, 1.3 m = 130 cm

Since 115 cm < 130 cm, the desk will fit in the crate.

▶ Or, you can divide to write a smaller unit as a larger one. Write 115 centimeters as meters:

> Meters are a larger unit than centimeters, so your answer will have fewer meters than you had centimeters.

$$115 \text{ cm} = \blacksquare \text{ m}$$

Since 100 cm = 1 m

Then 115 cm = (115 ÷ 100) m

So, 115 cm = 1.15 m

Since 1.15 m < 1.3 m, the desk will fit in the crate.

 Think

≡ • How is writing centimeters as meters like writing cents as dollars?

• If you write 12 meters as millimeters, will the number of millimeters be more than or less than 12? Explain.

GUIDED PRACTICE

Use the table. Write the letter of the equivalent measure.

1. 14 m
   a. 1.4 cm
   b. 140 cm
   c. 1400 cm

2. 22 mm
   a. 2.2 cm
   b. 220 cm
   c. 0.22 cm

3. 0.67 m
   a. 6.7 cm
   b. 67 cm
   c. 670 cm

4. 9.6 cm
   a. 96 mm
   b. 960 mm
   c. 0.96 mm

5. 9 km
   a. 9 m
   b. 900 m
   c. 9000 m

Complete.

6. 120 mm = ▦ cm

7. 0.67 km = ▦ m

8. 45,720 cm = ▦ mm

Complete. Write >, <, or =.

9. 800 cm ● 8000 mm

10. 36 km ● 360,000 m

11. 5.46 m ● 546 mm

12. When writing one unit of measure as another, how do you decide whether to multiply or divide?

INDEPENDENT PRACTICE

Use the table. Write the letter of the equivalent measure.

13. 3.642 m
  a. 3642 cm
  b. 36.42 cm
  c. 364.2 cm

14. 48 mm
  a. 480 m
  b. 0.48 m
  c. 0.048 m

15. 300 cm
  a. 3000 mm
  b. 30 mm
  c. 3 mm

16. 15 km
  a. 150,000 m
  b. 0.015 m
  c. 15,000 m

17. 95,000 m
  a. 9500 km
  b. 950 km
  c. 95 km

Complete.

18. 5.27 m = ▦ cm

19. 755 mm = ▦ m

20. 4.2 km = ▦ m

21. 14 km = ▦ m

22. 0.0062 m = ▦ mm

23. 7.53 cm = ▦ mm

Complete. Write >, <, or =.

24. 759 mm ● 64.3 cm

25. 1.089 m ● 1250 mm

26. 6 m ● 600 cm

27. 37.6 cm ● 1 m

28. 38,650 mm ● 3865 m

29. 84.7 m ● 1.2 km

Problem Solving

30. Alex nails a board 7 millimeters thick to another board 4.0 centimeters thick. How thick are the two boards nailed together?

31. Alex is installing a dishwasher 180 centimeters wide. The space for the dishwasher measures 1.25 meters wide. Is the space wide enough? Explain.

Maintain • Organizing Data

Write the mean, median, and range for each set of numbers.

1. 48, 42, 44, 42, 44

2. 1, 2, 3, 4, 5, 6, 7

3. 54, 88, 47, 88, 63

4. 15, 17, 15, 12, 26

ESTIMATING WITH MONEY

About how much does 1 bottle of apple juice cost?

Estimate: $6\overline{)\$2.49}$

Use compatible numbers. Replace $2.49 with an amount close to it that you can divide mentally by 6. Thinking of $2.49 as 249¢ may help.

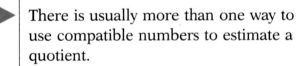

$6\overline{)\$2.49}$ $6\overline{)249¢} \longrightarrow 6\overline{)240¢} = 40¢$

One bottle of juice costs about $0.40.

 Think

- Will 1 bottle of juice cost more than or less than 40¢? Explain.

$2.49
6-pack Apple Juice

There is usually more than one way to use compatible numbers to estimate a quotient.

Estimate: $4\overline{)\$1.43}$

 $4\overline{)120¢} = 30¢$ $4\overline{)160¢} = 40¢$

Both $0.30 and $0.40 are reasonable estimates. Why?

Other Examples

Estimate: $6\overline{)\$361.47}$

$6\overline{)\$360} = \$60$

Estimate: $\$0.68 \div 8$

$72¢ \div 8 = 9¢$

$64¢ \div 8 = 8¢$

Estimate: $\$2.33 \div 5$

$250¢ \div 5 = 50¢$

$200¢ \div 5 = 40¢$

GUIDED PRACTICE

Tell what compatible numbers you would use, then estimate.

1. 3)$1.02

2. 6)$27.51

3. $8.32 ÷ 5

4. 7)$4.63

5. 5)$3.72

6. $2.04 ÷ 3

7. 4)$11.09

8. 9)$0.51

9. Do you think the actual quotient in exercise 4 is greater than or less than $0.60? Explain.

INDEPENDENT PRACTICE

Write the letter of the reasonable estimate. Write *a*, *b*, or *c*.

10. $3.27 ÷ 4
  a. $0.08
  b. $0.80
  c. $8.00

11. $0.83 ÷ 3
  a. $0.03
  b. $0.30
  c. $3.00

12. $126.75 ÷ 6
  a. $0.20
  b. $2.00
  c. $20.00

13. $0.39 ÷ 5
  a. $0.07
  b. $0.70
  c. $7.00

Tell what compatible numbers you would use, then estimate the quotient.

14. 6)$147

15. $2.61 ÷ 5

16. 7)$3.38

17. 4)$1.35

18. $28.46 ÷ 7

19. 6)$376.83

20. 4)$0.92

21. $0.37 ÷ 8

22. $3.32 ÷ 6

23. 4)$2.26

24. 67.99 ÷ 9

25. 5)$4.88

About how much does 1 of each of the following cost?

26.
27.
28.
29.

5 ORANGES for $1.39

4 CUPS for $9.89

TOMATOES 6 for $2.29

3 MELONS for $2.59

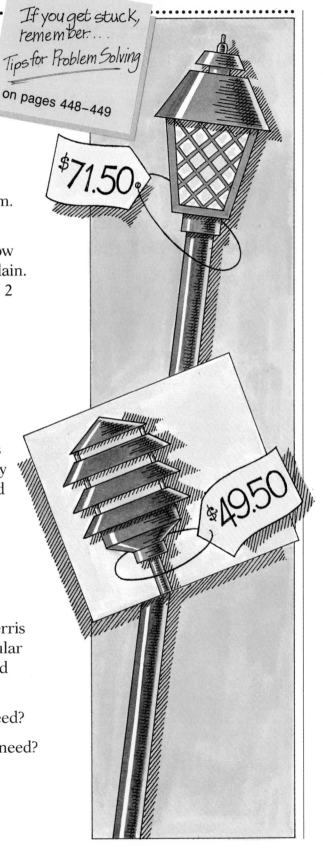

If you get stuck, remember...
Tips for Problem Solving
on pages 448–449

$71.50

$49.50

Mr. Ferris plans to put night lamps along one side of his walkway. He wants the lamps equally spaced with a lamp at each end. The walkway is 16.4 meters long.

Help Mr. Ferris by solving each problem. Explain how you got your answer.

1. If Mr. Ferris uses 12 lamps, about how far apart would they be spaced? Explain. HINT: First use smaller numbers, like 2 or 3 lamps.

2. The lamp company recommends placing the lamps 2 meters apart along the walkway. How many lamps will Mr. Ferris actually need?

3. The company also sells taller lamps that light up more area. These lamps are placed 3 meters apart. How many of these lamps would Mr. Ferris need for his walkway?

4. Mr. Ferris plans to put lamps along his driveway also. He can use either 9 tall lamps or 12 short ones. Which would cost less?

5. To complete his lighting plan, Mr. Ferris will place lamps around his rectangular patio. The patio is 18 meters long and 12 meters wide.

   a. How many tall lamps would he need?

   b. How many short lamps would he need?

   c. Which would cost less?

SECTION REVIEW

for pages 204–212

Write the letter of the correct answer. Use a model if it helps.

1. 4.2 ÷ 7
   a. 60
   b. 0.06
   c. 6
   d. 0.6

2. 2.1 ÷ 3
   a. 7
   b. 7.0
   c. 0.7
   d. 70

3. 2.5 ÷ 5
   a. 0.05
   b. 5
   c. 50
   d. 0.5

4. 7.2 ÷ 10
   a. 72
   b. 0.72
   c. 72.0
   d. 720

5. 2.2 ÷ 4
   a. 0.5
   b. 0.55
   c. 5.5
   d. 55

6. 5.1 ÷ 6
   a. 85
   b. 8.5
   c. 0.8
   d. 0.85

7. 27.4 ÷ 10
   a. 274
   b. 2740
   c. 0.274
   d. 2.74

8. 3.2 ÷ 8
   a. 40
   b. 0.4
   c. 4
   d. 0.04

9. 5.9 ÷ 100
   a. 0.59
   b. 0.059
   c. 590
   d. 59

10. 3.3 ÷ 6
    a. 0.055
    b. 0.505
    c. 0.55
    d. 5.5

11. 142.8 ÷ 1000
    a. 0.1428
    b. 1.428
    c. 14.28
    d. 1428

12. 1.2 ÷ 5
    a. 0.24
    b. 0.024
    c. 24
    d. 2.4

Write the letter of the correct equivalent measure.
Use the table on page 208 if it helps.

13. 46 cm
    a. 4.6 m
    b. 0.46 m
    c. 460 m
    d. 0.0046 m

14. 8 m
    a. 0.08 km
    b. 0.8 km
    c. 8000 km
    d. 0.008 km

15. 18 km
    a. 1800 m
    b. 1.8 m
    c. 18,000 m
    d. 180 m

16. 135 mm
    a. 13.5 cm
    b. 1350 cm
    c. 1.35 cm
    d. 0.135 cm

Solve each problem.

17. Rene paid $11.80 for 10 gallons of gas. What was the cost of 1 gallon?

18. A box of 100 pencils costs $16. How much does each pencil cost?

19. Stamps cost $0.25 each. David has $2.25. Does he have enough money to buy 10 stamps?

PLACING THE DECIMAL POINT

J.J. rode 4 laps on his bike in 8.24 minutes. What was his average time for each lap?

Divide: 8.24 ÷ 4

One way to solve this problem is to use a model to show 8.24 as 824 hundredths divided into 4 equal parts.

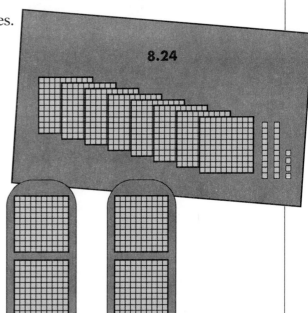

8.24

Regroup the tenths as hundredths.

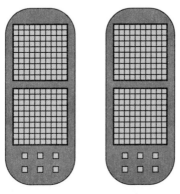

You can also solve the problem this way.

● **First, divide as you would with whole numbers.**

$$
\begin{array}{r}
206 \\
4\overline{)8.24} \\
-800 \\
\hline
24 \\
24 \\
\hline
0
\end{array}
$$

divisor → 4)8.24 ← dividend
206 ← quotient

● **Then, estimate to place the decimal point in the quotient.**

2.06
4)8.24

Estimate
4 × 2 = 8
4 × 20 = 80
The answer must be about 2.

● **Or, think of a related multiplication sentence to place the decimal point.**

2.06
4)8.24

Think of a related multiplication sentence:
4 × 2.06 = 8.24

J.J.'s average time for each lap was 2.06 minutes.

Think

- What do you notice about the placement of the decimal point in the quotient and in the dividend?

- Which is longer, 2.06 minutes or 2 minutes 6 seconds? Explain.

GUIDED PRACTICE

Write the quotient. Estimate or think about a related multiplication sentence to place the decimal point.

1. 7)7.07

2. 4)76.4

3. 8)$48.24

4. 3)0.54

5. How did you decide where to put the decimal point in exercise 4?

INDEPENDENT PRACTICE

Write the quotient. Estimate or think about a related multiplication sentence to place the decimal point.

6. 5)5.05

7. 6)64.8

8. 3)0.606

9. 7)71.4

10. 9)27.54

11. 4)$4.36

12. 9)0.063

13. 3)12.003

14. 0.16 ÷ 4

15. 18.81 ÷ 9

16. 3.642 ÷ 6

17. 0.915 ÷ 3

Problem Solving

18. Roberto rides the 4 laps in 9.58 minutes. What is his average time for each lap? Is that greater than or less than two and a half minutes?

19. What must Roberto's total time for the 4 laps be for his average to be less than 2 minutes?

CHALLENGE • Critical Thinking

Fill in the missing digits.

1.
```
   ■.0■
4)4.■6
 −■
  3■
 −■6
   0
```

2.
```
   ■.6■9
6)3.654
 −■■
   ■■
  −54
    0
```

3.
```
   0.■0■
8■)■.68■
 −8 6
   8■
  −■6
    ■
```

DECIMAL QUOTIENTS

Eight families want to share seven kilograms of frozen yogurt. They know that this means each family gets $\frac{7}{8}$ kilogram, but the scale they will use has a decimal display!

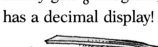

Since $\frac{7}{8}$ means 7 divided by 8, divide: $7 \div 8$.

● Write an equivalent decimal and divide as you would for whole numbers.

$$
\begin{array}{r}
8 \\
8\overline{)7.0} \\
-6\,4 \\
\hline
6
\end{array}
$$
7 = 70 tenths

● Revise your equivalent decimal if you need to. Repeat until division is complete or you answer your question.

$$
\begin{array}{r}
875 \\
8\overline{)7.000} \\
-6\,4 \\
\hline
60 \\
-56 \\
\hline
40 \\
-40 \\
\hline
0
\end{array}
$$
7 = 7000 thousandths

● Place the decimal point in the quotient.

$$
\begin{array}{r}
0.875 \\
8\overline{)7.000} \\
-6\,4 \\
\hline
60 \\
-56 \\
\hline
40 \\
-40 \\
\hline
0
\end{array}
$$
Estimate 8 × 0.8 = 6.4 or think of a related multiplication sentence: 8 × 0.875 = 7

Each family will get 0.875 kilogram of frozen yogurt.

Think

• What do you notice about the placement of the decimal point in the quotient and in the dividend?

By now you have had enough experience with dividing decimals to see that the decimal point in the quotient goes directly above the decimal point in the dividend. To use this rule, you must be very careful when lining up the digits as you divide.

Other Examples

$$4 \div 5 \longrightarrow 5\overline{)4.0}^{\,0.8}$$

$$7 \div 4 \longrightarrow 4\overline{)7.00}^{\,1.75}$$

$$\$10 \div 8 \longrightarrow 8\overline{)\$10.00}^{\,\$1.25}$$

GUIDED PRACTICE

Write the quotient.

1. $8\overline{)6}$
2. $8\overline{)2}$
3. $8\overline{)42}$
4. $5\overline{)\$12}$

5. $37 \div 5$
6. $\$5 \div 2$
7. $57 \div 4$
8. $5 \div 8$

9. How can you check your answers?

....

INDEPENDENT PRACTICE

Write the quotient.

10. $8\overline{)4}$
11. $8\overline{)12}$
12. $5\overline{)2}$
13. $6\overline{)27}$

14. $5\overline{)16}$
15. $8\overline{)3}$
16. $6\overline{)\$63}$
17. $4\overline{)33}$

18. $\$10 \div 4$
19. $3 \div 6$
20. $78 \div 5$
21. $\$15 \div 6$

Problem Solving

22. Hugh's log book shows how many kilometers he ran each weekday for 2 weeks. What is the average number of kilometers Hugh ran in a day?

23. During which week was Hugh's daily average greater? How much greater?

24. Hugh was supposed to run an average of 3 km per day for the 2 weeks. How many kilometers could he have run on the last Friday to make his goal?

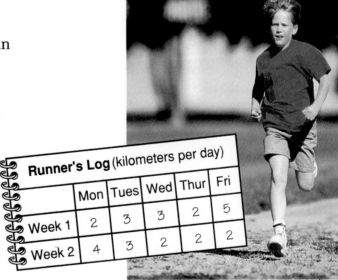

Runner's Log (kilometers per day)

	Mon	Tues	Wed	Thur	Fri
Week 1	2	3	3	2	5
Week 2	4	3	2	2	2

 • **Mixed Practice**

Write the answer.

1. 6.27×0.5
2. 0.05×0.7
3. $15 \div 10$
4. 0.21×1.2
5. $1986 \div 100$

USING DIVISION

Mr. Kraft owns Hands-On Hobbies. He is deciding which company to buy model rocket kits from. The kits are the same, so he will choose the company that charges less.

To compare, he can divide to find the cost of one kit from each company.

Count Down	**Blastoff**
$\dfrac{\$29.165}{6)\$174.990}$	$\dfrac{\$33.898}{5)169.490}$
Each Count Down kit costs $29.17.	Each Blastoff kit costs $33.90.

Or, Mr. Kraft can compare by estimating.

Count Down

If 6 kits cost $180, then each kit would cost $30. Since 6 kits cost less than $180, then each kit costs *less than* $30.

Blastoff

If the kits cost $30 each, then 5 would cost $150. But 5 kits cost more than $150, so each kit costs *more than* $30.

Think

- Which method gives a correct answer to Mr. Kraft's problem?

- Which method is easier for you to use?

INDEPENDENT PRACTICE

Problem Solving

1. Blastoff offers a special discount. For every 10 kits Mr. Kraft orders, $5 is deducted from his bill. If he wants to order 50 kits, should this affect his decision to buy from Count Down?

2. How much of a discount on 50 kits would Blastoff have to offer to convince you that Mr. Kraft should order from them?

Use the catalog pages to answer each question. You may use a calculator.

3. Mr. Kraft wants to buy a dozen Space Race video games. Where should he buy them?

4. Which catalog has the best buy for ten Vandenberg maps? Explain.

5. The Cape Canaveral tour book is a popular item at Hands-On Hobbies. Which catalog offers the best buy on 200 of them?

6. Look at Mr. Kraft's shopping list. Where would you recommend that he place his order? Explain.

7. Video games weigh 0.5 pound, tour books weigh 1.5 pounds, maps weigh 0.1 pound, and rocket kits weigh 2 pounds each. Look at Mr. Kraft's order and the table of shipping charges.

   a. Find the cost to ship the order.

   b. Find the total cost of ordering from Count Down, including shipping.

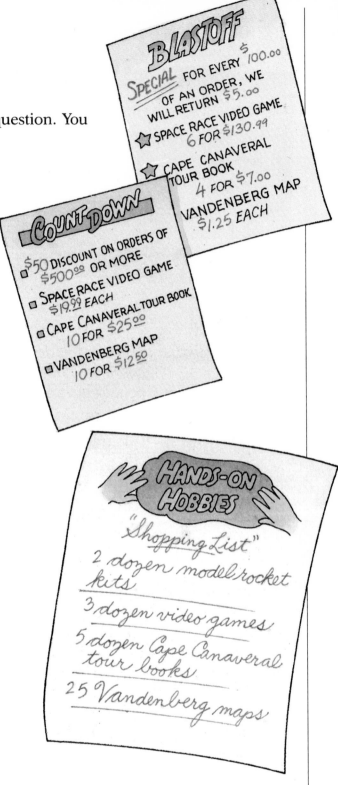

BLASTOFF

SPECIAL FOR EVERY $100.00 OF AN ORDER, WE WILL RETURN $5.00

☆ SPACE RACE VIDEO GAME
6 FOR $130.99

☆ CAPE CANAVERAL TOUR BOOK
4 FOR $7.00

VANDENBERG MAP
$1.25 EACH

COUNT DOWN

☐ $50 DISCOUNT ON ORDERS OF $500⁰⁰ OR MORE

☐ SPACE RACE VIDEO GAME
$19.⁹⁹ EACH

☐ CAPE CANAVERAL TOUR BOOK
10 FOR $25⁰⁰

☐ VANDENBERG MAP
10 FOR $12⁵⁰

HANDS-ON HOBBIES

"Shopping List"

2 dozen model rocket kits

3 dozen video games

5 dozen Cape Canaveral tour books

25 Vandenberg maps

Weight	Shipping Charge
0–20 lb	free
25–50 lb	$1.75 per pound
50–100 lb	$1.50 per pound
over 100 lb	$1.35 per pound

USING SIMPLER NUMBERS

Some kinds of numbers can make a problem seem hard. You can make the numbers simpler to get an idea about how to solve the problem. One time, I used simpler numbers when I worked in a dog kennel.

MY PROBLEM

We had 4 bags of Gro-Pup dog food left. They weighed 4.5 pounds, 6.6 pounds, 2.5 pounds, and 8.8 pounds. We use 6 pounds of Gro-Pup each day. I needed to know how long our supply would last.

MY SOLUTION

To help me come up with a plan, I made the numbers in the problem simpler. I rounded the weights to whole numbers.

Actual Numbers	Simpler Numbers
4.5	5
6.6	7
2.5	3
8.8	9

The simpler numbers helped me think of a plan. I would add the weights to find out how much Gro-Pup we had. Then I would divide the total by the amount we use each day.

$$\begin{array}{r} 5 \\ 7 \\ 3 \\ + 9 \\ \hline 24 \end{array}$$ Total $\quad 6\overline{)24} = 4$

Then I used the same plan with the actual numbers.

$$\begin{array}{r} 4.5 \\ 6.6 \\ 2.5 \\ + 8.6 \\ \hline 22.2 \end{array}$$ Actual Total $\quad 6\overline{)22.2} = 3.7$

So, the supply of Gro-Pup would last almost 4 days.

GUIDED PRACTICE

Finish choosing simpler numbers and use them to help you solve the problem.

1. Some teachers at the Payson School would like to buy a printer. Other teachers would like to buy 3 color monitors. Which would cost less? How much less?

	Actual Numbers	Simpler Numbers
cost of printer	$1399.98	$1400
cost of monitor	$419.95	■
number of monitors	3	■

....

APPLICATION

Work in groups to solve each problem. Use simpler numbers or try another strategy.

2. John is deciding what shape garden to make. One plan is for 6 sides that are each 1.9 meters long. Another plan is for a square that is 3.1 meters long. Which garden would need more fencing around it?

3. a. Which package of videocassettes costs more?

   b. Which package of videocassettes lets you record for a longer time?

4. The train travels at a steady speed. If you are going from Barkly to Emery, are you more than halfway there when you get to Chadwick? Explain.

5. How much longer does it take to go from Barkly to Chadwick than from Dixon to Emery?

6 TAPES
4 HOUR
VIDEO CASSETTES
$1 95 PER TAPE

4 TAPES
6 HOUR
VIDEO CASSETTES
$3 09 PER TAPE

Rapid Rails, Inc.	
Station	Arrives
Barkly	10:03 A.M.
Chadwick	12:28 P.M.
Dixon	12:58 P.M.
Emery	2:19 P.M.

221

FRACTIONS AND DECIMALS

Coach Stanley wants to find out who had the best batting average last season. Each player's total hits and at-bats can be written as a fraction. But since each player had a different number of at-bats, the fractions are hard to compare.

▶ Compute Amy's batting average.

Batting averages are usually written as decimals to the thousandths place. Since $\frac{28}{64}$ means 28 ÷ 64, Coach Stanley presses 28 ÷ 64 on his calculator. He gets 0.4375 as his quotient.

$$\frac{28}{64} = 0.4375$$

Remember: to round to a place, look at the digit in the next smaller place. If it is 5 or more, round up. Amy's batting average was 0.438.

Stanley's Sluggers	Number of Hits / Number of At-Bats
Amy	$\frac{28}{64}$
Omar	$\frac{24}{64}$
Jonathan	$\frac{28}{70}$
Curtis	$\frac{17}{50}$
Samuel	$\frac{28}{58}$
Kate	$\frac{26}{64}$

Batting Average Table

Name	Steps	Batting Average
Amy	28 ÷ 64	0.438
Omar		
Jonathan		
Curtis		
Samuel		
Kate		

You may use a calculator to do the exercises.

1. Copy and complete the batting average table. Remember to write the batting average to the nearest thousandth.

3. Order the players by their batting averages, from highest to lowest.

2. Order these fractions from least to greatest. It may help to write each fraction as a decimal to the nearest hundredth.

$\frac{7}{8}$ $\frac{3}{5}$ $\frac{9}{10}$ $\frac{46}{50}$ $\frac{9}{4}$ $\frac{28}{34}$ $\frac{15}{8}$ $\frac{54}{65}$ $\frac{21}{9}$ $\frac{89}{72}$

SECTION REVIEW

for pages 214–222

Write the answer.

1. 0.7 ÷ 4   **2.** 0.081 ÷ 9   **3.** 0.084 ÷ 6   **4.** 12.3 ÷ 3

5. 63.28 ÷ 8   **6.** 0.19 ÷ 5   **7.** 0.01 ÷ 2   **8.** 6.4 ÷ 4

Write the letter of the correct answer.

9. 6 ÷ 8
a. 1.333
b. 0.75
c. 0.075
d. 0.57

10. 0.34 ÷ 4
a. 0.81
b. 0.805
c. 0.081
d. 0.085

11. 36.9 ÷ 9
a. 41
b. 1.4
c. 0.41
d. 4.1

12. 70 ÷ 4
a. 17.5
b. 175
c. 1.75
d. 0.175

13. 0.07 ÷ 5
a. 0.124
b. 0.410
c. 0.014
d. 0.14

14. 16.32 ÷ 6
a. 2.72
b. 2.27
c. 0.272
d. 27.2

15. 27 ÷ 8
a. 33.75
b. 3.375
c. 3.357
d. 3.275

16. 0.054 ÷ 6
a. 0.9
b. 0.09
c. 0.090
d. 0.009

17. 1 ÷ 8
a. 0.125
b. 8.0
c. 1.25
d. 0.225

18. 30 ÷ 8
a. 0.266
b. 3.75
c. 5.73
d. 3.075

19. 0.8 ÷ 5
a. 1.6
b. 0.016
c. 0.16
d. 0.61

20. 254 ÷ 4
a. 0.635
b. 6.35
c. 635
d. 63.5

Solve each problem.

21. A store is selling 5-packs of cassettes for $12.45. What is the price of each cassette?

22. If 6 children cash in $8.40 worth of soda cans, how much money should each child receive?

CHAPTER REVIEW

Language Connection

Two is to *three* as *twins* is to *triplets.*

The sentence above is an analogy. Analogies are made up of two pairs of words. Each pair is related in the same way. In the analogy above, the second word in each pair is one more than the first word in each pair. Here are two other examples:

Two is to *hands* as *ten* is to *fingers.*   *Day* is to *night* as *odd* is to *even.*

Write a word to complete each analogy below.

Tenths is to _____ as *hundredths* is to *pennies.*
Add is to *subtract* as *multiply* is to _____.
Gram is to _____ as *meter* is to *kilometer.*

Test ● ● ● ● ● ● ●

Write the quotient.

1. $3.636 \div 6$
2. $\$7.15 \div 5$
3. $2.622 \div 2$
4. $31 \div 8$

5. $6\overline{)\$66.54}$
6. $5\overline{)27}$
7. $3\overline{)9.42}$
8. $9\overline{)18.486}$

9. $0.852 \div 6$
10. $5 \div 8$
11. $\$33.08 \div 4$
12. $4.221 \div 7$

13. $8\overline{)33}$
14. $7\overline{)\$5.46}$
15. $5\overline{)45.42}$
16. $3\overline{)0.57}$

17. $28.26 \div 4$
18. $0.66 \div 5$
19. $4\overline{)77.0}$
20. $7\overline{)\$63.98}$

21. $8\overline{)48.6}$
22. $5\overline{)56}$
23. $8\overline{)3.552}$
24. $6\overline{)\$58.92}$

25. $38.865 \div 5$
26. $12.264 \div 3$
27. $36 \div 5$
28. $\$79.60 \div 8$

29. $13\overline{)\$59.41}$
30. $8\overline{)3.32}$
31. $6\overline{)30.042}$
32. $8\overline{)9}$

PROBLEM SOLVING

Solve each problem.

33. Angela rode her new bicycle around the block 5 times. She began at 3:10 and finished at 3:28. About how long did it take Angela to ride around the block once?

34. Valerie is going to roller skate 4 miles for a fund-raiser. If she completes the route, she will raise $34. How much money will Valerie raise each mile?

35. The farmer's market charges $0.49 for a pound of potatoes. How much will Stuart pay for 7 pounds of potatoes?

36. Sydney earns $28.75 for working from 10:00 A.M. to 3:00 P.M. How much does Sydney earn each hour?

37. A long-distance runner ran 61.2 kilometers in 3 hours. About how many kilometers did he run each hour?

38. Roma paid $36 to rent cross-country skis for 5 days. About how much did it cost to rent the skis for one day?

CUMULATIVE REVIEW

Find the perimeter of each polygon.

39.

3 in.   3 in.

2 in.   2 in.

5 in.

40.

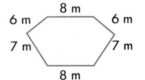

8 m

6 m   6 m

7 m   7 m

8 m

41.

4 ft

13 ft

42.

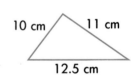

10 cm   11 cm

12.5 cm

Use a ruler to measure each object to the nearest inch, or fraction of an inch, as shown.

43. $\frac{1}{4}$ inch

44. inch

45. $\frac{1}{2}$ inch

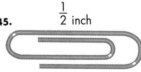

Write the product.

46.
$$\begin{array}{r} 0.201 \\ \times \quad 7 \\ \hline \end{array}$$

47.
$$\begin{array}{r} 3.065 \\ \times \quad 4 \\ \hline \end{array}$$

48.
$$\begin{array}{r} 1.55 \\ \times \quad 9 \\ \hline \end{array}$$

49.
$$\begin{array}{r} 8.3 \\ \times \quad 5 \\ \hline \end{array}$$

50.
$$\begin{array}{r} 4.08 \\ \times \quad 10 \\ \hline \end{array}$$

EXCURSION
USING TECHNOLOGY

MEAN AND MEDIAN

A calculator can be used to do a chain of computations. It is especially helpful to find the average, or mean, of a set of data.

Day	M	T	W	Th
Miles	48.8	75.6	36.2	56

Find the mean number of miles driven during the four days.

First find the sum of the data.

Enter: [4][8][.][8][+][7][5][.][6][+][3][6][.][2][+][5][6][=] [216.6]

Then divide by the number in the set.

[2][1][6][.][6][÷][4][=] [54.15]

The mean number of miles in this example is 54.15.

To find the median of a set of data, arrange the numbers in order. For an odd number of data, the median is the middle number. For an even number of data, the median is the mean of the two middle numbers. You can use a calculator to find the mean of the two middle numbers.

Find the median number of miles driven.

List data in order from least to greatest.
36.2, 48.8, 56, 75.6
Add the two middle numbers   **Divide by two.**

Enter: [4][8][.][8][+][5][6][=] [104.8]   Enter: [÷][2][=] [52.4]

The median number of miles in this example is 52.4.

Think

≥ • If the number of miles driven on Tuesday were changed to 85, would the mean change? Would the median change? Explain.

GUIDED PRACTICE

Use a calculator. Write the mean for each set of data.

1. $123, $117, $148, $109

2. 11,762; 14,341; 14,547

3. 9, 9, 8, 7, 6, 4, 8, 8

4. 54 in., 61 in., 55 in., 59 in.

Write the median for each set of data.

5. 122, 117, 148, 109

6. 11,762; 14,341; 14,549

7. 9, 9, 8, 7, 6, 4, 8, 8

8. 54 in., 61 in., 55 in., 59 in.

9. Which set of data in exercises 5–8 could represent a town's population? Explain.

INDEPENDENT PRACTICE

Use a calculator. Write the mean for each set of data.

1. $2.79, $3.69, $2.80, $3.20, $4, $2.48

2. 28 L, 30.5 L, 46.2 L, 39.3 L, 15.4 L

3. 102, 115, 135, 98, 77, 88, 96, 118

4. 26.42, 29.36, 48.1, 38.14, 56.3, 44

5. 62, 24, 57, 19, 41

6. 16, 71, 44, 29, 37

Write the median for each set of data.

7. $1.15, $2.30, $1.50, $1.75, $1.90, $2.70

8. 402.3, 728.4, 882.4, 298.8

9. 1400, 1736, 2146, 1891, 1580, 2020

10. 48 ft, 52 ft, 61 ft, 77 ft, 83 ft, 69 ft

11. 36,000; 24,800; 86,425; 61,212

12. $10.45, $26.40, $38.62, $20.36

Use the Almanac section of the Data Book and a calculator to solve.

13. Find the mean temperature for July in the following six cities: Albuquerque, Dallas, Houston, Oklahoma City, Phoenix, San Antonio.

14. Find the median of the average high temperature for November to February in Oklahoma City.

GEOMETRY

Science

Making a Weather Instrument The students shown on page 228 have built a weather instrument. It is used to estimate wind speed. You can build your own weather instrument. You will need some cardboard, white paper, tape, a Ping-Pong ball, and about 30 centimeters of fishing line.

Use the paper to trace the instrument shown below. Then paste the tracing onto a piece of cardboard, and use a scissors to cut out your instrument. Tape the ball to one end of the fishing line. Then tape the other end of the line to the center of your instrument.

Take your instrument outside on a windy day. Point it toward the wind, and read the angle of the fishing line. Then use the table to estimate the wind speed. Record the wind speed and weather for a few days to see if the weather changes when winds change.

Angle	Wind Speed km per hour
0	0
5	9
10	13
15	16
20	19
25	21
30	24
35	26
40	29
45	31
50	34
55	37
60	41
65	46
70	52

QUADRILATERALS

In this lesson, you will explore different types of quadrilaterals. You will need tracing paper.

▶ A quadrilateral is a polygon with four sides. The sides of quadrilateral *ABCD* are segment *AB*, segment *BC*, segment *CD*, and segment *AD*. A shorter way to write *segment AB* is $\overline{AB}$.

1. How would you write *segment BC*, *segment CD*, and *segment AD* a shorter way?

▶ In quadrilateral *ABCD*, $\overline{AD}$ extends in the same direction as $\overline{BC}$. No matter how long you drew each of the segments, $\overline{AD}$ and $\overline{BC}$ would never meet or cross. $\overline{AD}$ and $\overline{BC}$ are **parallel** line segments. We write $\overline{AD} \parallel \overline{BC}$.

2. Are $\overline{AB}$ and $\overline{DC}$ parallel? Explain.

▶ In quadrilateral *EFGH*, $\overline{EF}$ and $\overline{HG}$ are the same length. They are **congruent**. We write $\overline{EF} \cong \overline{HG}$.

Quadrilateral *EFGH* also has angles that have the same measure, or congruent angles. Angle *EFG* is congruent to angle *EHG*. We write $\angle EFG \cong \angle EHG$.

3. Copy and complete each statement. Use tracing paper if you need to.
   a. $\overline{JM} \cong$ ▩
   b. $\angle STU \cong$ ▩
   c. $\overline{WZ} \parallel$ ▩

Use the figures above to answer each question. Use tracing paper if you need to.

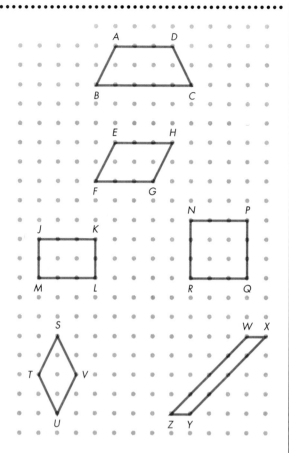

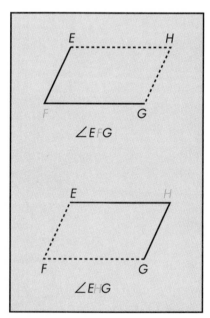

∠EFG

∠EHG

4. Figure *ABCD* has four vertices. Which of the other figures also have four vertices?

5. Which figures have two pairs of parallel sides?

6. A quadrilateral with two pairs of parallel sides is a **parallelogram**. Which figures are parallelograms?

7. How many pairs of congruent sides does each parallelogram have?

8. Which figures have at least one pair of congruent angles?

9. A **rhombus** is a figure that has two pairs of parallel sides and four congruent sides. Is a square a rhombus?

10. Which two figures are rhombuses?

11. Figure *ABCD* is a **trapezoid**. How is it like the other quadrilaterals? How is it different?

SUMMING IT UP

Write *yes* or *no*.
Use tracing paper.

12. Is Figure A a:
    a. square?
    b. rectangle?
    c. parallelogram?

13. Is Figure B a:
    a. square?
    b. rectangle?
    c. parallelogram?

14. Is Figure C a:
    a. square?
    b. rhombus?
    c. parallelogram?

15. Is Figure D a:
    a. square?
    b. rhombus?
    c. parallelogram?

16. Is Figure E a:
    a. square?
    b. trapezoid?
    c. parallelogram?

17. Discuss your answers to exercises 12–16 with the class.

Figure A

Figure B

Figure C

Figure D

Figure E

SLIDES AND FLIPS

This lesson is about slides and flips. You will need the recording sheet, tracing paper, crayons (one red, one green, one blue), and a centimeter ruler.

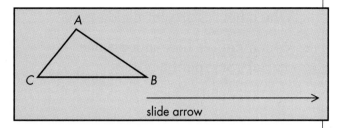

Follow these directions. Draw a slide image of triangle *ABC* (△*ABC*) in section A of your recording sheet.

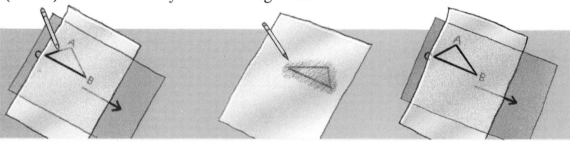

Trace the figure. Bear down hard on your pencil.

Turn the paper over. Darken the area on the back of the figure.

Turn the paper back over. Place the tracing on top of the figure.

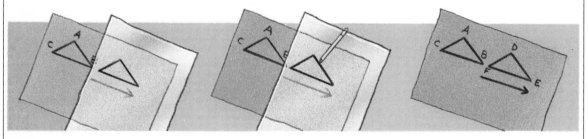

Slide the tracing along the slide arrow to the end of the arrow.

Draw over the traced figure.

Remove the tracing paper. Label the image.

1. **Congruent figures** are the same size and shape. Are △*ABC* and △*DEF* congruent?

2. Copy and complete each statement.

   a. $\angle CAB \cong$ ▓   b. $\overline{AC} \cong$ ▓   c. $\overline{AC} \parallel$ ▓
   d. $\angle BCA \cong$ ▓   e. $\overline{AB} \cong$ ▓   f. $\overline{AB} \parallel$ ▓
   g. $\angle ABC \cong$ ▓   h. $\overline{BC} \cong$ ▓   i. $\overline{BC} \parallel$ ▓

   Use tracing paper to check.

3. What is the distance between points *A* and *D*? Between points *B* and *E*? Between points *C* and *F*? What do you notice?

Follow these directions. Draw a flip image of △ABC in section A of your recording sheet.

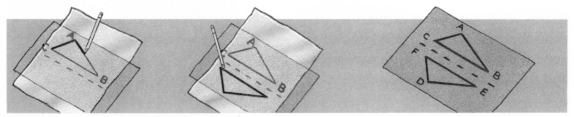

● Trace the figure and the flip line. Bear down hard on your pencil.

● Flip the paper over. Match up flip lines. Draw over the tracing.

● Remove the tracing paper. Label the image.

4. Are △ABC and △DEF congruent? Explain.

5. Copy and complete each statement.
   a. ∠ABC ≅ ■
   b. ∠CAB ≅ ■
   c. ∠ACB ≅ ■
   d. $\overline{AB}$ ≅ ■
   e. $\overline{BC}$ ≅ ■
   f. $\overline{AC}$ ≅ ■
   Use tracing paper to check.

6. Is any segment in △ABC parallel to its image in △DEF? Explain.

7. What is the distance between points A and D? Between points B and E? Between points C and F? What do you notice?

▶ **8.** Draw and label the slide or flip image of each figure in section B of your recording sheet.

9. For each pair of figures in exercise 8, color:
   a. one pair of congruent line segments red.
   b. one pair of congruent angles blue.
   c. any pair of parallel line segments green.

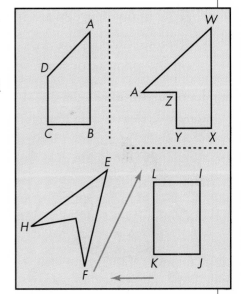

· ·

SUMMING IT UP

10. Use the figures in section A of your recording sheet. Write S if the statement is true for the slide, F if the statement is true for the flip.
   a. △DEF ≅ △ABC
   b. $\overline{DE} \parallel \overline{AB}$
   c. Each line segment is congruent to its image.
   d. Each angle is congruent to its image.
   e. The distance from A to D is the same as the distance from B to E and from C to F.

MEASURING AND DRAWING ANGLES

In this lesson, you will explore measuring and drawing angles. You will need the recording sheet, a protractor, and a ruler.

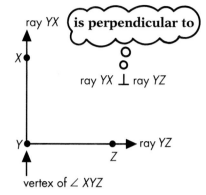

ray YX **is perpendicular to**

ray YX ⊥ ray YZ

vertex of ∠ XYZ

You know that angles are measured in degrees. Angles are any degree measure from 0° to 360°. A right angle measures 90°. Rays that form a right angle are **perpendicular**.

Look at your protractor. Notice that it has two scales. One is read clockwise from 0° to 360°. The other is read counterclockwise from 0° to 360°.

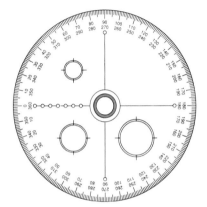

1. How many degrees are in a circle?

2. How many degrees does each line on the protractor represent?

To measure an angle:

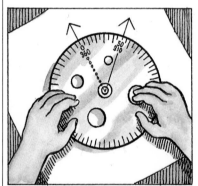

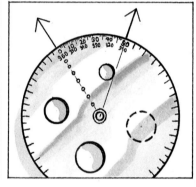

- Place the center point in the red circle at the vertex of the angle. Turn the protractor so that 0° lines up with one of the rays.

- Read along the scale (going from 0 to 10 to 20 . . .) in the direction of the other ray.

- Read the degree measure at that ray. The measure of this angle is 50°.

3. Measure the angles in section A of your recording sheet. Write each measure.

4. Which of these is a right angle?

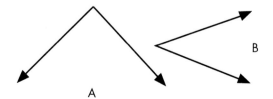

A

B

To draw an angle:

● **Draw a ray.**

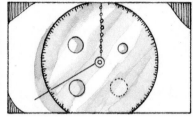

● **Place the center point of the protractor on the end of the ray. The end of the ray will be the vertex of the angle.**

● **Turn the protractor so that 0° lines up with the ray.**

● **Read along the scale (going from 0 to 10 to 20 . . .) until you've reached the measure you want. Mark it with a dot.**

● **Remove the protractor. With your ruler draw a ray connecting the vertex and the dot.**

5. Draw angles with the following measures in section B of your recording sheet.
   a. 35°   **b.** 120°

6. Angles that measure between 90° and 180° are called **obtuse angles**. Draw an obtuse angle in section C of your recording sheet. Write the measure.

7. Angles that measure less than 90° are called **acute angles**. Draw an acute angle in section C of your recording sheet. Write the measure.

SUMMING IT UP

Write *true* or *false*.

8. A circle has 360°.
9. Ray *BA* ⊥ ray *BC*.
10. The angle at the right is obtuse.
11. All angles are either obtuse or acute.

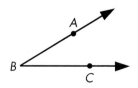

235

TURNS

In this lesson, you will review turns and discover some new things about them. You will need the recording sheet, tracing paper, dot paper, a ruler, and crayons.

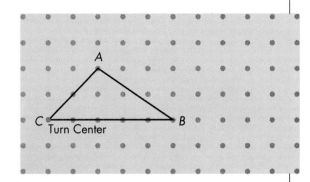

Follow these directions to draw a turn image of △ABC.

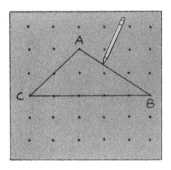

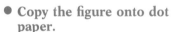

- Copy the figure onto dot paper.

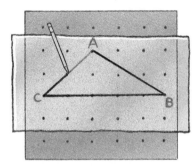

- Trace the figure.

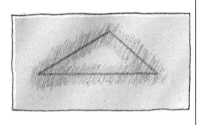

- Turn the tracing paper over. Darken the area on the back of the figure.

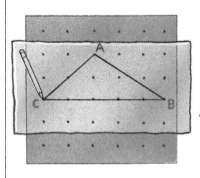

- Turn the paper back over. Place your pencil point on the turn center.

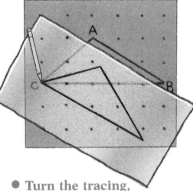

- Turn the tracing, holding the turn center steady.

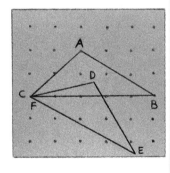

- Draw over the tracing. Remove the tracing. Label the turn image.

1. Are △ABC and △DEF congruent? Explain.

2. Copy and complete each statement.
   - a. ∠BAC ≅ ▨ $\overline{BA}$ ≅ ▨
   - b. ∠ABC ≅ ▨ $\overline{AC}$ ≅ ▨
   - c. ∠ACB ≅ ▨ $\overline{AB}$ ≅ ▨

Use tracing paper to check.

Look at the examples of a quarter turn, half turn, and three-quarter turn below.

$\frac{1}{4}$ turn

$\frac{1}{2}$ turn

$\frac{3}{4}$ turn

3. Practice making quarter, half, and three-quarter turns. Trace the pentagon above. Holding the turn center steady, turn your paper a quarter turn so the pentagon fits over the blue lines. Repeat for a half turn and a three-quarter turn.

$\frac{1}{4}$ turn  $\frac{1}{2}$ turn  $\frac{3}{4}$ turn

4. Draw quarter, half, and three-quarter turn images of the figure in section A of your recording sheet.

5. For each figure and turn image in exercise 4, color one pair of congruent angles and one pair of congruent line segments.

6. A turn can also be described in degrees. Use the circles on your recording sheet.
   a. Shade a circle to represent each fraction: $\frac{1}{4}$, $\frac{1}{2}$, and $\frac{3}{4}$. Start shading at zero and go clockwise.
   b. Write the number of degrees in each shaded fraction of the circle.

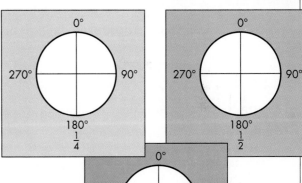

SUMMING IT UP

7. Complete each statement, based on the figure and turn image shown at the right.
   a. The image shows a turn of ▓°.
   b. figure *DEFG* ≅ ▓
   c. $\overline{EF}$ ≅ ▓

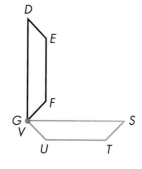

237

SYMMETRY

In this lesson, you will explore line symmetry and half-turn symmetry. Work in small groups. You will need the recording sheet, scissors, and tracing paper.

If a figure can be folded along a line so that the two halves match exactly, then the figure has **line symmetry**. The line is called the **line of symmetry**.

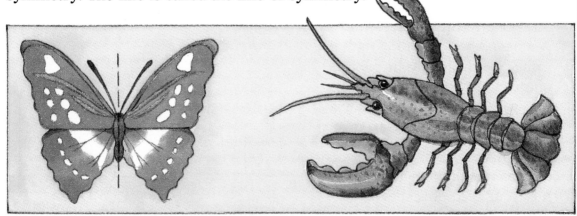

This figure has line symmetry.

This figure does *not* have line symmetry.

Trace each figure below. Include the dotted line in your tracing. Cut out each figure. Fold each drawing along the dotted line.

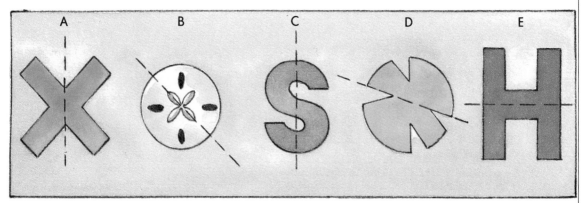

1. Write the letter of each figure above that has line symmetry.

2. Look at figure B. Try to fold it along another line so that the two halves match exactly. Can you do it?

3. Predict which figures on your recording sheet have line symmetry. Trace and cut out each figure. Draw each line of symmetry you find. Find as many as you can.

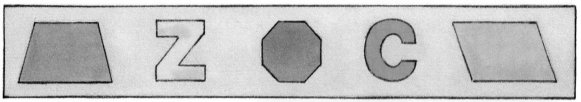

4. Record your findings in the chart on your recording sheet.

▶ If a figure can be turned halfway around a turn center so that it looks exactly the same, the figure has **half-turn symmetry**.

Figure	Number of Lines of Symmetry	Half-Turn Symmetry (yes/no)
⬭		
Z		
⬢		
C		
▱		

after half turn

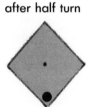

This figure has half-turn symmetry.

after half turn

This figure does *not* have half-turn symmetry.

5. Trace each figure on your recording sheet again.

6. On your recording sheet, draw the half-turn image for each figure.

7. Record your findings in the chart on your recording sheet.

························
SUMMING IT UP

8. Write *yes* or *no*. Can a figure have:
   a. more than two lines of symmetry?
   b. line symmetry and half-turn symmetry?
   c. line symmetry but no half-turn symmetry?
   d. half-turn symmetry but no line symmetry?

9. Discuss your results with the class.

USING STRATEGIES

An old circular building is being turned into a cinema with six theaters. Ms. Shen is designing the theaters. She must make all six of them the same size and shape.

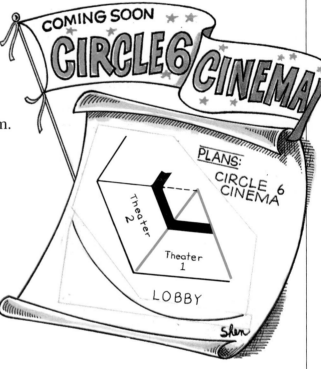

Help Ms. Shen by solving each problem.

1. What size angle will be formed by the two side walls (shown in blue) of Theater 1?

2. What would that angle be if 8 theaters were planned instead of 6?

3. How many theaters would fit if that angle were 30 degrees?

4. What shape will the outside walls of the 6 theaters make?

5. If the theaters are numbered in order, which theater will be directly opposite Theater 3?

6. Each theater will have 15 rows of seats. The front row will have 10 seats. Each row will have 2 more seats than the one in front of it. How many seats will be in each theater?

7. Half the theaters will be painted blue and the rest will be painted red. How many different ways are there to arrange that? HINT: These two pictures show the same arrangement.

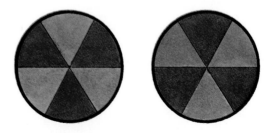

SECTION REVIEW

for pages 230–240

1. △*MNO* is the slide image of △*HIJ*. Copy and complete each statement.
   a. △*HIJ* ≅ ▨
   b. ∠*NOM* ≅ ▨
   c. $\overline{HJ}$ ▨ $\overline{MO}$

2. Copy trapezoid *STUV* onto dot paper. Use tracing paper to draw its flip image.
   a. Circle the vertices of one pair of congruent angles.
   b. Darken one pair of congruent line segments.

3. Use tracing paper. Write the letter of each figure that is a:
   a. quadrilateral.
   b. rhombus.

4. Use a protractor to draw:
   a. an acute angle.
   b. an obtuse angle.
   c. a right angle.

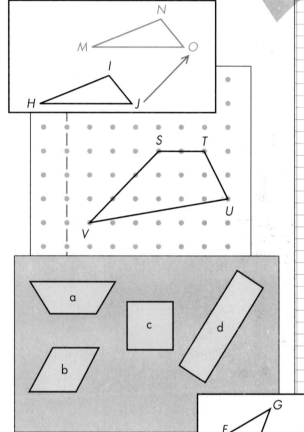

Use △*FGH* and its turn image △*XYZ* to answer each question.

5. Image △*XYZ* shows a turn of ▨°.

6. Name a pair of congruent angles.

7. Name a pair of congruent line segments.

8. Copy each figure at the right onto dot paper.
   a. Which figures have half-turn symmetry? (The red dot is the turn center.)
   b. Which figures have line symmetry?

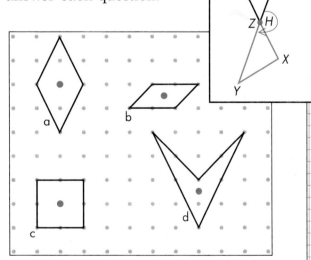

TRIANGLES

In this lesson, you will measure triangles and discover something all triangles have in common. Work in pairs. You will need the recording sheet, tracing paper, a protractor, and a centimeter ruler.

Triangle	Angle Measures	Measure $\angle E$	$\angle F$	$\angle G$	Sum of Angle Measures ($\angle E + \angle F + \angle G$)
1	66°, 48°, 66°	66°	66°	48°	
2	60°, 60°, 60°				
3	17°, 38°, 125°				

A short way to name an angle is to use just the letter that names the vertex of the angle.

$\angle A\mathbf{B}C$ can be written $\angle B$.

$\angle F\mathbf{G}H$ can be written $\angle G$.

1. Write each angle using a single letter.
   a. $\angle AEO$
   b. $\angle RSK$
   c. $\angle MNO$

2. Trace each triangle on this page. Measure all three angles in each triangle. Select the correct measurement in chart A on your recording sheet, and write it under the angle. The first one has been done for you.

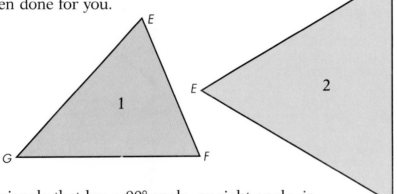

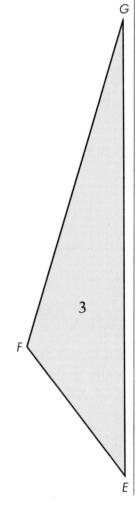

3. A triangle that has a 90° angle, or right angle, is called a **right triangle**. Is any one of these a right triangle?

4. Complete chart A. What do you notice about the sum of the angles for every triangle?

5. Look at what you wrote for exercise 4. This is true for all triangles. Write this as a rule.

6. Use your ruler to measure the sides of each triangle. Complete chart B on your recording sheet.

▶ A triangle that has two sides congruent is an **isosceles triangle**.

▶ An **equilateral triangle** is a special isosceles triangle. It has all sides congruent.

▶ A triangle that has no sides congruent is a **scalene triangle**.

7. Look at chart B. Which triangle is:
   a. isosceles?
   b. scalene?
   c. equilateral?

Chart B

Triangle	Length (cm) $\overline{EF}$	$\overline{FG}$	$\overline{GE}$
1			
2			
3			

SUMMING IT UP

8. Write the missing angle measure for each triangle.
   a. △RSK   ∠R = 70°   ∠S = 35°   ∠K = ▨
   b. △MSW   ∠M = 45°   ∠S = 90°   ∠W = ▨
   c. △LTV   ∠L = 22°   ∠T = 64°   ∠V = ▨

9. Explain how you got your answers for exercise 8.

10. Can a triangle have more than one right angle? How do you know?

11. Try to draw a right triangle that is also:
    a. isosceles. Can you do it?
    b. scalene. Can you do it?
    c. equilateral. Can you do it?

12. What are three things all triangles have in common?

13. Name four types of triangles.

ORDERED PAIRS

This lesson explores the positions of figures and slide images on a grid. Work in small groups. You will need the recording sheet and tracing paper.

▶ To identify the point where two lines intersect, give the number of each line.

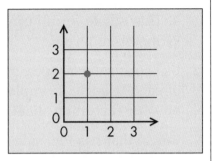

● First read across from zero.	● Then read up from that number.	● Write each number.
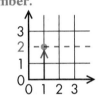		(1, 2)

1. Which letter is on the grid at the right at the point (3,1)? (1,3)?

2. How do you name point *C*? Point *F*? Point *G*?

3. Name another point, like point *C*, where both numbers are the same.

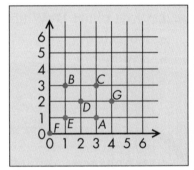

▶ Because order is important in identifying the point, the numbers identifying it are called an **ordered pair**.

4. What point does each ordered pair below name?
   - **a.** (2,3)
   - **b.** (3,2)
   - **c.** (1,5)
   - **d.** (5,1)
   - **e.** (4,0)
   - **f.** (0,4)

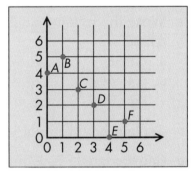

5. Write the ordered pair for each vertex of △*ABC* in section A of your recording sheet.

Figure	Ordered Pairs Vertex		
	A	*B*	*C*
△ ABC			
△ ABC image			

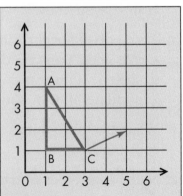

6. Use tracing paper to draw the slide image of △ABC in section A of your recording sheet. Record in the chart the ordered pair that names each vertex of the slide image.

7. Circle the first number in each ordered pair of △ABC and the first number in each ordered pair of the slide image. What pattern do you notice?

A

(①, 4)

(③, 5)

8. Underline the second number in each ordered pair of △ABC and the second number in each ordered pair of the slide image. What pattern do you notice?

A

(1, 4)

(3, 5)

9. Draw the slide image of △ABC in section B of your recording sheet by moving the figure two units to the right and one unit up.

Figure	Ordered Pairs Vertex		
	A	**B**	**C**
△ABC image			

10. Write the ordered pair that names each vertex of the slide image in section B of your recording sheet. Are these the same ordered pairs as in exercise 6?

11. Write the ordered pair that names each vertex of trapezoid *GHIJ* in section C of your recording sheet.

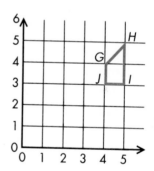

12. Predict what the ordered pair for each vertex will be if you slide the trapezoid two units to the left and two units down. Write your prediction.

13. Check your prediction in exercise 12 by drawing the slide image in section C of your recording sheet. Write the ordered pairs in the chart.

Figure	Ordered Pairs Vertex			
	G	**H**	**I**	**J**
Trapezoid GHIJ				
Trapezoid GHIJ image				

....

SUMMING IT UP

14. How do the numbers identifying the position of a figure change when you slide it?

SIMILAR FIGURES

In this lesson, you will explore similar figures on a grid. Work in pairs. You will need the recording sheet, squared paper, and tracing paper.

1. Write the ordered pair for each vertex of rectangle GHIJ in the chart in section A of your recording sheet.

2. Multiply the numbers in each ordered pair by 2. For example, (1,2) would become (2,4). Write the new ordered pairs in the chart.

3. Use the new ordered pairs to draw a figure on the same grid. What do you notice when you compare the new figure with the original?

4. How many times as long is each side of the new figure compared with the original figure?

5. Use tracing paper to compare the angles in the new figure to the angles in the original figure. What do you notice?

6. Write the ordered pair that names each vertex of figure PQRSTU in the chart in section B of your recording sheet.

7. Multiply the numbers in each ordered pair by 3. Predict how the measures of the sides and angles of figure 2 will compare with those of figure 1.

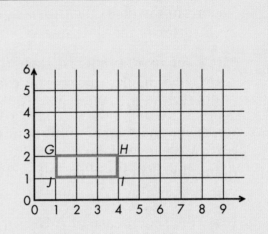

Figure	Ordered Pairs Vertex			
	G	H	I	J
1				
2				

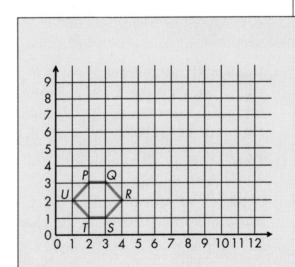

Figure	Ordered Pairs Vertex					
	P	Q	R	S	T	U
1						
2						

8. Draw figure 2 from exercise 7, and check your prediction.

9. Write the ordered pair for each vertex of △ABC in the chart in Section C of your recording sheet.

10. Divide the numbers in each ordered pair by 2. Predict how the measures of the sides and angles of figure 2 will compare with figure 1.

11. Draw figure 2 from exercise 10, and check your prediction.

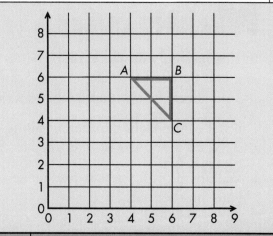

| Figure | Ordered Pairs Vertex | | |
	A	B	C
1			
2			

SUMMING IT UP

12. In each pair of figures you drew, the figures are **similar**. Answer each question, based on the pairs of similar figures.
   a. Are the similar figures the same shape?
   b. Are the angles of the similar figures congruent?

13. What kind of figure do you get if you multiply or divide each number in the ordered pairs of a figure by the same number?

14. How are similar figures different from congruent figures?

15. Write a definition for similar figures.

16. Discuss your definition with the class.

CHALLENGE • Critical Thinking

Trace each figure four times. Cut the figures out. Use the four congruent figures to make a larger, similar figure for each of the original figures shown.

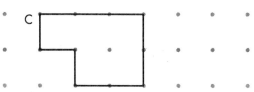

MAKING CUBES

In this lesson, you will explore patterns, or **nets**, that can be used to make cubes. You will need several sheets of dot paper, scissors, and tape.

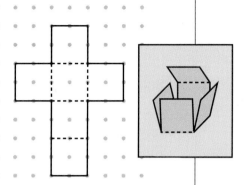

The net at the right can be cut along the solid lines and folded along the dotted lines to make a cube.

1. Will each of the nets below make a cube? Write your predictions.

A.
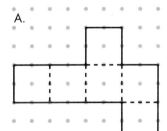

B.
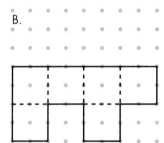

C.
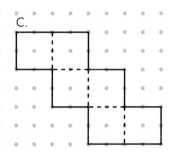

2. Copy the nets onto dot paper. Then cut, fold, and tape them. Check your predictions.

3. Write the letter of each net that made a cube.

4. Each of the nets below will make a cube. Copy each net onto dot paper. Include the *X* drawn on each.

A.
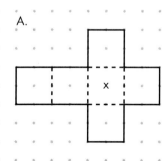

B.
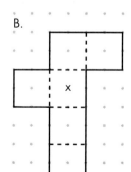

C.
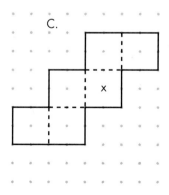

5. The *X* marks the bottom of each cube. Predict which square of the net will be the top, front, right face, left face, and back of the cube. Label your predictions on the net.

   T for top   *R* for right face
   L for left face   *B* for back
   F for front

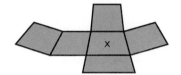

6. Cut, fold, and tape each cube to check your prediction. Remember to place the *X* square flat on your desk before you begin folding.

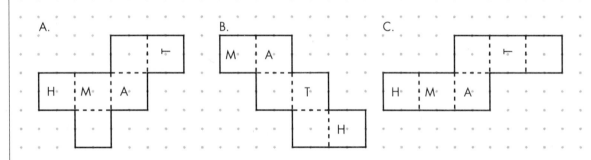

7. Each of the nets below will make a cube. Copy each net onto dot paper.

   A.

   B.

   C.

8. Predict which of the nets above will spell the word *MATH* so that the letters appear right side up and in the right order. Cut, fold, and tape the nets to check your predictions.

•
SUMMING IT UP

9. Design your own cube to spell out the word *CUBE*. Cut, fold, and tape it.

10. Compare your design with another student's design. Are they the same?

11. Discuss your design with the class.

12. How many different designs did your class find?

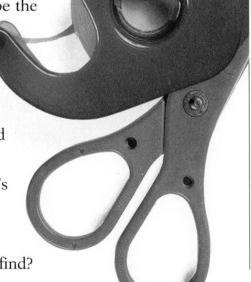

THE PLANE IN GEOMETRY

In this lesson, you will explore planes. You will need your recording sheet, scissors, and tape.

Your desktop is a flat surface. A **plane** is a flat surface that goes on forever in *all directions*. Your desktop is part of a plane.

Look around the room. Find other flat surfaces. Since each one is part of a plane, we can say that each represents a plane.

1. Which of these could represent a plane?

   wall   floor   window

   ceiling   globe   blackboard

2. Look at the door. How many planes are represented by surfaces on the door?

3. When two planes meet, or **intersect**, they form a line. How many lines are represented by the intersections of the walls and ceiling of your room?

4. Since planes go on forever, what can you say about lines formed by intersecting planes?

5. Look at a spot where two walls and the ceiling meet. What does the intersection of three planes form?

▶ Cut out the net on your recording sheet. Fold and tape the net to form a cube. Use your cube to answer each question.

6. How many planes are represented by the faces on the cube?

7. How many pairs of parallel planes are represented?

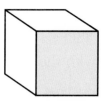

8. How many planes meet at each vertex?

9. Look at the pyramid. Count the number of faces meeting at each vertex. How does it compare with your answer to exercise 8?

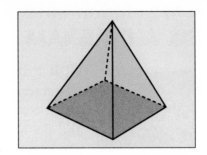

SUMMING IT UP

10. What is a plane?

11. Could you measure a real plane? Discuss your reasons.

PROJECT • Model Building

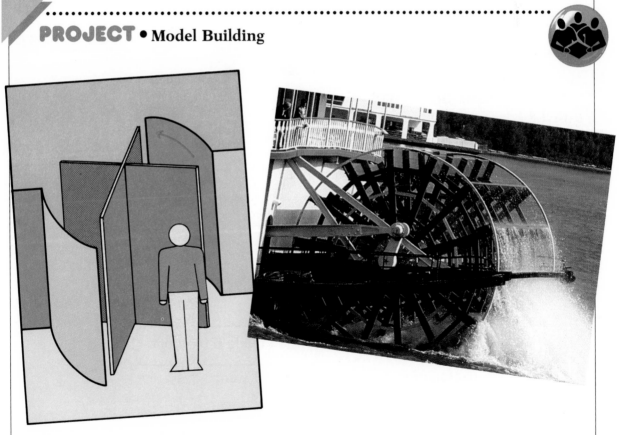

Work in groups. Make your own paddle wheel or revolving door. You can use cardboard, construction paper, or any other material you have available.

How many planes are represented in your model wheel or door?

MAKE A DIAGRAM, MAKE A MODEL

Often, people use different strategies to solve the same problem.

One time, I made a model to help a magician plan his show.

OUR PROBLEM

The magician planned to line up 8 trunks on the stage. Starting from the left, he would count 3 trunks and push away the third trunk. Starting where he left off, he would again count and push away the third trunk. He would keep doing this until only 1 trunk remained. Then the trunk would pop open, and his assistant would jump out. How did the magician know in which trunk his assistant should hide?

MAKE A MODEL SOLUTION

I used 8 counters to stand for the 8 trunks. I acted out each step of the show until only 1 counter remained. I always counted from left to right.

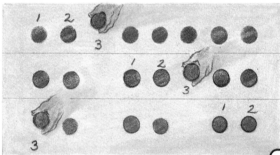

And I made a diagram.

MAKE A DIAGRAM SOLUTION

I drew 8 boxes to stand for the 8 trunks. Then I went through each step, crossing out boxes until only 1 remained.

Although we used different strategies, we got the same answer. The assistant should hide in the seventh trunk. Try these yourself and see if you agree.

GUIDED PRACTICE

Make a model or diagram to help.

1. Look at the clues that lead to the treasure. What would be a more direct way to go from Rugged Rock to the treasure?

~ Clues for ~
Finding Treasure

Start at Rugged Rock.

Walk east 10 meters.

Turn 90 degrees to the left.

Walk 10 meters.

Turn 90 degrees to the right.

Walk 20 meters.

Turn 90 degrees to the right.

Walk 10 meters.

Dig up the treasure.

....

APPLICATION

Work in pairs to solve each problem. Make a model or diagram or try another strategy.

2. John plans to make a box from a sheet of paper 11 inches long and $8\frac{1}{2}$ inches wide. He will cut out a 2-inch square from each corner. Then he will fold the flaps up and tape them. What will be the dimensions of his box?

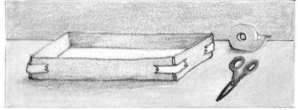

3. Draw the shape that Mindy is thinking of.

> I'm thinking of a shape that has 4 sides. Two sides are 6 inches each, and the other two sides are 3 inches each. Two of its angles are 90 degrees. I'm NOT thinking of a rectangle.

4. The Mill City train is entering a 200-yard tunnel. The train has 5 cars. Each car is 16 yards long, and there is a 5-yard space between cars. If the train is moving 100 yards each minute, how much time will pass before the end of the train comes out of the tunnel?

5. Design a net for a cube with the numbers 1–6 so that opposite sides have a sum of 7.

USING STRATEGIES

Mr. Jacobs creates snacks. His latest idea is called the Fro Yo, a cube of frozen yogurt. He wants to make a small box to hold a single FroYo and a large box to hold 8 FroYos.

Mr. Jacobs has begun drawing a plan for the small box. He is going to make a plan for the large box by doubling the ordered pairs.

Help Mr. Jacobs by solving each problem. Use squared paper.

1. Copy the plan for the small FroYo box. Complete it.

2. How many small squares are in the plan?

3. Write the ordered pairs for the corners of each square drawn on your plan.

4. On a separate sheet of squared paper, make a large plan by multiplying each number in the ordered pairs by 2.

5. Is your large plan twice as long as your small plan?

6. How many small squares are in your large plan?

7. Cut, fold, and tape each plan to make the two boxes. Do you think the large box will hold 8 FroYos? Explain.

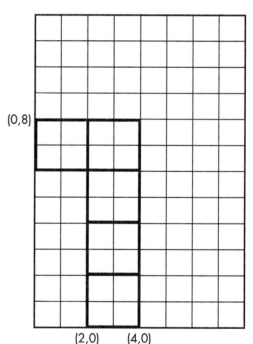

SECTION REVIEW

for pages 242–254

1. Write the letter of each triangle that is:
   a. equilateral.
   b. isosceles.
   c. scalene.

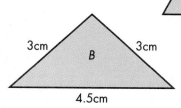

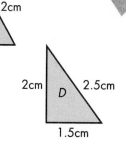

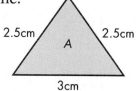

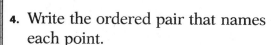

2. Write the missing angle measure for each triangle.
   a. $\triangle ANT$ $\angle A = 90°$ $\angle N = 30°$ $\angle T = $ ■
   b. $\triangle COW$ $\angle C = 50°$ $\angle O = 20°$ $\angle W = $ ■
   c. $\triangle BAT$ $\angle B = 36°$ $\angle A = 82°$ $\angle T = $ ■

3. Which of the triangles in exercise 2 is a right triangle?

Use Figure *CDEF* and its grid to answer each question.

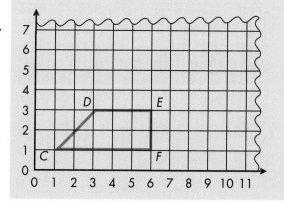

4. Write the ordered pair that names each point.
   a. *C*
   b. *D*
   c. *E*
   d. *F*

5. Multiply the numbers in each ordered pair in exercise 4 by 3. Write the new ordered pairs.

6. Copy figure *CDEF* and its grid onto squared paper. Draw a new figure using the ordered pairs in exercise 5.

7. Write *yes* or *no*. Is the figure you drew in exercise 6:
   a. congruent to figure *CDEF*?
   b. similar to figure *CDEF*?

CHAPTER REVIEW

Language Connection

Words can be used in many ways. The word *square* can be a noun or an adjective. Understanding how a word is used helps you understand its meaning better.

You learned many new words in this chapter. Decide how each can be used. Copy the list of words and phrases. Over each word, write *n* if it is a noun. Write *adj* if it is an adjective. Write *v* if it is a verb. Use a dictionary if you need help.

WORDS

trapezoid	parallelogram	equilateral	rhombus
parallel	congruent	isosceles	angle
fold	nets	scalene	turn

Test ● ● ● ● ● ●

Use the figures to answer each question. You may use tracing paper.

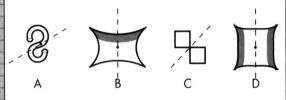

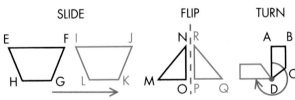

1. Which lines are lines of symmetry?

2. Which figures have both line and half-turn symmetry?

3. ∠*FGH* in figure *EFGH* is congruent to which angle in slide image *IJKL*?

4. The image of *ABCD* shows a turn of how many degrees?

5. $\overline{EH}$ in figure *EFGH* is congruent to which line in the slide image?

6. $\overline{MN}$ in △*MNO* is congruent to which line in the flip image?

256

Use tracing paper. Identify the type of quadrilateral in each figure.

 E
 F
 G H

7. figure E   **8.** figure F   **9.** figure G   **10.** figure H

Identify each type of triangle on the grid.

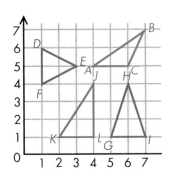

11. △DEF

12. △ABC

13. △GHI

14. △JKL

Use the grid to write the ordered pair that names each vertex.

15. K   **16.** E   **17.** J   **18.** G

PROBLEM SOLVING

Solve each problem.

19. In a game of Pin the Tail on the Donkey, Carl was facing north. He made a $\frac{3}{4}$ turn to the right and another $\frac{3}{4}$ turn to the right. What direction was he facing then?

20. Dora walked 20 feet and then made a $\frac{1}{4}$ turn to the right. She did this three more times. What shape was her path?

21. Dale has two isosceles triangles made of wood. If he puts them together, which of the following figures will he be able to form: rectangle, trapezoid, parallelogram, or rhombus?

22. If this net is folded to form a cube, two opposite faces will have the same color. What color will they be?

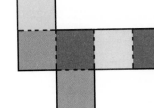

CUMULATIVE REVIEW

Write the answer.

23. 5.73×6.4 **24.** $1.3 \div 4$ **25.** $21 \div 4$ **26.** 2.61×4.4

27. $52.35 \div 6$ **28.** $17 \div 8$ **29.** 21.6×0.04 **30.** $14.6 \div 8$

EXCURSION
ART

CREATING TESSELLATIONS

Figures that cover a surface without overlapping or leaving gaps **tessellate**. The pattern they form is called a **tessellation**. To create your own tessellating figures you will need tracing paper, scissors, tape, and crayons.

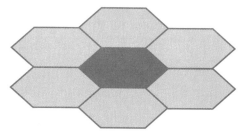

Figures that tessellate may be made up of simple geometric figures like the triangles and hexagons at the right. Or the figures may be more complicated, like those below, by the artist M.C. Escher.

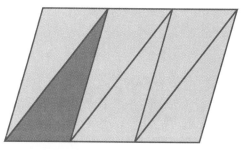

1. Trace the parallelogram at the right six times. Cut out each figure.

2. Place the parallelograms on another piece of paper so that they tessellate.

3. Tape down your design.

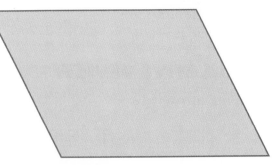

To make a more complicated tessellating figure,
follow these steps:

Draw and cut out a figure you know
will tessellate.

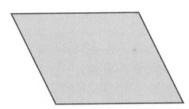

Cut a piece out of one side of the
figure.

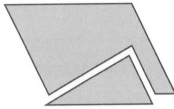

Move the piece to the opposite side of
the figure. Tape it there. Repeat for as
many pairs of opposite sides as you wish.

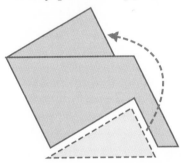

Decorate the figure. It can be a design
or look like a real object.

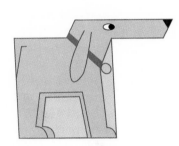

Trace the figure several times to form a tessellation.
Decorate each figure the same way.

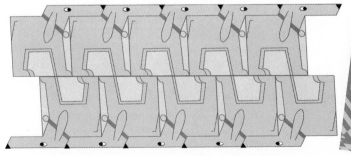

4. Make your own figure by tracing the triangle,
hexagon, or parallelogram on page 258. Follow
the directions above.

5. Share your tessellation with the class.

Connections
Measurement

Finding Your Hat Size Did you know that hat sizes are measured in fractions? You can use this activity to find your hat size.

Work with a partner. You will need scissors, a ruler, and long strips of paper. Wrap a strip around your partner's forehead just above the ears and eyebrows. Make sure the strip is not too loose or too tight, and mark its length.

Remove the strip and measure its length to the nearest eighth of an inch. Then use the table to find your partner's hat size. Now have your partner help you find your hat size.

YOUR HEAD SIZE	YOUR HAT SIZE
$20\frac{1}{2}$ in.	$6\frac{1}{2}$
$20\frac{3}{4}$ in.	$6\frac{5}{8}$
$21\frac{1}{8}$ in.	$6\frac{3}{4}$
$21\frac{1}{2}$ in.	$6\frac{7}{8}$
$21\frac{7}{8}$ in.	7
$22\frac{1}{4}$ in.	$7\frac{1}{8}$
$22\frac{5}{8}$ in.	$7\frac{1}{4}$
23 in.	$7\frac{3}{8}$
$23\frac{1}{2}$ in.	$7\frac{1}{2}$
$23\frac{7}{8}$ in.	$7\frac{5}{8}$

FRACTIONS

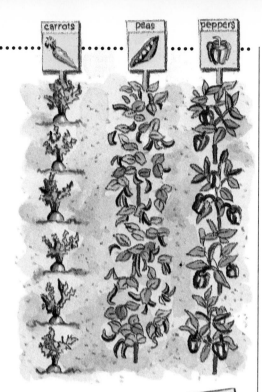

Ryan's garden is divided into 3 equal parts. What part of the garden is planted with carrots?

▶ You can write a fraction to represent part of a whole.

numerator $\rightarrow$ $\dfrac{1}{3}$ $\leftarrow$ **number of parts planted in carrots**

denominator $\rightarrow$ $\leftarrow$ **total number of equal parts**

Standard form: $\frac{1}{3}$ Word form: one third

One third of the garden is planted with carrots.

 Think

- What fraction of the garden is planted with peas? Green peppers? Green vegetables?

▶ A fraction can also represent part of a set.

What fraction of the signs are for vegetables?

$\dfrac{2}{3}$ $\leftarrow$ **number of signs for vegetables**
$\leftarrow$ **total number of signs**

Standard form: $\frac{2}{3}$ Word form: two thirds

Two thirds of the signs are for vegetables.

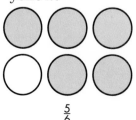

Other Examples

Five sixths of the circle is blue.	*Five sixths* of the circles are yellow.	*Four fourths* of the square is green.	*Four fourths* of the squares are red.
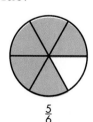 $\frac{5}{6}$	$\frac{5}{6}$	$\frac{4}{4}$	$\frac{4}{4}$

GUIDED PRACTICE

Write the word form and standard form of the fraction that tells what part is shaded.

1. 　　2. 　　3. 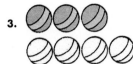　　4.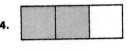

Write the standard form of the fraction.

5. eight fifteenths　6. two thirds　　7. seven tenths　　8. one eighth

9. Copy this rectangle three times.

a. Shade $\frac{1}{3}$ of the first rectangle.　　b. Shade $\frac{1}{5}$ of the second rectangle.　　c. Shade $\frac{1}{8}$ of the third rectangle.

Which fraction is the largest—$\frac{1}{3}$, $\frac{1}{5}$, or $\frac{1}{8}$?

....
INDEPENDENT PRACTICE

Write the word form and standard form of the fraction that tells what part is shaded.

10. 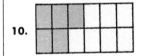　11. 　12. 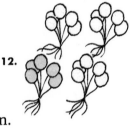　13.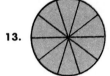

Write the standard form of each fraction.

14. two twelfths　15. five sixths　　16. one fourth　　17. sixteen twentieths

Problem Solving Draw a picture if it helps.

18. Rachel's garden is divided into equal areas for growing corn, tomatoes, beets, and pumpkins. What fraction of her garden is planted in corn?

19. Rachel picks $\frac{5}{8}$ of her tomatoes the last week in August. Is she picking more than or less than $\frac{1}{2}$ of her tomato crop?

....
CHALLENGE • Critical Thinking

Write a fraction that represents the shaded area. Explain your reasoning.

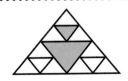

Should I cut your pizza into 6 slices or 8 slices?

Cut it into 6 slices, please. We're not hungry enough to eat 8.

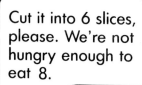

That doesn't make sense. Either way it's a whole pizza.

Work in groups. Read each story. Does the underlined sentence make sense? Explain.

1. Amy, Ben, and Carla shared some grapes. Amy ate $\frac{1}{2}$ of them, Ben ate $\frac{1}{2}$ of them, and Carla ate $\frac{1}{2}$ of them.

2. Amy, Ben, and Carla played a new tape. Amy listened to $\frac{1}{2}$ of the tape, Ben listened to $\frac{1}{2}$ of it, and Carla listened to $\frac{1}{2}$ of it.

3. A recipe calls for 8 egg whites and half as many egg yolks. So, Andy needs 1 dozen eggs to make the recipe.

4. Kevin spent twice as much for a radio as Rachel did. So, Rachel must have spent half as much as Kevin.

5. In Tanya's class, $\frac{2}{3}$ of the students are boys, $\frac{1}{3}$ of the students are girls, and $\frac{1}{3}$ of the students have blond hair.

6. There were some boxes of comic books at a book sale. Lauren, Marcus, and Nick each bought $\frac{1}{3}$ of the boxes. But Lauren got $\frac{1}{2}$ of the comic books.

7. Jan's basketball team scored $\frac{1}{3}$ of its points in the second quarter.

8. Leroy's basketball team scored $\frac{1}{3}$ of its points in each quarter.

9. Nancy was cutting a sandwich to share with Jay. "I'll take the middle half," said Sam.

10. Gilbert worked from 12 noon to 2:50 P.M. "Since 50 is $\frac{1}{2}$ of 100, I must have worked $2\frac{1}{2}$ hours", he said.

11. A pilot was flying to Holton. He began with a full tank and flew $\frac{1}{4}$ of the way there. Then, he flew back. When he got back the fuel tank was $\frac{1}{4}$ full. "I did not have enough fuel to make it to Holton," he said.

12. A pilot was flying to Hafton. She flew $\frac{2}{3}$ of the way there and saw that she didn't have enough fuel to get there. So, she flew back.

EQUIVALENT FRACTIONS

How long is the caterpillar?

Think

• What fraction of an inch does the red line on each ruler represent?

Equivalent fractions have the same value. You can use a ruler or number line to find equivalent fractions. $\frac{3}{4}$ and $\frac{6}{8}$ are equivalent fractions.

The caterpillar is $\frac{3}{4}$ inch, or $\frac{6}{8}$ inch, long.

▶ Here is a second way to find an equivalent fraction:

Multiply the numerator and the denominator by the same number. That number cannot be zero.

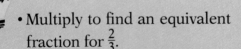

$$\frac{3}{4} \overset{\times\,2}{\underset{\times\,2}{=}} \frac{6}{8} \qquad \frac{3}{4} \overset{\times\,3}{\underset{\times\,3}{=}} \frac{9}{12}$$

The fractions $\frac{3}{4}$, $\frac{6}{8}$, and $\frac{9}{12}$ are all equivalent. You can check this by using number lines.

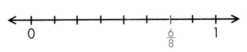

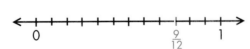

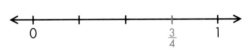

Think

• Multiply to find an equivalent fraction for $\frac{2}{3}$.

▶ Here is a third way to find an equivalent fraction:

Divide the numerator and the denominator by the same number.

$$\frac{6}{8} \overset{\div\,2}{\underset{\div\,2}{=}} \frac{3}{4} \qquad \frac{9}{12} \overset{\div\,3}{\underset{\div\,3}{=}} \frac{3}{4}$$

Again, $\frac{3}{4}$, $\frac{6}{8}$, and $\frac{9}{12}$ are equivalent.

GUIDED PRACTICE

Complete to make equivalent fractions.

1. $\frac{1}{3} = \frac{\blacksquare}{9}$ **2.** $\frac{3}{6} = \frac{\blacksquare}{2}$ **3.** $\frac{2}{8} = \frac{4}{\blacksquare}$ **4.** $\frac{1}{2} = \frac{\blacksquare}{6}$ **5.** $\frac{4}{10} = \frac{2}{\blacksquare}$

6. Write another equivalent fraction for each pair of fractions in exercises 1–5.

7. Is $\frac{1000}{3000}$ an equivalent fraction for $\frac{1}{3}$? Explain.

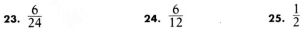

INDEPENDENT PRACTICE

Complete to make equivalent fractions.

8. $\frac{1}{4} = \frac{\blacksquare}{8}$ **9.** $\frac{2}{4} = \frac{\blacksquare}{8}$ **10.** $\frac{3}{4} = \frac{\blacksquare}{8}$ **11.** $\frac{4}{4} = \frac{\blacksquare}{8}$ **12.** $\frac{5}{4} = \frac{\blacksquare}{8}$

Multiply to find an equivalent fraction.

13. $\frac{1}{3}$ **14.** $\frac{3}{5}$ **15.** $\frac{7}{8}$ **16.** $\frac{4}{36}$ **17.** $\frac{5}{6}$

Divide to find an equivalent fraction.

18. $\frac{2}{8}$ **19.** $\frac{6}{12}$ **20.** $\frac{9}{12}$ **21.** $\frac{21}{28}$ **22.** $\frac{3}{15}$

Use the numbers in the circle to write an equivalent fraction.

23. $\frac{6}{24}$ **24.** $\frac{6}{12}$ **25.** $\frac{1}{2}$

26. $\frac{4}{9}$ **27.** $\frac{6}{7}$ **28.** $\frac{7}{9}$

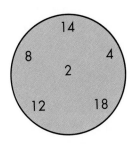

Problem Solving Use the picture below.

29. Travis baked a carrot cake. He put icing on the top and 4 sides. Then he sliced it into 16 pieces. What fraction of the pieces have icing on:
  a. 3 sides?   **b.** 2 sides?   **c.** 1 side?

30. Divide to write an equivalent fraction for each fraction in exercise 29.

SIMPLEST FORM

The fractions $\frac{1}{4}$ and $\frac{6}{24}$ are equivalent fractions.

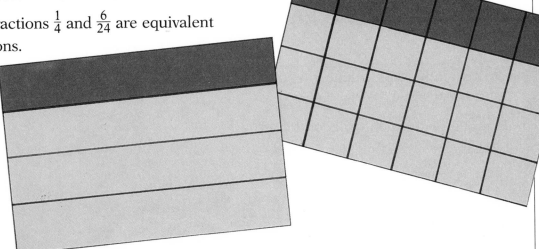

The fraction $\frac{1}{4}$ is the fraction $\frac{6}{24}$ written in **simplest form**.

> A fraction is in simplest form when the numerator and denominator have no common factors greater than 1.

▶ One way to find the simplest form of a fraction is to divide the numerator and the denominator by a common factor.

$$\frac{6}{24} \begin{array}{c} \nearrow \div 2 \searrow \\ = \\ \searrow \div 2 \nearrow \end{array} \frac{3}{12}$$

Continue dividing until the numerator and denominator have no common factors greater than 1.

$$\frac{6}{24} \begin{array}{c} \nearrow \div 2 \searrow \\ = \\ \searrow \div 2 \nearrow \end{array} \frac{3}{12} \begin{array}{c} \nearrow \div 3 \searrow \\ = \\ \searrow \div 3 \nearrow \end{array} \frac{1}{4}$$

▶ Another way to find the simplest form of a fraction is to look for the greatest common factor (GCF) of the numerator and denominator.

Factors of 6: 1, 2, **3**, **6**
Factors of 24: 1, 2, **3**, 4, **6**, 8, 12, 24

The GCF of 6 and 24 is 6. Divide the numerator and denominator by 6.

$$\frac{6}{24} \begin{array}{c} \nearrow \div 6 \searrow \\ = \\ \searrow \div 6 \nearrow \end{array} \frac{1}{4}$$

Again, $\frac{1}{4}$ is the simplest form of $\frac{6}{24}$.

Think

- Name two other fractions whose simplest form is $\frac{1}{4}$.

GUIDED PRACTICE

List the factors for each number. Circle the greatest common factor.

1. 8, 20   **2.** 16, 24   **3.** 40, 50   **4.** 7, 13

Write an equivalent fraction that is in simplest form. Show your work.

5. $\frac{5}{15}$ **6.** $\frac{8}{24}$ **7.** $\frac{6}{12}$ **8.** $\frac{50}{70}$ **9.** $\frac{12}{16}$

10. For which of exercises 5–9 did you use the greatest common factor?

INDEPENDENT PRACTICE

List the factors for each number. Circle the greatest common factor.

11. 27, 36   **12.** 18, 32   **13.** 14, 21   **14.** 18, 24

15. 18, 21   **16.** 9, 10   **17.** 8, 28   **18.** 7, 8

Write an equivalent fraction that is in simplest form.

19. $\frac{8}{18}$ **20.** $\frac{24}{36}$ **21.** $\frac{5}{15}$ **22.** $\frac{4}{12}$ **23.** $\frac{20}{32}$

24. $\frac{6}{15}$ **25.** $\frac{4}{24}$ **26.** $\frac{24}{30}$ **27.** $\frac{21}{28}$ **28.** $\frac{12}{36}$

Problem Solving Use the scoreboard.

29. What fraction of their games have the Tigers won? Lost? Write your answers in simplest form.

30. Would the Tigers have needed to win 30, 32, or 33 games in order to have won $\frac{2}{3}$ of their games?

WINS	LOSSES	TIES	TOTAL NUMBER OF GAMES
27	15	3	45

MATH LOG

What are two ways to find the simplest form of a fraction? Which do you prefer? Explain why.

ESTIMATING FRACTIONS

This piece of fabric is $\frac{3}{8}$ yard long. You can report the length in another way as *about* $\frac{1}{2}$ yard.

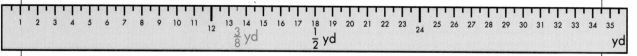

A fraction is equal to $\frac{1}{2}$ when the denominator is twice the numerator.

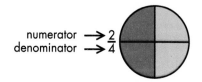

numerator $\rightarrow 2$
denominator $\rightarrow 4$

$\frac{5}{10}$ $\frac{8}{16}$

A fraction is equal to 1 when the numerator and the denominator are the same.

$\frac{3}{3}$ $\frac{7}{7}$ $\frac{4}{4}$

Fractions can be estimated as close to 0, $\frac{1}{2}$, or 1.

A fraction is:

- **close to 0** when the numerator is very small compared to the denominator.

| $\frac{1}{15}$ | $\frac{2}{67}$ | $\frac{3}{14}$ | $\frac{5}{100}$ | $\frac{1}{8}$ |

- **close to $\frac{1}{2}$** when the denominator is about twice as large as the numerator.

| $\frac{4}{9}$ | $\frac{3}{7}$ | $\frac{58}{100}$ | $\frac{7}{12}$ | $\frac{5}{8}$ |

- **close to 1** when the numerator and the denominator are about the same size.

| $\frac{7}{8}$ | $\frac{13}{12}$ | $\frac{97}{100}$ | $\frac{11}{9}$ | $\frac{8}{9}$ |

Think

- Explain how you can use estimation to decide whether $\frac{11}{25}$ is greater than or less than $\frac{5}{6}$.

- When a fraction is a bit larger than 1, which is larger, the numerator or the denominator?

GUIDED PRACTICE

Write whether each fraction is close to 0, $\frac{1}{2}$, or 1.

1. $\frac{1}{16}$ **2.** $\frac{9}{10}$ **3.** $\frac{5}{8}$ **4.** $\frac{4}{9}$ **5.** $\frac{3}{25}$

Make each fraction close to $\frac{1}{2}$, but not exactly $\frac{1}{2}$.

6. $\frac{4}{\blacksquare}$ **7.** $\frac{6}{\blacksquare}$ **8.** $\frac{9}{\blacksquare}$ **9.** $\frac{\blacksquare}{10}$ **10.** $\frac{\blacksquare}{7}$

11. How would you make the fraction in exercise 6 close to 1, but not exactly 1? Explain.

INDEPENDENT PRACTICE

Write whether each fraction is close to 0, $\frac{1}{2}$, or 1.

12. $\frac{11}{13}$ **13.** $\frac{3}{8}$ **14.** $\frac{1}{8}$ **15.** $\frac{7}{12}$ **16.** $\frac{8}{7}$

Make each fraction close to 0, but not exactly 0.

17. $\frac{\blacksquare}{10}$ **18.** $\frac{\blacksquare}{6}$ **19.** $\frac{2}{\blacksquare}$ **20.** $\frac{4}{\blacksquare}$ **21.** $\frac{\blacksquare}{27}$

Make each fraction close to $\frac{1}{2}$, but not exactly $\frac{1}{2}$.

22. $\frac{5}{\blacksquare}$ **23.** $\frac{3}{\blacksquare}$ **24.** $\frac{\blacksquare}{8}$ **25.** $\frac{\blacksquare}{12}$ **26.** $\frac{\blacksquare}{9}$

Make each fraction close to 1, but not exactly 1.

27. $\frac{\blacksquare}{6}$ **28.** $\frac{\blacksquare}{10}$ **29.** $\frac{4}{\blacksquare}$ **30.** $\frac{\blacksquare}{15}$ **31.** $\frac{\blacksquare}{100}$

Problem Solving Estimate to solve.

32. Erin needs about 1 yard of cloth to make a pillow. Which piece of fabric should she choose?

33. Which is the longest piece of cloth? The shortest?

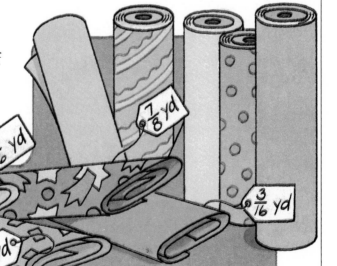

PROBLEM SOLVING

USING STRATEGIES

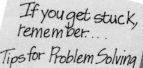

If you get stuck, remember...
Tips for Problem Solving
on pages 448–449

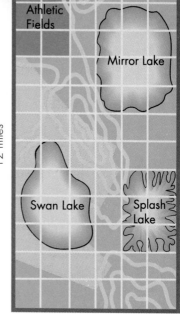

Athletic Fields

Mirror Lake

12 miles

Swan Lake

Splash Lake

6 miles

Use the map of Granger State Park to solve each problem. Remember to show how you got your answer.

1. What fraction of the park is taken up by the athletic fields?

2. Which takes up more area inside the park, the athletic fields or Splash Lake?

3. Which is a longer distance, once around the shore of Splash Lake or once around the edge of the athletic fields?

4. By just looking, make a quick estimate of the fraction of Granger State Park covered by water.

5. Make a more careful estimate of the fraction covered by water. HINT: Group partially covered squares to make whole squares.

6. Compare the methods you used in exercises 4 and 5 with the methods other students used. How are they different? How are they alike?

SECTION REVIEW

for pages 262–272

Write the letter of the correct answer.

1. Bill is baking banana bread. He only has $\frac{1}{2}$ pound of flour instead of the 1 pound that the recipe calls for. If he wants to continue baking, he should:
   a. add $\frac{1}{2}$ pound to each of the ingredients in the recipe.
   b. double the amounts in the rest of the recipe.
   c. use $\frac{1}{2}$ of each ingredient in the recipe.
   d. subtract $\frac{1}{4}$ pound from each ingredient in the recipe.

2. The elevator in Chuck's building can carry up to 2500 pounds in weight. Chuck has 3 crates weighing 1200 pounds, 1250 pounds, and 2700 pounds. How many trips will it take Chuck to bring all the crates up by elevator?
   a. 2 trips
   b. 3 trips
   c. 1 trip
   d. Chuck cannot bring all the crates up by elevator.

Write the letter of the equivalent fraction.

3. $\frac{6}{20}$
   a. $\frac{3}{20}$
   b. $\frac{10}{24}$
   c. $\frac{2}{5}$
   d. $\frac{3}{10}$

4. $\frac{8}{24}$
   a. $\frac{1}{3}$
   b. $\frac{6}{22}$
   c. $\frac{4}{24}$
   d. $\frac{1}{6}$

5. $\frac{4}{5}$
   a. $\frac{5}{6}$
   b. $\frac{12}{15}$
   c. $\frac{8}{15}$
   d. $\frac{2}{5}$

6. $\frac{16}{18}$
   a. $\frac{4}{9}$
   b. $\frac{8}{9}$
   c. $\frac{10}{12}$
   d. $\frac{6}{8}$

7. $\frac{5}{8}$
   a. $\frac{4}{7}$
   b. $\frac{10}{24}$
   c. $\frac{20}{32}$
   d. $\frac{20}{24}$

8. $\frac{28}{36}$
   a. $\frac{7}{12}$
   b. $\frac{7}{36}$
   c. $\frac{24}{32}$
   d. $\frac{14}{18}$

Write the letter of the fraction in simplest form.

9. $\frac{4}{32}$
   a. 4
   b. $\frac{2}{16}$
   c. $\frac{1}{8}$
   d. $\frac{1}{32}$

10. $\frac{12}{60}$
    a. $\frac{1}{5}$
    b. $\frac{1}{60}$
    c. 12
    d. $\frac{4}{20}$

11. $\frac{16}{48}$
    a. $\frac{1}{48}$
    b. 16
    c. $\frac{8}{24}$
    d. $\frac{1}{3}$

12. $\frac{32}{40}$
    a. 48
    b. $\frac{4}{5}$
    c. 12
    d. $\frac{8}{10}$

13. $\frac{18}{45}$
    a. $\frac{1}{3}$
    b. $\frac{2}{9}$
    c. $\frac{6}{15}$
    d. $\frac{2}{5}$

14. $\frac{15}{50}$
    a. $\frac{1}{5}$
    b. $\frac{1}{3}$
    c. $\frac{3}{10}$
    d. $\frac{3}{5}$

WHOLE NUMBERS AND MIXED NUMBERS

You can use Fraction Bars to learn how to write whole numbers and mixed numbers as fractions. Work in groups. You will need the recording sheet, scissors, and five copies of the Fraction Bars worksheet. Cut out the bars on each worksheet.

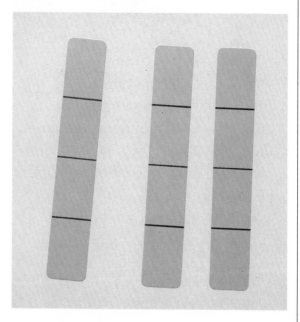

Use your fourths Fraction Bars for the following activity.

There are 4 fourths, or $\frac{4}{4}$, on one bar.

There are 8 fourths, or $\frac{8}{4}$, on two bars.

1. How many fourths are there in all on the three bars?

Complete Table A on your recording sheet.

2. What pattern do you notice in the numerators in Table A?

3. Complete Table B on your recording sheet. Use your halves, fifths, and sixths Fraction Bars.

4. Look at Table B. How could you find a numerator without using your Fraction Bars?

5. What do you think the numerator for $2 = \frac{\blacksquare}{3}$ is? Check your answer with the Fraction Bars.

6. Write the numerator. Check your answer with the Fraction Bars.

   a. $1 = \frac{\blacksquare}{5}$

   b. $2 = \frac{\blacksquare}{5}$

   c. $4 = \frac{\blacksquare}{6}$

   d. $5 = \frac{\blacksquare}{8}$

Table A

Number of Bars	Fraction in Fourths
2	$\frac{8}{4}$
3	$\frac{\blacksquare}{4}$
4	$\frac{\blacksquare}{4}$
5	$\frac{\blacksquare}{4}$

Table B

Fraction Bar	Number of Bars	Fraction
halves	2	$\frac{4}{2}$
fifths	2	$\frac{\blacksquare}{5}$
sixths	2	$\frac{\blacksquare}{6}$
halves	3	$\frac{\blacksquare}{2}$
fifths	3	$\frac{\blacksquare}{5}$
sixths	3	$\frac{\blacksquare}{6}$

The picture at the right shows $1\frac{1}{3}$ shaded Fraction Bars. You can see that there are four thirds. A mixed number like $1\frac{1}{3}$ can be written as the fraction $\frac{4}{3}$.

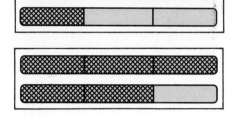

7. In the Fraction Bars at the right, how many thirds are shaded?

Complete Table C on your recording sheet.

8. Does the denominator change when you write a mixed number as a fraction?

9. Look at Table C. How could you find a numerator without using your Fraction Bars?

10. What do you think the numerator for $3\frac{1}{4} = \frac{\blacksquare}{4}$ is? Check your answer with the Fraction Bars.

11. Write a fraction for each mixed number. Check your answer with the Fraction Bars.

   a. $2\frac{1}{4}$

   b. $3\frac{3}{5}$

   c. $2\frac{3}{6}$

   d. $1\frac{1}{8}$

   e. $2\frac{2}{12}$

Table C

Model	Number	Fraction
	1	$\frac{4}{4}$
	$1\frac{1}{4}$	$\frac{\blacksquare}{4}$
	$1\frac{2}{4}$	$\frac{\blacksquare}{4}$
	$1\frac{3}{4}$	$\frac{\blacksquare}{4}$
	2	$\frac{\blacksquare}{4}$
	3	$\frac{\blacksquare}{5}$
	$3\frac{1}{5}$	$\frac{\blacksquare}{5}$
	$3\frac{2}{5}$	$\frac{\blacksquare}{5}$
	2	$\frac{\blacksquare}{6}$
	$2\frac{1}{6}$	$\frac{\blacksquare}{6}$
	$2\frac{2}{6}$	$\frac{\blacksquare}{6}$

SUMMING IT UP

12. How do you write a whole number as a fraction? Write this as a rule.

13. How do you write a mixed number as a fraction? Write this as a rule.

14. Discuss your rules with the class.

WRITING FRACTIONS

Adrian is cutting orange wedges to be given to
runners at the end of a marathon. If each wedge is
$\frac{1}{8}$ of an orange, how many eighths will he have after
cutting 4 oranges?

Adrian will get 8 eighths from each orange. So he
will get 4×8, or 32 eighths, from 4 oranges.

Here is another way to change 4 wholes to eighths.

● Write the denominator.

$$4 = \frac{\blacksquare}{8}$$

● Then multiply the whole number
by the denominator to get the
numerator.

$$4 = \frac{32}{8} \quad \boxed{8 \times 4 = 32}$$

If Adrian cuts $5\frac{4}{8}$ oranges, how many
eighths, or wedges, will he have?

To write $5\frac{4}{8}$ as a fraction:

● Write the whole number
as a fraction.

$$\boxed{5 \times 8 = 40}$$

$$5 = \frac{\blacksquare}{8} \quad 5 = \frac{40}{8}$$

● Add the fraction part of
the mixed number.

$$\frac{40}{8} + \frac{4}{8} = \frac{44}{8}$$

So, $5\frac{4}{8} = \frac{44}{8}$.

Adrian will have 44 eighths, or 44 wedges.

 Think

• Why do you use the denominator 8 when
you write the whole number 5 as a fraction
in the example above?

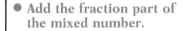

Complete each equivalent fraction.

1. $5 = \frac{\blacksquare}{3}$ 2. $3\frac{6}{7} = \frac{\blacksquare}{7}$ 3. $4\frac{3}{11} = \frac{\blacksquare}{11}$ 4. $3 = \frac{\blacksquare}{8}$ 5. $1 = \frac{\blacksquare}{4}$

Write each mixed number as an equivalent fraction.

6. $1\frac{2}{9}$ 7. $4\frac{3}{8}$ 8. $5\frac{1}{12}$ 9. $2\frac{5}{6}$ 10. $3\frac{5}{6}$

11. How many different ways can you answer exercise 5? Write two more examples.

Complete each equivalent fraction.

12. $2 = \frac{\blacksquare}{10}$ 13. $4\frac{2}{3} = \frac{\blacksquare}{3}$ 14. $1\frac{3}{12} = \frac{\blacksquare}{12}$ 15. $4 = \frac{\blacksquare}{3}$ 16. $2 = \frac{\blacksquare}{\blacksquare}$

Write each number as an equivalent fraction in fifths.

17. 2 18. 7 19. 3 20. 5 21. 9

Write each mixed number as an equivalent fraction.

22. $2\frac{1}{4}$ 23. $7\frac{1}{2}$ 24. $3\frac{2}{6}$ 25. $2\frac{3}{27}$ 26. $7\frac{3}{20}$

27. $5\frac{3}{8}$ 28. $9\frac{5}{7}$ 29. $4\frac{6}{11}$ 30. $1\frac{14}{15}$ 31. $3\frac{5}{8}$

32. $4\frac{5}{9}$ 33. $7\frac{6}{7}$ 34. $2\frac{3}{5}$ 35. $12\frac{2}{3}$ 36. $9\frac{1}{9}$

Problem Solving

37. Alberto has run $12\frac{1}{2}$ miles. How many half miles has he run? If a water station is located every $\frac{1}{2}$ mile along the route, how many water stations has he passed?

38. Shelby has run 21 of the 26 miles of the race.

   a. What fraction of the race does she have left to run?

   b. Does she have more than or less than $\frac{1}{2}$ of the race left to run?

Maintain • **Least Common Multiple**

Write the least common multiple.

1. 9, 6 2. 8, 5 3. 12, 3 4. 3, 10

WRITING MIXED NUMBERS

At lunchtime, 16 students from Tami's class sit down at the Jazz 'n Pizza Palace. Each student orders 2 slices of cheese pizza. If there are 6 slices in each pizza, how many pizzas will the students eat in all?

Number of Students	Number of Slices	Number of Pizzas in Sixths	Number of Pizzas
12	24	$\frac{24}{6}$	4
13	26	$\frac{26}{6}$	$4\frac{2}{6}$
14	28	$\frac{28}{6}$	$4\frac{4}{6}$
15	30	$\frac{30}{6}$	5
16	32	$\frac{32}{6}$	$5\frac{2}{6}$

Think

- What patterns do you see in the chart?

- How many slices will 16 students eat? What fraction tells how many pizzas this is?

The students will eat $5\frac{2}{6}$, or $5\frac{1}{3}$, pizzas in all.

▶ Here is a quick way to write a fraction as a mixed number or a whole number.

$$\frac{32}{6} = \blacksquare$$

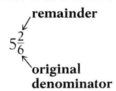

● Divide the numerator by the denominator.	● If there is a remainder, write it as a fraction.	● Simplify if you can.
$\frac{32}{6} \longrightarrow 6\overline{)32} \longrightarrow \begin{array}{r} 5\,R\,2 \\ 6\overline{)32} \\ -30 \\ \hline 2 \end{array}$	$5\frac{2}{6}$ ↗ remainder ↘ original denominator	$5\frac{2}{6} = 5\frac{1}{3}$

So, $\frac{32}{6} = 5\frac{2}{6} = 5\frac{1}{3}$. The fraction and the mixed numbers are equal.

GUIDED PRACTICE

Write each fraction as a mixed number in simplest form
or as a whole number.

1. $\frac{9}{2}$ 2. $\frac{10}{5}$ 3. $\frac{27}{9}$ 4. $\frac{34}{12}$ 5. $\frac{15}{9}$

6. In exercise 5, if you write $\frac{15}{9}$ in simplest form
first and then divide, what do you notice?

INDEPENDENT PRACTICE

Write each fraction as a mixed number in simplest form
or as a whole number.

7. $\frac{11}{5}$ 8. $\frac{23}{6}$ 9. $\frac{50}{10}$ 10. $\frac{44}{8}$ 11. $\frac{14}{8}$

12. $\frac{77}{11}$ 13. $\frac{18}{8}$ 14. $\frac{33}{9}$ 15. $\frac{13}{8}$ 16. $\frac{65}{15}$

Problem Solving Use the menu below.

17. Soon, 3 additional students arrive
from Tami's class. Each of them
orders and eats 2 slices of pizza.
Adding this number of slices to the
32 already eaten, how many pizzas
are eaten in all by Tami's class?

18. If each student eats 2 slices of
pizza, would it be cheaper for 15
students to order whole pizzas or
order by the slice? How much
money will they save?

 **• Estimation**

Is there enough money to buy the items?

1. eight boxes of cat food with $7

2. two cat collars with $6

3. eight cat leashes with $30

4. two cat leashes with $10

COMPARING AND ORDERING

Sandy is buying chili from the Hoppin' Hot Chili booth. He has a $\frac{3}{4}$-pint thermos. Can the thermos hold a Regular-size serving?

Sandy compares $\frac{1}{4}$ and $\frac{3}{4}$.

$\frac{1}{4}$ ● $\frac{3}{4}$ ← **common denominator**

$1 < 3$, so $\frac{1}{4} < \frac{3}{4}$

Sandy's thermos can hold a Regular-size serving.

The serving sizes are to be listed on the sign from smallest to largest. What should the order be?

● Find the least common multiple (LCM) of the denominators.

$\frac{1}{4}$ $\frac{5}{6}$ $\frac{2}{3}$ $\frac{3}{4}$

3: 3, 6, 9, 12, 15 . . .
4: 4, 8, 12, 16 . . .
6: 6, 12, 18 . . .
The LCM of 3, 4, and 6 is 12.

● Write equivalent fractions with the least common denominator. Use the LCM.

$\frac{1}{4} = \frac{3}{12}$

$\frac{5}{6} = \frac{10}{12}$

$\frac{2}{3} = \frac{8}{12}$

$\frac{3}{4} = \frac{9}{12}$

● Compare numerators and write the fractions in order.

$3 < 8 < 9 < 10$
so
$\frac{3}{12} < \frac{8}{12} < \frac{9}{12} < \frac{10}{12}$
so
$\frac{1}{4} < \frac{2}{3} < \frac{3}{4} < \frac{5}{6}$

The serving sizes should be listed in the following order: Regular, Deluxe, Super, and El Grande.

Think

• Would the order need to be changed if the serving sizes were: Regular—$1\frac{1}{4}$ pint, Deluxe—$2\frac{2}{3}$ pints, Super—$1\frac{3}{4}$ pints, and El Grande—$1\frac{5}{6}$ pints? Explain.

Write the least common denominator for each pair of numbers.

1. $\frac{3}{4}, \frac{2}{5}$ 2. $\frac{1}{3}, \frac{5}{6}$ 3. $\frac{7}{10}, \frac{1}{6}$ 4. $2\frac{2}{9}, 2\frac{5}{6}$ 5. $4\frac{2}{3}, 4\frac{3}{7}$

Compare. Write >, <, or =.

6. $\frac{2}{5} \bullet \frac{1}{5}$ 7. $\frac{1}{3} \bullet \frac{2}{6}$ 8. $1\frac{3}{8} \bullet 2\frac{3}{5}$ 9. $6\frac{7}{8} \bullet 6\frac{11}{12}$ 10. $3\frac{3}{4} \bullet 2\frac{7}{9}$

Write the numbers in order from least to greatest.

11. $\frac{1}{4}, \frac{2}{5}, \frac{3}{8}$ 12. $\frac{2}{5}, \frac{4}{5}, \frac{3}{5}$ 13. $2\frac{2}{7}, 2\frac{2}{9}, 1\frac{3}{11}$

14. In exercise 7, if you used the common denominator 24, would you still get the same answer? Explain.

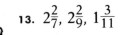

INDEPENDENT PRACTICE

Write the least common denominator for each pair of numbers.

15. $\frac{2}{3}, \frac{3}{5}$ 16. $1\frac{1}{7}, 1\frac{2}{14}$ 17. $\frac{5}{12}, \frac{1}{8}$ 18. $\frac{3}{7}, \frac{4}{5}$ 19. $2\frac{1}{3}, 2\frac{3}{8}$

Compare. Write >, <, or =.

20. $1\frac{3}{4} \bullet 2\frac{1}{4}$ 21. $\frac{3}{8} \bullet \frac{3}{9}$ 22. $\frac{3}{5} \bullet \frac{9}{10}$ 23. $4\frac{5}{8} \bullet 4\frac{2}{3}$ 24. $2\frac{5}{8} \bullet 1\frac{2}{3}$

25. $\frac{5}{7} \bullet \frac{2}{7}$ 26. $6\frac{7}{10} \bullet 6\frac{3}{5}$ 27. $4\frac{3}{6} \bullet 4\frac{1}{2}$ 28. $\frac{3}{8} \bullet \frac{7}{12}$ 29. $1\frac{3}{8} \bullet 1\frac{7}{12}$

Write the numbers in order from least to greatest.

30. $1\frac{2}{3}, \frac{11}{12}, 1\frac{5}{12}$ 31. $\frac{1}{3}, \frac{2}{9}, \frac{1}{5}$ 32. $\frac{1}{4}, \frac{1}{9}, \frac{3}{5}$ 33. $\frac{7}{8}, \frac{11}{6}, \frac{3}{4}$

34. $\frac{14}{15}, \frac{9}{20}, \frac{1}{11}$ 35. $\frac{1}{5}, \frac{1}{3}, \frac{1}{8}$ 36. $3, 2\frac{7}{8}, 2\frac{3}{4}$ 37. $\frac{5}{8}, \frac{1}{4}, \frac{3}{8}$

Problem Solving Use the information on page 280.

38. Chris says he can't eat a whole Super serving, so he'll get 2 Regular servings instead. Does that make sense? Explain.

39. Does an El Grande serving have more or less chili than 2 Regular servings?

EQUIVALENT FORMS

Amar lives three tenths of a kilometer from the soccer field where he practices. You know how to write three tenths as a fraction and as a decimal.

three tenths $= \frac{3}{10} = 0.3$

It is easy to write a fraction as a decimal when the fraction has a denominator that is a number such as 10, 100, or 1000.

Look at these examples.

Number	Fraction	Decimal
9 tenths	$\frac{9}{10}$	0.9
7 hundredths	$\frac{7}{100}$	0.07
157 thousandths	$\frac{157}{1000}$	0.157

If a fraction does not have a denominator of 10, 100, or 1000, you can often rewrite it as an equivalent fraction that does.

Write $\frac{1}{25}$ as a decimal.

- Multiply to find an equivalent fraction with a denominator of 10, 100, or 1000.

$$\frac{1}{25} \overset{\times 4}{\underset{\times 4}{=}} \frac{4}{100}$$

$$25 \times 4 = 100$$

- Then write the equivalent fraction as a decimal.

$$\frac{4}{100} = 0.04$$

Think

- If $\frac{40}{1000}$ were used as the equivalent fraction for $\frac{1}{25}$, would the decimal equivalent change? Would its value change?

GUIDED PRACTICE

Write each fraction as a decimal.

1. $\frac{4}{100}$ **2.** $\frac{3}{1000}$ **3.** $\frac{1}{10}$ **4.** $\frac{45}{100}$

5. $\frac{1}{4}$ **6.** $\frac{7}{20}$ **7.** $\frac{9}{25}$ **8.** $\frac{1}{20}$

9. Write equivalent fractions for $\frac{1}{10}$ with denominators of 100 and 1000. Write each as a decimal. What do you notice?

....

INDEPENDENT PRACTICE

Write each fraction as a decimal.

10. $\frac{5}{10}$ **11.** $\frac{1}{100}$ **12.** $\frac{23}{1000}$ **13.** $\frac{2}{5}$

14. $\frac{3}{20}$ **15.** $\frac{7}{25}$ **16.** $\frac{3}{5}$ **17.** $\frac{3}{50}$

18. For each fraction pair, write an equivalent decimal from the box.

a. $\frac{2}{10}, \frac{1}{5}$

b. $\frac{1}{2}, \frac{50}{100}$

c. $\frac{3}{100}, \frac{30}{1000}$

d. $\frac{3}{4}, \frac{9}{12}$

0.25	0.2	0.03
0.75		0.5

Problem Solving Use the picture if it helps.

19. Amar has 3 quarters. Can he buy the wristbands?

20. A regulation soccer ball can weigh between 0.397 and 0.454 kilogram. Alice's soccer ball weighs $\frac{1}{4}$ kilogram. Is her ball over, under, or within regulation weight?

$0.69
Per Pair

FRACTIONS AND DECIMALS

Fractions can mean different things.

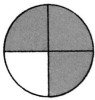  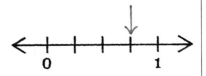

$\frac{3}{4}$ of the circle is red.

$\frac{3}{4}$ of the flowers are blue.

The arrow points to $\frac{3}{4}$ on the number line.

A fraction can also mean division.

$\frac{3}{4}$ can mean $3 \div 4$.

One way to find equivalent decimals for fractions and mixed numbers is to divide.

- **Fractions: Divide the numerator by the denominator.**

$$\frac{3}{4} = 4\overline{)3.00} \quad \begin{array}{r} 0.75 \\ \hline -28 \\ \hline 20 \\ -20 \\ \hline 0 \end{array}$$

So, $\frac{3}{4} = 0.75$.

- **Mixed Numbers: Find the decimal equivalent of the fraction part. Add it to the whole number part.**

$$8\overline{)1.000} \quad \begin{array}{r} 0.125 \\ \hline -8 \\ \hline 20 \\ -16 \\ \hline 40 \\ -40 \\ \hline 0 \end{array}$$

$2\frac{1}{8} = 2 + \frac{1}{8} = 2 + 0.125 = 2.125$

So, $2\frac{1}{8} = 2.125$.

Think

- Show two ways to find the equivalent decimal of $1\frac{3}{5}$.

▶ You can also write a decimal as a fraction or a mixed number.

- **Decide whether the decimal is in tenths, hundredths, or thousandths.**

    1.4 = 1 and 4 tenths

- **Write an equivalent fraction or mixed number.**

    $1\frac{4}{10}$

- **Simplify if you can.**

    $1\frac{4}{10} = 1\frac{2}{5}$

284

GUIDED PRACTICE

Write each number as a decimal.

1. $1\frac{4}{5}$ 2. $\frac{7}{100}$ 3. $\frac{1}{2}$ 4. $\frac{17}{20}$ 5. $2\frac{5}{8}$

Write the decimal as a fraction or mixed number in simplest form.

6. 0.45   7. 0.625   8. 0.9   9. 1.65   10. 2.02

11. Name three other fractions that have the same decimal answer as exercise 3.

INDEPENDENT PRACTICE

Write each number as a decimal.

12. $5\frac{3}{8}$ 13. $2\frac{77}{100}$ 14. $\frac{8}{40}$ 15. $\frac{47}{94}$ 16. $3\frac{18}{24}$

Write the decimal as a fraction or mixed number in simplest form.

17. 3.25   18. 8.6   19. 0.050   20. 0.35   21. 0.375

22. Copy and complete the chart. What pattern do you see? HINT: Write each decimal to the thousandths place.

Fraction	$\frac{1}{8}$	$\frac{2}{8}$	$\frac{3}{8}$	$\frac{4}{8}$	$\frac{5}{8}$	$\frac{6}{8}$	$\frac{7}{8}$
Decimal	0.125	0.250					

Problem Solving Write each answer as a fraction or mixed number.

23. Victor's garden has 6 equal-size rows. There are 2 rows each of corn and carrots, and 2 rows of lettuce. What part of the garden is planted with lettuce?

24. Kelly has run the first 2.5 kilometers of a 10-kilometer race. How much of the race does she have left to run?

285

Paula stays in shape by running around an outdoor track. When the weather is bad, she uses an indoor track. It is $\frac{1}{4}$ mile around the outdoor track and $\frac{1}{6}$ mile around the indoor track.

I usually run 14 times around the outdoor track.

I want to run the same distance around the indoor track.

Help Paula by solving each problem.

1. How many times does Paula run around the outdoor track to run 1 mile? The indoor track?

2. When Paula runs 14 times around the outdoor track, she runs 14 quarter miles. How would you write that distance as a fraction? A mixed number?

3. Would 14 times around the indoor track be a longer or shorter distance than 14 times around the outdoor track?

4. How many miles would 14 times around the indoor track be?

5. How many times should Paula run around the indoor track to equal the distance of running 14 times around the outdoor track?

6. Make up your own problem about two tracks.

SECTION REVIEW

for pages 274–286

Write the mixed number as a fraction.

1. $7\frac{1}{2}$ 2. $5\frac{4}{9}$ 3. $8\frac{2}{3}$ 4. $2\frac{1}{2}$

Write the fraction as a whole number or a mixed number in simplest form.

5. $\frac{8}{6}$ 6. $\frac{19}{5}$ 7. $\frac{24}{2}$ 8. $\frac{64}{10}$

Write the letter of the correct fraction for each mixed number.

9. $7\frac{3}{4}$ 10. $3\frac{3}{7}$ 11. $9\frac{3}{8}$ 12. $6\frac{1}{3}$

a. $\frac{25}{4}$ b. $\frac{14}{4}$ a. $\frac{24}{7}$ b. $\frac{16}{7}$ a. $\frac{35}{8}$ b. $\frac{75}{8}$ a. $\frac{19}{3}$ b. $\frac{9}{3}$

c. $\frac{31}{4}$ d. $\frac{21}{4}$ c. $\frac{13}{6}$ d. $\frac{9}{7}$ c. $\frac{27}{8}$ d. $\frac{20}{8}$ c. $\frac{10}{3}$ d. $\frac{6}{3}$

Write the letter of the mixed number in simplest form.

13. $\frac{75}{9}$ 14. $\frac{21}{6}$ 15. $\frac{27}{8}$ 16. $\frac{44}{5}$

a. $8\frac{1}{3}$ b. $7\frac{5}{9}$ a. 3 b. $3\frac{3}{6}$ a. 3 b. $4\frac{3}{8}$ a. $8\frac{4}{5}$ b. $4\frac{4}{5}$

c. $8\frac{3}{9}$ d. 8 c. $2\frac{1}{6}$ d. $3\frac{1}{2}$ c. $3\frac{3}{8}$ d. $3\frac{1}{4}$ c. $9\frac{4}{5}$ d. $8\frac{2}{3}$

Use the fractions and mixed numbers in the box to answer the question.

$$1\frac{1}{2} \quad \frac{3}{4} \quad \frac{4}{3} \quad \frac{1}{2} \quad \frac{5}{4} \quad \frac{3}{8} \quad \frac{1}{16}$$

17. Compare and order the numbers from least to greatest.

Solve each problem.

18. Katie needs $1\frac{1}{2}$ yards of material to finish a quilt she is making. She finds a piece of material that measures $1\frac{3}{8}$ yards. Is that enough material for Katie to finish the quilt?

19. Travis lives 0.6 kilometer from the Lanier School. Crystal lives $\frac{3}{4}$ of a kilometer from the same school. Who lives farther from the school?

CHAPTER REVIEW

Language Connection

Imagine a marketplace many years ago. The world has no standard measures. It uses the cubit, the distance from a person's elbow to the tip of the middle finger, as a measure of length. Sellers measure cubits with their own bodies. You do not have much money, but you need lots of rope. The first seller is tiny, so you keep walking. The next seller is bigger, but shaped wrong. You walk past him, too. Then you see the perfect seller, down the street. Describe what this seller looks like.

Test ● ● ● ● ● ●

Write each fraction in simplest form.

1. $\frac{7}{42}$ **2.** $\frac{15}{35}$ **3.** $\frac{36}{45}$ **4.** $\frac{6}{60}$ **5.** $\frac{8}{24}$

Complete to make an equivalent fraction.

6. $\frac{18}{27} = \frac{\blacksquare}{3}$ **7.** $\frac{1}{9} = \frac{\blacksquare}{36}$ **8.** $\frac{21}{35} = \frac{\blacksquare}{5}$ **9.** $\frac{4}{44} = \frac{\blacksquare}{11}$ **10.** $\frac{5}{6} = \frac{\blacksquare}{36}$

Complete each equivalent fraction.

11. $5 = \frac{\blacksquare}{25}$ **12.** $3 = \frac{\blacksquare}{4}$ **13.** $3\frac{3}{4} = \frac{\blacksquare}{\blacksquare}$ **14.** $2\frac{3}{10} = \frac{\blacksquare}{\blacksquare}$ **15.** $4\frac{7}{9} = \frac{\blacksquare}{\blacksquare}$

Write each fraction as a mixed number in simplest form or as a whole number.

16. $\frac{12}{9}$ **17.** $\frac{21}{7}$ **18.** $\frac{18}{5}$ **19.** $\frac{22}{8}$ **20.** $\frac{21}{5}$

Compare. Write >, <, or =.

21. $\frac{7}{9}$ ● $\frac{4}{8}$ **22.** $\frac{1}{4}$ ● $\frac{1}{5}$ **23.** $\frac{14}{21}$ ● $\frac{10}{15}$ **24.** $2\frac{1}{3}$ ● $1\frac{2}{3}$ **25.** $\frac{5}{9}$ ● $\frac{8}{10}$

Write the numbers in order from least to greatest.

26. $\frac{1}{2}, \frac{3}{10}, \frac{9}{20}$ **27.** $\frac{5}{6}, 1\frac{5}{6}, \frac{5}{12}$ **28.** $2\frac{3}{8}, 1, 2\frac{7}{10}$

PROBLEM SOLVING

Solve each problem.

29. Lisa lives 0.25 mile from the library. Terrence lives $\frac{2}{5}$ of a mile from the same library. Who lives farther from the library?

30. In Manny's kite collection, there are 3 blue kites, 3 red kites, and 6 green kites. What fraction of Manny's kite collection is green?

31. Erika sees two packages of material at the fabric store. Package A contains $1\frac{2}{3}$ yards of material and package B contains $1\frac{5}{6}$ yards of material. Which package contains more material?

32. Sam has $1\frac{1}{3}$ cups of blueberries and wants to bake some muffins. The recipe calls for $1\frac{1}{4}$ cups of blueberries. Does Sam have enough blueberries to make the muffins?

CUMULATIVE REVIEW

Decide if the figure is a parallelogram. Write *yes* or *no*.

33.   **34.**   **35.**   **36.**

Write the quotient.

37. $10.845 \div 9$ **38.** $0.72 \div 8$ **39.** $9.012 \div 3$ **40.** $44.842 \div 7$

EXCURSION

MATH HISTORY

MEASUREMENT, THEN AND NOW

Ancient people used objects such as sticks to measure the length of other objects. Sticks were not always useful because they could become lost or broken.

Egyptians also created units based on their arms and hands. The distance from a person's elbow to the tip of the middle finger was called a **cubit.** The width of a person's four fingers was called a **palm.** One cubit was equal to 7 palms.

Early civilizations also used body parts to measure length. In some places, the king would use his own foot as a unit of length. While the king ruled, people would use the "king's foot" as a standard of measurement for buying, selling, and trading things. You can imagine what happened when a new king took over.

Another unit, called the **uncia,** was based on the width of a person's thumb. There were about 12 uncias in one foot. The **yard** was the distance from the tip of a person's nose to the tip of the middle finger. There were about 3 feet in one yard.

For this activity work in pairs. You will need four sheets of paper, tape, and a 36-inch piece of string.

1. Use string to find the length of your foot. Mark this length on paper and label it *foot*. Mark three of these lengths end to end on the paper, and label that length *yard*.

2. Use the string to determine the width of your thumb. Mark this length on paper and label it *uncia*. Mark 12 of these lengths end to end and label it *foot*.

3. Compare the lengths of both of the lines labeled *foot*. What do you notice?

4. How do you think your measures will compare with those of your classmates?

5. Use the string to determine the distance from your elbow to the tip of your middle finger. Mark this length and label it *cubit*.

6. How do you think your classmates' cubits will compare with yours?

7. Do you think that the cubit is a reliable unit of measure to use in your class? Explain.

A **standard** is an amount that everyone agrees on. In Egypt, the standard for cubit became 21 inches. The Roman cubit was 17.5 inches. The Hebrews used a cubit that measured 17.58 inches, and the English cubit measured 18 inches.

8. What problems may have been solved by using standard cubits? What problems may not have been solved?

9. Why is it important that everyone agrees on a standard unit for length? Give an example.

10. Why is it important that a unit of measure not change? Give an example.

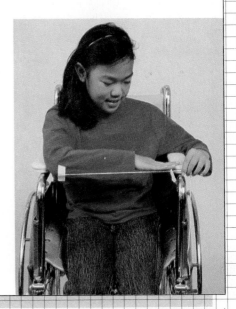

ADDITION AND
SUBTRACTION OF FRACTIONS

Money Sense

Walking the Dogs Andrew started his own business. Each day after school he walks his neighbors' dogs. They each agreed to pay him $2.00 per hour. He now has five customers.

Andrew decided to make a chart to keep track of his hours. He walks each dog for a fraction of an hour every weekday. He walks all the dogs the same amount of time. Using the information in the chart below for one dog, he can figure out how much money he will earn for the week.

First, Andrew must add the fractions to find the total number of hours he walks one dog. Then he must multiply that total by the hourly rate of $2.00. How much money will he collect from each customer? How much money will he collect in all?

Day	Time Minutes	Hours
Monday	20	$\frac{1}{3}$
Tuesday	20	$\frac{1}{3}$
Wednesday	30	$\frac{1}{2}$
Thursday	20	$\frac{1}{3}$
Friday	30	$\frac{1}{2}$
Total		

FRACTIONS WITH LIKE DENOMINATORS

You add and subtract fractions with the same denominator, such as $\frac{3}{5}$ and $\frac{1}{5}$, just as you would numbers whose units of measure are the same.

3 meters + 1 meter = 4 meters

$3 + $1 = $4

$$\frac{3}{5} + \frac{1}{5} = \frac{4}{5}$$

▶ Add: $\frac{7}{8} + \frac{3}{8}$

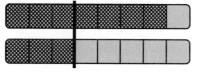

• Check that the denominators are the same.	• Add the numerators.	• Simplify if you can.
$\frac{7}{8} + \frac{3}{8}$	$\frac{7}{8} + \frac{3}{8} = \frac{10}{8}$	$\frac{10}{8} = 1\frac{2}{8}$ or $1\frac{1}{4}$

▶ Subtract: $\frac{7}{8} - \frac{3}{8}$

• Check that the denominators are the same.	• Subtract the numerators.	• Simplify if you can.
$\frac{7}{8} - \frac{3}{8}$	$\frac{7}{8} - \frac{3}{8} = \frac{4}{8}$	$\frac{4}{8} = \frac{1}{2}$

The addition properties for whole numbers also apply to fractions.

Zero Property	$0 + \frac{3}{5} = \frac{3}{5}$	The sum of zero and one other addend is the other addend.
Commutative Property	$\frac{1}{6} + \frac{4}{6} = \frac{4}{6} + \frac{1}{6}$	The sum stays the same when the order of addends is changed.
Associative Property	$(\frac{3}{8} + \frac{4}{8}) + \frac{4}{8} = \frac{3}{8} + (\frac{4}{8} + \frac{4}{8})$	The sum stays the same when the grouping of addends is changed.

Think

- How do the addition properties of fractions compare with the addition properties of decimals?

GUIDED PRACTICE

Write the answer in simplest form.

1. $\frac{2}{4} + \frac{1}{4}$ **2.** $\frac{5}{6} - \frac{2}{6}$ **3.** $\frac{10}{11} + \frac{4}{11}$ **4.** $\frac{3}{9} + \frac{5}{9}$

5. $\frac{8}{12} - \frac{6}{12}$ **6.** $\frac{4}{7} - \frac{1}{7}$ **7.** $\frac{7}{16} + \frac{13}{16}$ **8.** $\frac{8}{9} - \frac{5}{9}$

Complete.

9. $\frac{3}{10} + \left(\frac{2}{10} + \frac{4}{10}\right) = \left(\frac{3}{10} + \blacksquare\right) + \frac{4}{10}$ **10.** $\frac{1}{8} + \frac{6}{8} = \blacksquare + \frac{1}{8}$ **11.** $\frac{3}{4} + \blacksquare = \frac{3}{4}$

12. Look at exercise 7. What would you add to the sum to get 2?

INDEPENDENT PRACTICE

Write the answer in simplest form.

13. $\frac{1}{5} + \frac{1}{5}$ **14.** $\frac{6}{9} + \frac{4}{9}$ **15.** $\frac{1}{6} + \frac{2}{6}$ **16.** $\frac{12}{16} - \frac{2}{16}$

Copy and complete.

17. $\frac{12}{16} + 0 = \blacksquare$ **18.** $\left(\frac{2}{16} + \frac{5}{16}\right) + \frac{5}{16} = \blacksquare + \left(\frac{5}{16} + \frac{5}{16}\right)$ **19.** $\frac{3}{16} + \frac{4}{16} = \frac{4}{16} + \blacksquare$

Problem Solving Use the diagram. Write the answer in simplest form.

20. How large is the Pine View Tree Farm in acres?

21. **a.** What fraction of the entire farm is balsam fir or pitch pine?
     b. What fraction of the entire farm is shortleaf or pitch pine?
     c. What fraction of the entire farm is not shortleaf or pitch pine?

22. The owner wants to replace some balsam fir with white spruce so that half the farm will be spruce trees. What fraction of the balsam fir will need to be replaced?

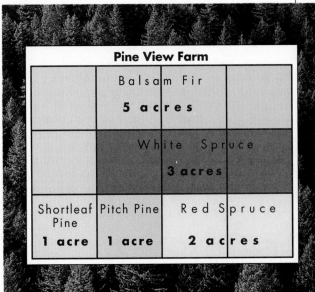

Pine View Farm

	Balsam Fir 5 acres	
	White Spruce 3 acres	
Shortleaf Pine 1 acre	Pitch Pine 1 acre	Red Spruce 2 acres

FRACTIONS

Netta is building a birdhouse. She wants the floor to be about $1\frac{1}{2}$ inches thick. Will these two boards nailed together be about $1\frac{1}{2}$ inches thick?

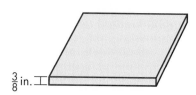

$\frac{15}{16}$ in.

Estimate: $\frac{15}{16} + \frac{3}{8}$

She uses what she knows about fractions that are close to 0, $\frac{1}{2}$, or 1.

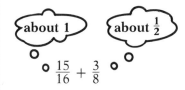

about 1   about $\frac{1}{2}$

$\frac{15}{16} + \frac{3}{8}$

$\frac{3}{8}$ in.

Estimate: $1 + \frac{1}{2} = 1\frac{1}{2}$

Together the boards are about $1\frac{1}{2}$ inches thick.

? in.

Think

- Will the combined thickness be more than or less than $1\frac{1}{2}$ inches? How can you tell?

▶ You can also estimate differences.

For example: $\frac{97}{100} - \frac{5}{8}$

about 1   about $\frac{1}{2}$

Estimate: $1 - \frac{1}{2} = \frac{1}{2}$

Other Examples

Estimate: $\frac{23}{25} - \frac{9}{10}$

about 1   about 1

Estimate: $1 - 1 = 0$

Estimate: $\frac{1}{15} + \frac{7}{8}$

about 0   about 1

Estimate: $0 + 1 = 1$

Estimate: $\frac{7}{9} + \frac{1}{2}$

about 1

Estimate: $1 + \frac{1}{2} = 1\frac{1}{2}$

Estimate the fraction as close to 0, $\frac{1}{2}$, or 1.

1. $\frac{7}{6}$ **2.** $\frac{5}{12}$ **3.** $\frac{5}{81}$ **4.** $\frac{3}{5}$ **5.** $\frac{100}{8765}$

Estimate the answer.

6. $\frac{1}{8} + \frac{13}{16}$ **7.** $\frac{2}{5} + \frac{9}{10}$ **8.** $\frac{11}{12} - \frac{7}{8}$ **9.** $\frac{3}{20} + \frac{4}{9}$

10. $\frac{8}{9} - \frac{1}{16}$ **11.** $\frac{20}{21} - \frac{5}{8}$ **12.** $\frac{7}{12} + \frac{3}{8}$ **13.** $\frac{6}{7} - \frac{6}{11}$

14. In exercises 1–5, how did you decide what your estimate was?

Estimate the fraction as close to 0, $\frac{1}{2}$, or 1.

13. $\frac{5}{6}$ **14.** $\frac{7}{12}$ **15.** $\frac{16}{100}$ **16.** $\frac{3}{7}$ **17.** $\frac{13}{16}$

Estimate the answer.

20. $\frac{9}{10} + \frac{13}{15}$ **21.** $\frac{8}{9} + \frac{5}{12}$ **22.** $\frac{5}{4} - \frac{1}{8}$ **23.** $\frac{3}{8} + \frac{5}{9}$

24. $\frac{10}{11} + \frac{1}{12}$ **25.** $\frac{1}{10} + \frac{2}{30}$ **26.** $\frac{5}{8} - \frac{7}{12}$ **27.** $\frac{12}{13} - \frac{1}{6}$

28. $\frac{5}{6} - \frac{11}{20}$ **29.** $\frac{23}{29} - \frac{4}{9}$ **30.** $\frac{5}{6} + \frac{1}{5}$ **31.** $\frac{1}{12} - \frac{1}{16}$

CHALLENGE • Number Sense

Complete each statement. Use each fraction in the circle once.

1. $\frac{9}{10} +$ ▇ is about 1   **2.** $\frac{4}{25} -$ ▇ is about 0

3. $\frac{47}{50} -$ ▇ is about $\frac{1}{2}$ **4.** ▇ $+ \frac{10}{13}$ is about 2

5. ▇ $+$ ▇ is about 2   **6.** ▇ $- \frac{2}{27}$ is about $\frac{1}{2}$

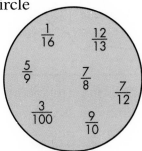

FRACTIONS WITH UNLIKE DENOMINATORS

To add or subtract fractions with different, or unlike, denominators, you need to rewrite the fractions with like denominators.

▶ Add: $\frac{2}{9} + \frac{5}{6}$ about 0 $\frac{2}{9}$ + about 1 $\frac{5}{6}$ Estimate: $0 + 1 = 1$

● **Find the least common denominator (LCD).**

$$\frac{2}{9} = \frac{\blacksquare}{18}$$
$$+\frac{5}{6} = \frac{\blacksquare}{18}$$

The least common multiple (LCM) of 9 and 6 is 18. So, 18 is the LCD.

● **Write equivalent fractions with the LCD.**

$$\frac{2}{9} \xrightarrow{\times 2} = \frac{4}{18}$$

$$+\frac{5}{6} \xrightarrow{\times 3} = \frac{15}{18}$$

● **Add. Simplify if you can.**

$$\frac{4}{18}$$
$$+\frac{15}{18}$$
$$\overline{\frac{19}{18}}, \text{ or } 1\frac{1}{18}$$

This is close to our estimate of 1. So, $1\frac{1}{18}$ is reasonable.

▶ Subtract: $\frac{5}{7} - \frac{1}{2}$. about $\frac{1}{2}$ $\frac{5}{7} - \frac{1}{2}$ Estimate: $\frac{1}{2} - \frac{1}{2} = 0$

● **Find the least common denominator (LCD).**

$$\frac{5}{7} = \frac{\blacksquare}{14}$$
$$-\frac{1}{2} = \frac{\blacksquare}{14}$$

The LCM of 7 and 2 is 14. So, 14 is the LCD.

● **Write equivalent fractions with the LCD.**

$$\frac{5}{7} \xrightarrow{\times 2} = \frac{10}{14}$$

$$+\frac{1}{2} \xrightarrow{\times 7} = \frac{7}{14}$$

● **Subtract. Simplify if you can.**

$$\frac{10}{14}$$
$$-\frac{7}{14}$$
$$\overline{\frac{3}{14}}$$

This is close to our estimate of zero. So, $\frac{3}{14}$ is reasonable.

Think

• How is subtracting fractions with unlike denominators similar to adding fractions with unlike denominators?

GUIDED PRACTICE

Write the answer in simplest form.

1. $\frac{1}{4}$
$+ \frac{5}{8}$

2. $\frac{7}{12}$
$- \frac{1}{4}$

3. $\frac{3}{4}$
$+ \frac{1}{3}$

4. $\frac{15}{16}$
$- \frac{1}{2}$

5. $\frac{7}{8}$
$+ \frac{4}{5}$

6. Solve exercise 1 by using any common denominator. What do you notice when you compare the answer with the one you got using the LCD?

INDEPENDENT PRACTICE

Write the answer in simplest form.

7. $\frac{5}{6}$
$+ \frac{1}{2}$

8. $\frac{4}{5}$
$- \frac{2}{10}$

9. $\frac{3}{5}$
$- \frac{2}{12}$

10. $\frac{2}{8}$
$+ \frac{2}{6}$

11. $\frac{5}{6}$
$- \frac{2}{10}$

12. $\frac{1}{2} - \frac{3}{8}$

13. $\frac{5}{6} + \frac{3}{5}$

14. $\frac{9}{12} + \frac{1}{6}$

15. $\frac{1}{4} + \frac{2}{5}$

16. $\frac{11}{16} - \frac{2}{4}$

Problem Solving Write the answer in simplest form.

17. Nick's results are not shown. He walked backward $\frac{1}{4}$ mile. Between which two walkers did he finish?

18. The top two walkers will represent Tucson in the statewide team competition. Who are these two walkers? What is their combined distance?

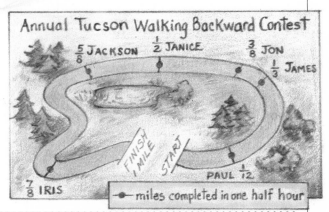

Annual Tucson Walking Backward Contest

$\frac{5}{8}$ JACKSON $\frac{1}{2}$ JANICE $\frac{3}{8}$ JON $\frac{1}{3}$ JAMES

FINISH 1 MILE START

PAUL $\frac{1}{12}$

$\frac{7}{8}$ IRIS

← miles completed in one half hour

CHALLENGE • Missing Number

Solve. Choose your answer from the box at the right.

a. $\frac{1}{2} - \blacksquare = \frac{3}{8}$

b. $\blacksquare - \frac{5}{12} = \frac{5}{12}$

c. $\blacksquare + \frac{1}{2} = \frac{3}{4}$

d. $\frac{2}{3} + \blacksquare = 1\frac{7}{33}$

$\frac{6}{11}$	$\frac{1}{4}$
$\frac{5}{6}$	
$\frac{1}{8}$	$\frac{1}{2}$

PROBLEM SOLVING
··
USING STRATEGIES

If you get stuck, remember....

Tips for Problem Solving

on pages 448–449

Solve each problem.

1. Mrs. Butler's class took a vote to decide how to raise money for a field trip. Half the class voted for a raffle, 8 voted for a bake sale, and the other 4 voted for a plant sale. How many students voted?

2. Jacob is making banana bread. The recipe calls for 1 cup of flour. Jacob has already mixed in $\frac{1}{4}$ cup of flour. How much more flour should he add?

3. In Eaton's Old Spice Shop, Mr. Eaton has 5 antique brass weights and a pan balance. Which weights can he use to balance a bag of spices that weighs $1\frac{1}{2}$ pounds?

4. Can Mr. Eaton use his weights to balance a bag of spices that weighs 2 pounds? Why?

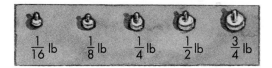

$\frac{1}{16}$ lb $\frac{1}{8}$ lb $\frac{1}{4}$ lb $\frac{1}{2}$ lb $\frac{3}{4}$ lb

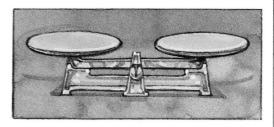

5. Jan is making pancakes from a special recipe. Her measuring cup is marked in quarter cups on one side and in thirds of a cup on the other side. How can Jan measure out $\frac{7}{12}$ cup of water?

6. Joan, Reggie, and Paula each have an empty glass, but each glass is a different size. Joan pours 8 ounces of juice into each one. Now Joan's glass is full, Reggie's glass is $\frac{1}{2}$ full, and Paula's glass is $\frac{2}{3}$ full. About what size is each person's glass?

Solve each problem. Use your Data Book.

7. A plane left New York City at 1:00 P.M., Eastern time. It landed in Chicago $1\frac{1}{4}$ hours later. Then the plane flew for $3\frac{1}{2}$ more hours and landed in Los Angeles. It reached Los Angeles at 3:30 P.M., Pacific time. How long was the plane on the ground in Chicago?

8. Over 1 million dogs were registered with the American Kennel Club in 1986. Were more than $\frac{1}{10}$ of these dogs poodles? Explain how you got your answer.

SECTION REVIEW

for pages 294–300

Add or subtract. Write the letter of the correct answer in its simplest form.

1. $\frac{5}{8} + \frac{5}{8}$
   a. $\frac{10}{16}$
   b. $\frac{10}{64}$
   c. $1\frac{1}{4}$
   d. $\frac{10}{8}$

2. $\frac{7}{12} - \frac{3}{12}$
   a. $\frac{4}{12}$
   b. $\frac{3}{12}$
   c. $\frac{1}{3}$
   d. $\frac{10}{12}$

3. $\frac{3}{4} - \frac{5}{16}$
   a. $\frac{2}{12}$
   b. $\frac{7}{16}$
   c. $\frac{1}{6}$
   d. $\frac{1}{8}$

4. $\frac{7}{10} + 0$
   a. 0
   b. $\frac{70}{10}$
   c. $\frac{7}{10}$
   d. 1

5. $\frac{1}{2} + \frac{3}{8}$
   a. $\frac{7}{8}$
   b. $\frac{4}{10}$
   c. $\frac{2}{5}$
   d. $\frac{1}{2}$

6. $\frac{9}{10} + \frac{1}{4}$
   a. $1\frac{3}{20}$
   b. $1\frac{6}{40}$
   c. $\frac{5}{7}$
   d. $\frac{46}{40}$

7. $\frac{5}{8} - \frac{3}{12}$
   a. $\frac{9}{24}$
   b. $\frac{2}{4}$
   c. $\frac{3}{8}$
   d. $\frac{1}{2}$

8. $\frac{2}{3} - \frac{3}{10}$
   a. $\frac{1}{7}$
   b. $\frac{11}{30}$
   c. $\frac{1}{10}$
   d. $\frac{1}{3}$

9. $\frac{3}{5} - \frac{1}{3}$
   a. $\frac{2}{2}$
   b. 1
   c. $\frac{2}{15}$
   d. $\frac{4}{15}$

10. $\frac{1}{10} + \frac{7}{8}$
    a. $\frac{8}{18}$
    b. $\frac{4}{9}$
    c. $\frac{8}{9}$
    d. $\frac{39}{40}$

11. $\frac{5}{6} + \frac{3}{4}$
    a. $1\frac{7}{12}$
    b. $1\frac{14}{24}$
    c. $\frac{38}{24}$
    d. $\frac{4}{5}$

12. $\frac{5}{12} - \frac{1}{4}$
    a. $\frac{2}{12}$
    b. $\frac{1}{2}$
    c. $\frac{1}{6}$
    d. $\frac{4}{12}$

Use the chart at the right to solve each problem.

13. What fraction of the class has a pet?

14. Suppose each student with no pet got a cat. Would more students have a pet dog or a pet cat?

Mr. Li's 5th-Grade Class	
Pet	**Fraction of the Class**
Cat	$\frac{1}{4}$
Dog	$\frac{1}{2}$
No Pet	$\frac{1}{6}$
Other Animal	$\frac{1}{12}$

MIXED NUMBERS WITH LIKE DENOMINATORS

Each week, Paul works $2\frac{1}{4}$ hours doing chores at home and $4\frac{1}{4}$ hours helping neighbors. How many hours does he work altogether?

▶ Add: $2\frac{1}{4}$ h + $4\frac{1}{4}$ h

● Check that the denominators are the same.

$$2\frac{1}{4} \text{ h}$$
$$+ \ 4\frac{1}{4} \text{ h}$$

● Add the fractions. Then add the whole numbers.

$$2\frac{1}{4} \text{ h}$$
$$+ \ 4\frac{1}{4} \text{ h}$$
$$6\frac{2}{4} \text{ h}$$

● Simplify if you can.

$$6\frac{2}{4} \text{ h} = 6\frac{1}{2} \text{ h}$$

Paul works $6\frac{1}{2}$ hours.

▶ Now try subtraction: $5\frac{3}{4} - 2\frac{1}{4}$

● Check that the denominators are the same.

$$5\frac{3}{4}$$
$$- \ 2\frac{1}{4}$$

● Subtract the fractions. Then subtract the whole numbers.

$$5\frac{3}{4}$$
$$- \ 2\frac{1}{4}$$
$$3\frac{2}{4}$$

● Simplify if you can.

$$3\frac{2}{4} = 3\frac{1}{2}$$

Think

• How can thinking about quarters and half dollars help you work with the fractions $\frac{1}{4}$ and $\frac{1}{2}$?

Other Examples

$$15\frac{7}{8} + 6 = 21\frac{7}{8}$$

$$6\frac{1}{4} - 5 = 1\frac{1}{4}$$

$$8\frac{3}{5} - 1\frac{3}{5} = 7$$

GUIDED PRACTICE

Write the answer in simplest form.

1. $5\frac{1}{4}$
   $-\ \frac{1}{4}$

2. $3\frac{1}{6}$
   $+\ 2\frac{1}{6}$

3. $3\frac{5}{8}$
   $+\ 3\frac{1}{8}$

4. $13\frac{1}{2}$
   $-\ \ 5$

5. $2\frac{7}{9}$
   $+\ 3\frac{1}{9}$

6. $3\frac{1}{3} + 2\frac{1}{3}$

7. $8\frac{5}{6} - 2\frac{1}{6}$

8. $3\frac{1}{2} + 2$

9. $12\frac{7}{8} - 7\frac{7}{8}$

10. How could you check your answers to exercises 1–9?

INDEPENDENT PRACTICE

Write the answer in simplest form.

11. $6\frac{5}{6}$
    $-\ 2\frac{5}{6}$

12. $3\frac{5}{8}$
    $+\ 4$

13. $7\frac{4}{7}$
    $+\ 2\frac{1}{7}$

14. $12\frac{5}{8}$
    $-\ 6\frac{1}{8}$

15. 16
    $+\ \ 3\frac{2}{5}$

16. $12\frac{3}{5} - 7$

17. $4\frac{7}{8} - 4\frac{5}{8}$

18. $8\frac{7}{8} - 4$

19. $8\frac{2}{5} + 7\frac{1}{5}$

PROJECT • Decision Making

Plan a two-week work schedule for the jobs listed in the chart.

- Each job must be done once in the two weeks.

- The total number of hours for each week cannot be more than $6\frac{3}{4}$.

- Show on which day of the week the job is to be done.

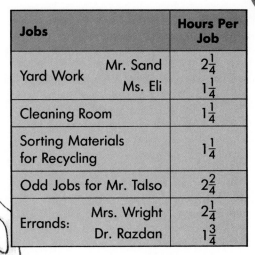

Jobs		Hours Per Job
Yard Work	Mr. Sand	$2\frac{1}{4}$
	Ms. Eli	$1\frac{1}{4}$
Cleaning Room		$1\frac{1}{4}$
Sorting Materials for Recycling		$1\frac{1}{4}$
Odd Jobs for Mr. Talso		$2\frac{2}{4}$
Errands:	Mrs. Wright	$2\frac{1}{4}$
	Dr. Razdan	$1\frac{3}{4}$

MIXED NUMBERS

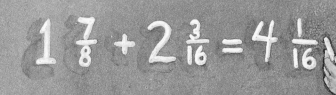

$$1\tfrac{7}{8} + 2\tfrac{3}{16} = 4\tfrac{1}{16}$$

▶ You can estimate to see if a sum is reasonable.

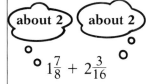

about 2　about 2

$1\tfrac{7}{8} + 2\tfrac{3}{16}$ 　　　　Estimate: 2 + 2 = 4

The estimate tells us the sum should be about 4.
The answer $4\tfrac{1}{16}$ is close to 4. So, the answer is
reasonable.

Think

- Do you think $1\tfrac{8}{15}$ is a reasonable sum for

  the problem $1\tfrac{7}{8} + \tfrac{1}{7}$? Explain.

▶ You can estimate to see if a difference is reasonable.

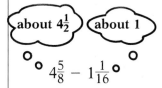

about $4\tfrac{1}{2}$　about 1

$4\tfrac{5}{8} - 1\tfrac{1}{16}$ 　　　　Estimate: $4\tfrac{1}{2} - 1 = 3\tfrac{1}{2}$

The estimate tells us the difference should be about
$3\tfrac{1}{2}$. The answer $3\tfrac{9}{16}$ is close to $3\tfrac{1}{2}$. So, the answer is
reasonable.

GUIDED PRACTICE

Write your estimate.

1. $2\frac{1}{8} + 3\frac{9}{10}$ 　　 2. $4\frac{3}{7} + 1\frac{1}{4}$ 　　 3. $3\frac{5}{8} + 3\frac{3}{5}$ 　　 4. $\frac{8}{9} + \frac{14}{16} + 2\frac{1}{7}$

5. $5\frac{7}{8} - 2\frac{1}{5}$ 　　 6. $8\frac{3}{5} - 4\frac{1}{10}$ 　　 7. $6\frac{9}{10} - 3\frac{4}{7}$ 　　 8. $9\frac{3}{5} - 7\frac{4}{9}$

9. Is an estimate always greater than the exact answer? Explain.

INDEPENDENT PRACTICE

Write your estimate.

10. $2\frac{3}{7} + 1\frac{5}{9}$ 　　 11. $7\frac{2}{15} + 3\frac{9}{10}$ 　　 12. $3\frac{1}{7} - 2\frac{5}{6}$ 　　 13. $4\frac{1}{10} + 3\frac{2}{17} + 1\frac{1}{6}$

14. $8\frac{1}{10} - 5\frac{1}{7}$ 　　 15. $7\frac{6}{7} - 4\frac{1}{15}$ 　　 16. $5\frac{4}{5} - 2\frac{1}{6}$ 　　 17. $7\frac{18}{19} - \frac{9}{10}$

Estimate the total weight for each.

18. Bananas 　　 $4\frac{1}{2}$ lb 　　　　 19. Asparagus 　　 $4\frac{1}{8}$ lb

　　 Kiwis 　　 $2\frac{1}{10}$ lb 　　　　　　 Artichokes 　　 $1\frac{15}{16}$ lb

　　 Strawberries 　 $1\frac{7}{8}$ lb 　　　　　 Snow Peas 　　 $2\frac{1}{2}$ lb

　　 Papayas 　　 $5\frac{2}{3}$ lb 　　　　　　 Cauliflower 　　 $4\frac{5}{8}$ lb

　　　　 Estimate: ▨ 　　　　　　　　　　 Estimate: ▨

20. Estimate to find the three mistakes Tom made.
Write the letter of each incorrect answer.

Tom

a. $2\frac{3}{4} + 4\frac{3}{4} = 7\frac{1}{2}$

b. $3\frac{1}{5} + 3\frac{1}{10} = 6\frac{3}{10}$

c. $4\frac{4}{5} + 2\frac{1}{75} = 6\frac{5}{80}$

d. $\frac{5}{6} + \frac{1}{8} = \frac{6}{14}$

e. $5\frac{3}{10} - 3\frac{1}{6} = 2\frac{2}{15}$

f. $\frac{13}{15} - \frac{5}{6} = \frac{8}{9}$

ADDING MIXED NUMBERS

Joyce is trying a new recipe. She will mix $1\frac{2}{3}$ cups of flour with $2\frac{5}{6}$ cups of other ingredients. How many cups must her mixing bowl be able to hold?

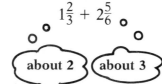

Add: $1\frac{2}{3}$ c + $2\frac{5}{6}$ c $1\frac{2}{3}$ + $2\frac{5}{6}$ Estimate: 2 + 3 = 5

about 2   about 3

Think

- How many full fraction bars can you make from the shaded areas? What fraction is left over?

To add mixed numbers with unlike denominators, rewrite them with like denominators.

- **Find the least common denominator (LCD).**

$$\begin{array}{r} 1\frac{2}{3}\text{ c} \\ + 2\frac{5}{6}\text{ c} \\ \hline \end{array}$$

The LCM of 3 and 6 is 6. So, 6 is the LCD.

- **Write equivalent fractions with the LCD.**

$$\begin{array}{r} 1\frac{2}{3}\text{ c} = 1\frac{4}{6}\text{ c} \\ + 2\frac{5}{6}\text{ c} = 2\frac{5}{6}\text{ c} \\ \hline \end{array}$$

- **Add the fractions. Then add the whole numbers. Simplify if you can.**

$$\begin{array}{r} 1\frac{4}{6}\text{ c} \\ + 2\frac{5}{6}\text{ c} \\ \hline \end{array}$$

This is close to our estimate of 5. So, $4\frac{1}{2}$ is reasonable.

$$3\frac{9}{6}\text{ c} = 4\frac{3}{6}\text{ c} = 4\frac{1}{2}\text{ c}$$

Joyce's mixing bowl must be able to hold $4\frac{1}{2}$ cups.

Other Examples

$$\begin{array}{r} 3\frac{1}{3} = 3\frac{8}{24} \\ + 5\frac{5}{8} = 5\frac{15}{24} \\ \hline 8\frac{23}{24} \end{array}$$

$$\begin{array}{r} 6\frac{3}{4} = 6\frac{15}{20} \\ + \frac{2}{5} = \frac{8}{20} \\ \hline 6\frac{23}{20} = 7\frac{3}{20} \end{array}$$

GUIDED PRACTICE

Write the mixed number in simplest form.

1. $3\frac{8}{6}$ 2. $5\frac{5}{3}$ 3. $2\frac{11}{8}$ 4. $1\frac{9}{6}$ 5. $7\frac{8}{4}$

Write the sum in simplest form.

6. $\begin{array}{r} 4\frac{3}{5} \\ + 5\frac{2}{8} \\ \hline \end{array}$
7. $\begin{array}{r} 3\frac{1}{3} \\ + \frac{1}{4} \\ \hline \end{array}$
8. $\begin{array}{r} 2\frac{1}{2} \\ + 7 \\ \hline \end{array}$
9. $\begin{array}{r} 5\frac{7}{8} \\ + 6\frac{1}{4} \\ \hline \end{array}$
10. $\begin{array}{r} 5\frac{9}{12} \\ + 4\frac{3}{4} \\ \hline \end{array}$

11. How do you know $1\frac{5}{4}$ is not in simplest form?

INDEPENDENT PRACTICE

Write the sum in simplest form.

12. $3\frac{1}{12} + \frac{7}{8}$ 13. $1\frac{2}{5} + 6\frac{3}{6}$ 14. $3\frac{1}{4} + 3$ 15. $\frac{1}{5} + 4\frac{5}{8}$

16. $6\frac{3}{8} + \frac{11}{12}$ 17. $\frac{3}{8} + 6\frac{11}{12}$ 18. $2\frac{1}{2} + 2\frac{3}{7}$ 19. $4\frac{1}{2} + \frac{2}{3}$

20. $\begin{array}{r} 1\frac{2}{5} \\ + \frac{3}{8} \\ \hline \end{array}$
21. $\begin{array}{r} 8\frac{2}{3} \\ + 1 \\ \hline \end{array}$
22. $\begin{array}{r} 3\frac{1}{4} \\ + 2\frac{1}{8} \\ \hline \end{array}$
23. $\begin{array}{r} 7\frac{2}{3} \\ + 4\frac{1}{5} \\ \hline \end{array}$
24. $\begin{array}{r} 5\frac{1}{3} \\ + 8\frac{3}{8} \\ \hline \end{array}$

Problem Solving Write the answer in simplest form.

25. Are there more than 2 cups of nuts in the recipe? Explain.

26. How much fruit is in the recipe?

27. How much cereal is in the recipe?

28. If each person eats 1 cup of party snack, will the recipe make enough party snack for 8 people?

CHALLENGE • Three Addends

Write the sum in simplest form.

1. $2\frac{3}{4} + 3\frac{1}{6} + 1\frac{5}{3}$ 2. $1\frac{5}{8} + 2\frac{2}{4} + 1\frac{3}{16}$ 3. $4\frac{1}{5} + \frac{3}{3} + 1\frac{2}{30}$ 4. $4\frac{3}{4} + 1\frac{2}{5} + 3\frac{1}{10}$

SUBTRACTING MIXED NUMBERS

Jared is exercising with $3\frac{1}{5}$-pound weights. His goal is to work with $5\frac{1}{2}$-pound weights. How many more pounds is this?

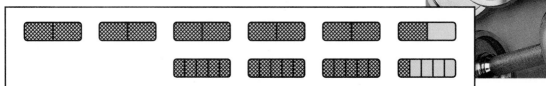

Subtract: $5\frac{1}{2}$ lb $-$ $3\frac{1}{5}$ lb $5\frac{1}{2}$ lb $-$ $3\frac{1}{5}$ lb   Estimate: $5\frac{1}{2} - 3 = 2\frac{1}{2}$

about 3

Think

- What must you do before you can subtract $\frac{1}{5}$ pound from $\frac{1}{2}$ pound?

● Find the least common denominator (LCD).

$$5\frac{1}{2} \text{ lb}$$
$$- 3\frac{1}{5} \text{ lb}$$

The LCM of 2 and 5 is 10. So, 10 is the LCD.

It is $2\frac{3}{10}$ pounds more.

● Write equivalent fractions with the LCD.

$$5\frac{1}{2} \text{ lb} = 5\frac{5}{10} \text{ lb}$$
$$- 3\frac{1}{5} \text{ lb} = 3\frac{2}{10} \text{ lb}$$

● Subtract the fractions. Then subtract the whole numbers. Simplify if you can.

$$5\frac{5}{10} \text{ lb}$$
$$- 3\frac{2}{10} \text{ lb}$$
$$2\frac{3}{10} \text{ lb}$$

This is close to our estimate of $2\frac{1}{2}$. So, $2\frac{3}{10}$ is reasonable.

Other Examples

$$3\frac{1}{2} = 3\frac{2}{4}$$
$$-2\frac{1}{4} = 2\frac{1}{4}$$
$$\overline{1\frac{1}{4}}$$

$$2\frac{2}{3} = 2\frac{10}{15}$$
$$- \frac{1}{5} = \frac{3}{15}$$
$$\overline{2\frac{7}{15}}$$

Write the difference in simplest form.

1. $3\frac{7}{10} = 3\frac{21}{30}$
    $- 1\frac{1}{6} = 1\frac{5}{30}$

2. $4\frac{2}{3} = 4\frac{10}{15}$
    $- 1\frac{2}{5} = 1\frac{6}{15}$

3. $6\frac{4}{5}$
    $- 1\frac{2}{7}$

4. $3\frac{3}{4}$
    $- \frac{1}{16}$

5. Solve exercise 2 using the common denominator 30. How does your answer compare to the answer using the LCD?

Write the difference in simplest form.

6. $12\frac{3}{8}$
    $- 2\frac{1}{16}$

7. $6\frac{4}{5}$
    $- 4\frac{3}{10}$

8. $8\frac{1}{2}$
    $- 5\frac{1}{5}$

9. $5\frac{1}{8}$
    $- 2$

10. $1\frac{3}{8}$
    $- \frac{1}{12}$

11. $4\frac{3}{4} - 4\frac{1}{3}$

12. $14\frac{7}{8} - 4\frac{12}{16}$

13. $9\frac{2}{3} - 3\frac{1}{5}$

14. $2\frac{1}{3} - \frac{1}{8}$

Problem Solving

15. Rebecca increased the weight she was exercising with by $1\frac{1}{2}$ pounds. Now she works out with $4\frac{5}{6}$ pounds. How many pounds was she using before?

16. Steve wants to put together a $2\frac{1}{4}$-pound weight. He puts on a $\frac{1}{2}$-pound weight and then a $\frac{3}{4}$-pound weight. How many more pounds does he need?

CHALLENGE • Three Addends

In an addition magic square, each row, column, and diagonal has the same sum. Copy and complete the magic square at the right using numbers from the box below.

$1\frac{7}{12}$		$\frac{1}{6}$
	$1\frac{2}{3}$	
$1\frac{3}{4}$		2

?	$\frac{1}{12}$	1
$\frac{1}{4}$	$\frac{11}{12}$	?
$\frac{5}{6}$	?	$\frac{1}{6}$

RENAMING FOR SUBTRACTION

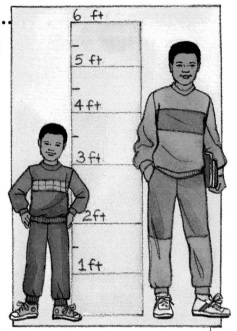

Derek is $5\frac{1}{2}$ feet tall. His younger brother, Jamie, is $3\frac{3}{4}$ feet tall. How much taller is Derek than Jamie?

▶ Subtract: $5\frac{1}{2}$ ft $- 3\frac{3}{4}$ ft

The denominators are not the same, so write equivalent fractions with a common denominator.

$$5\frac{1}{2} \text{ ft} = 5\frac{2}{4} \text{ ft}$$
$$- \; 3\frac{3}{4} \text{ ft} = 3\frac{3}{4} \text{ ft}$$

$\frac{3}{4}$ is greater than $\frac{2}{4}$, so write one of the 5 wholes as four fourths.

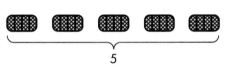 →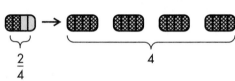

$$\underbrace{}_{5} \quad \underbrace{}_{\frac{2}{4}} \qquad \underbrace{}_{4} \quad \underbrace{}_{\frac{4}{4}} \; \underbrace{}_{\frac{2}{4}}$$

$$5\frac{2}{4} = 4 + \frac{4}{4} + \frac{2}{4}, \text{ or } 4\frac{6}{4}$$

Now we can subtract $3\frac{3}{4}$.

$$\begin{array}{r} 4\frac{6}{4} \text{ ft} \\ - \; 3\frac{3}{4} \text{ ft} \\ \hline 1\frac{3}{4} \text{ ft} \end{array}$$

Derek is $1\frac{3}{4}$ feet taller than Jamie.

▶ Here is a shorter way to write it.

● Write equivalent fractions with the LCD if you need to.	● Rename if you need to.	● Subtract. Simplify if you can.
$5\frac{1}{2} \text{ ft} = 5\frac{2}{4} \text{ ft}$ $- \; 3\frac{3}{4} \text{ ft} = 3\frac{3}{4} \text{ ft}$	$5\frac{2}{4} \text{ ft} = 4\frac{6}{4} \text{ ft}$ $- \; 3\frac{3}{4} \text{ ft} = 3\frac{3}{4} \text{ ft}$	$\begin{array}{r} 4\frac{6}{4} \text{ ft} \\ - \; 3\frac{3}{4} \text{ ft} \\ \hline 1\frac{3}{4} \text{ ft} \end{array}$

Think

• How would you rename if the problem were $5 - 3\frac{3}{4}$?

GUIDED PRACTICE

Write the difference in simplest form.

1. $6\frac{1}{5}$
   $-2\frac{4}{5}$

2. $5\frac{1}{5}$
   $-\frac{4}{5}$

3. 4
   $-3\frac{3}{8}$

4. $3\frac{1}{4}$
   $-1\frac{7}{8}$

5. $3\frac{1}{3}$
   $-2\frac{3}{5}$

6. Are the number of steps in exercises 1 and 4 the same? Explain.

INDEPENDENT PRACTICE

Write the difference in simplest form.

7. $4\frac{1}{3}$
   $-2\frac{2}{3}$

8. $8\frac{1}{8}$
   $-\frac{3}{8}$

9. 5
   $-1\frac{1}{3}$

10. $3\frac{1}{5}$
    $-1\frac{3}{5}$

11. $7\frac{1}{4}$
    $-\frac{3}{4}$

12. $5\frac{2}{5} - 3\frac{7}{10}$

13. $7 - 1\frac{3}{4}$

14. $2\frac{1}{16} - 1\frac{1}{8}$

15. $6\frac{1}{12} - 1\frac{2}{3}$

16. $3\frac{3}{5} - 1\frac{2}{3}$

17. $1\frac{1}{4} - \frac{1}{3}$

18. $7\frac{1}{8} - 2\frac{2}{3}$

19. $5\frac{1}{5} - 2\frac{3}{8}$

Problem Solving Write each answer in simplest form.

20. Li was $61\frac{3}{4}$ inches tall a year ago. Today he is $62\frac{1}{2}$ inches tall. How much has Li grown over the past year?

21. Carol Sue is $4\frac{1}{2}$ feet tall. With her arms extended she can reach up to $5\frac{1}{4}$ feet. About how long do you think her arms are?

 MATH LOG

How is subtracting $3\frac{3}{4}$ from $5\frac{2}{4}$ like subtracting 33 from 52? How is it different?

Olivia is growing peas for a science experiment.

Work in groups to solve each problem.

1. Olivia read that she should expect only $\frac{3}{4}$ of the seeds she plants to sprout. If that is so, what fraction will not sprout?

2. Olivia wants to grow about 60 plants. If only $\frac{3}{4}$ of her seeds will sprout, should she plant more than or fewer than 60 seeds? Explain.

3. The seed package states that the peas will be ready for harvesting about 55 days after planting. Olivia wants to harvest the peas around June 1st. When should she plant the seeds?

4. Olivia puts $1\frac{3}{4}$ inches of pebbles in the bottom of a pot. Then she adds soil until it's $1\frac{1}{4}$ inches from the top of the pot. The pot is $9\frac{1}{2}$ inches tall. How many inches of soil are in it?

5. The chart at the right shows the growth of one plant during one week. How much did it grow from Monday to Tuesday?

6. According to the chart, during what two-day period did the plant grow the most?

7. If the plant keeps growing at about the same rate as that shown on the chart, in how many more weeks will it be a foot tall?

Day	Height (in.)
Monday	$6\frac{3}{4}$
Tuesday	$7\frac{3}{8}$
Wednesday	$7\frac{7}{8}$
Thursday	$8\frac{1}{4}$
Friday	$8\frac{3}{4}$
Saturday	$9\frac{1}{8}$
Sunday	$9\frac{1}{2}$

8. Olivia is making a poster to explain her science experiment. She is using sheets of paper that are $8\frac{1}{2}$ inches wide and 11 inches long. She allows 1 inch for the width of each letter. How far from the left side of the sheet should she start the letter *G* so the word *GROWING* is in the center of the page?

9. On the same poster, how far from the left side of the sheet should Olivia start the letter *P* so the word *PEAS* is in the center of the page?

10. Make a cover for your next report. Draw a rectangle in the center of a sheet of paper. Make the rectangle 6 inches wide and 4 inches high. What is the measure of the side margins? What is the measure of the top and bottom margins?

1 in.

? GROWING

? PEAS

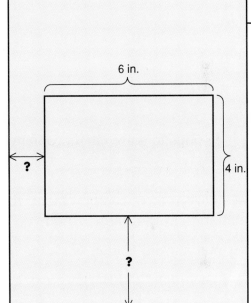

6 in.

?

4 in.

?

....

Maintain • **Equivalent Forms**

Write each fraction as a decimal.

1. $\frac{1}{4}$ 2. $\frac{3}{12}$ 3. $\frac{3}{4}$ 4. $\frac{6}{8}$ 5. $\frac{3}{5}$ 6. $\frac{9}{15}$

PROBLEM SOLVING
···
USING STRATEGIES

When Harlan gets home from school he goes to work at a supermarket. Last week he kept track of the time he worked.

Day	Time Arrived	Time Left
Monday	2:45	5:30
Tuesday	2:45	5:15
Wednesday	3:40	5:10
Thursday	3:15	5:30
Friday	2:15	5:15

Use the chart to solve each problem. If there is not enough information, tell what information you need.

1. On which day did Harlan work the fewest hours?

2. How many hours did Harlan work on Monday?

3. Did Harlan work more than 10 hours that week? How did you get your answer?

4. Harlan lives $2\frac{1}{2}$ miles from the supermarket. How many miles does he travel each week going to and from work?

5. What time did Harlan leave home to go to work on Friday?

6. Harlan earns $4.25 per hour. On what day did he earn the most money?

7. Harlan earned $51 last week. Now he has $85. If he keeps earning $51 a week and saves it all, in how many more weeks will he have the $475 he needs to buy a drum set?

SECTION REVIEW

for pages 302–314

Add or subtract. Write the letter of the answer that is in simplest form.

1. $1\frac{3}{4} + 4\frac{3}{4}$

  a. $\frac{6}{4}$

  b. $6\frac{1}{2}$

  c. 5

  d. $6\frac{2}{4}$

2. $7\frac{13}{16} - 5\frac{3}{16}$

  a. 2

  b. $2\frac{5}{8}$

  c. $2\frac{10}{16}$

  d. $\frac{5}{8}$

3. $3\frac{3}{8} - \frac{1}{8}$

  a. $3\frac{1}{4}$

  b. $2\frac{1}{4}$

  c. $3\frac{2}{8}$

  d. $\frac{2}{8}$

4. $3\frac{5}{6} + 2\frac{1}{3}$

  a. $\frac{7}{6}$

  b. 6

  c. $6\frac{1}{6}$

  d. 5

5. $4\frac{3}{8} + 6\frac{3}{4}$

  a. $11\frac{1}{8}$

  b. 10

  c. $\frac{9}{8}$

  d. $10\frac{3}{4}$

6. $2\frac{3}{5} - \frac{1}{10}$

  a. $2\frac{5}{10}$

  b. $\frac{1}{2}$

  c. $2\frac{1}{5}$

  d. $2\frac{1}{2}$

7. $4\frac{1}{3} + 5\frac{25}{27}$

  a. 9

  b. $10\frac{7}{27}$

  c. $\frac{34}{27}$

  d. $9\frac{26}{27}$

8. $5\frac{3}{4} - 4\frac{5}{12}$

  a. 1

  b. $1\frac{1}{3}$

  c. $\frac{1}{3}$

  d. $1\frac{4}{12}$

9. $1\frac{1}{3} + 5\frac{5}{12}$

  a. $6\frac{3}{4}$

  b. 6

  c. $6\frac{1}{2}$

  d. $6\frac{9}{12}$

10. $2\frac{2}{3} - \frac{3}{8}$

  a. $3\frac{1}{24}$

  b. $\frac{7}{24}$

  c. $2\frac{5}{24}$

  d. $2\frac{7}{24}$

11. $8\frac{1}{4} - 4\frac{2}{3}$

  a. $4\frac{7}{12}$

  b. $3\frac{7}{12}$

  c. $4\frac{5}{12}$

  d. $3\frac{2}{12}$

12. $3\frac{4}{5} - 2\frac{5}{6}$

  a. $1\frac{1}{6}$

  b. $1\frac{29}{30}$

  c. $\frac{1}{30}$

  d. $\frac{29}{30}$

Use the diagram at the right to solve each problem.

13. According to the plans, how tall is the birdhouse?

14. What is the diameter of the circular opening?

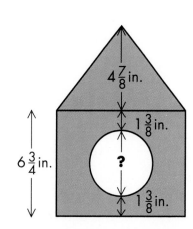

$4\frac{7}{8}$ in.

$1\frac{3}{8}$ in.

$6\frac{3}{4}$ in.

?

$1\frac{3}{8}$ in.

CHAPTER REVIEW

Language Connection

When objects are alike in some way, we say they have something in common. For example, fractions with a common denominator have the same number as their denominators.

What do books, wallpaper, and dollar bills have in common? They all contain paper. Think of other groups of objects that have something in common. Write each group on one side of a card. On the other side, write what they have in common. Then exchange cards with classmates. Try to guess what each group of objects has in common.

Test ● ● ● ● ● ● ●

Write the answer in simplest form.

1. $\frac{5}{6} + \frac{3}{6}$

2. $\frac{11}{12} - \frac{4}{9}$

3. $\frac{3}{4} - \frac{2}{4}$

4. $8\frac{4}{10} + 2\frac{1}{10}$

5. $\begin{array}{r} 7\frac{1}{6} \\ -\ 5\frac{1}{4} \end{array}$

6. $\begin{array}{r} \frac{4}{5} \\ -\ \frac{1}{3} \end{array}$

7. $\begin{array}{r} \frac{3}{8} \\ +\ \frac{3}{8} \end{array}$

8. $\begin{array}{r} 6\frac{3}{8} \\ -\ 1\frac{4}{5} \end{array}$

9. $12\frac{4}{5} + 10\frac{2}{5}$

10. $\frac{10}{12} - \frac{2}{12}$

11. $7\frac{1}{5} + 9\frac{2}{3}$

12. $5\frac{1}{3} - 4\frac{1}{3}$

13. $\begin{array}{r} \frac{2}{16} \\ +\ \frac{4}{8} \end{array}$

14. $\begin{array}{r} 12\frac{15}{16} \\ -\ 3\frac{3}{16} \end{array}$

15. $\begin{array}{r} \frac{3}{18} \\ +\ \frac{2}{6} \end{array}$

16. $\begin{array}{r} 10\frac{1}{3} \\ -\ 8\frac{1}{2} \end{array}$

17. $4\frac{13}{30} - 2\frac{7}{10}$

18. $\frac{9}{10} + \frac{7}{10}$

19. $8 - 3\frac{1}{10}$

20. $\frac{1}{2} + \frac{1}{5}$

21. $\begin{array}{r} \frac{14}{15} \\ -\ \frac{4}{15} \end{array}$

22. $\begin{array}{r} \frac{7}{12} \\ +\ \frac{3}{4} \end{array}$

23. $\begin{array}{r} 5\frac{3}{5} \\ +\ 3 \end{array}$

24. $\begin{array}{r} 10 \\ -\ 6\frac{5}{6} \end{array}$

PROBLEM SOLVING

Solve each problem. Write each answer in simplest form.

25. Rhonda has a bowl of flour. She puts another $1\frac{1}{2}$ cups of flour into the bowl. Now there are $8\frac{1}{2}$ cups of flour in the bowl. How many cups of flour were in the bowl to begin with?

26. Yesterday, Tina spent $1\frac{1}{2}$ hours doing her math homework and $1\frac{3}{4}$ hours doing the rest of her homework. She also played soccer for $1\frac{1}{2}$ hours. How many hours did Tina spend doing homework yesterday?

27. Jaime measured $50\frac{3}{4}$ inches tall two years ago. Today he measures $53\frac{3}{8}$ inches tall. How much has Jaime grown in the past two years?

28. During his first week of exercising, Lee uses a $1\frac{1}{2}$-pound weight. Each week, he is supposed to increase the weight by $\frac{3}{4}$ pound. How much weight will he be exercising with during the fourth week?

CUMULATIVE REVIEW

Write each fraction in simplest form.

29. $\frac{24}{32}$

30. $\frac{10}{16}$

31. $\frac{4}{40}$

32. $\frac{14}{35}$

Use the figures to answer each question.

A.

B.

C.

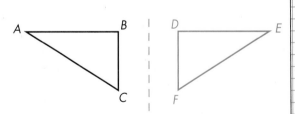

Copy and complete.

33. Which figures have both line and half-turn symmetry?

34. $\overline{AC} \cong$ ▨

35. $\angle B \cong$ ▨

EXCURSION
USING TECHNOLOGY

COMPUTING WITH MIXED NUMBERS

 You can use a calculator to write fractions and mixed numbers as decimals.

Write $\frac{1}{5}$ as a decimal.

$$\frac{1}{5} = 1 \div 5$$ $\boxed{0.2}$

1. Why can you write $\frac{1}{5}$ as $1 \div 5$?

Write $4\frac{3}{8}$ as a decimal.

$$4\frac{3}{8} = 4 + \frac{3}{8}$$ $\boxed{0.375}$ $4 + 0.375 = 4.375$

Write each fraction or mixed number as a decimal.

2. $\frac{11}{25}$ 3. $\frac{5}{8}$ 4. $4\frac{3}{5}$ 5. $2\frac{1}{4}$ 6. $7\frac{11}{16}$

You already know one way to compute with mixed numbers.

Add: $3\frac{3}{4} + 1\frac{2}{5}$

● Find the least common denominator (LCD).	● Write equivalent fractions with the LCD.	● Add the fractions. Then add the whole numbers. Simplify if you can.
$\begin{array}{r} 3\frac{3}{4} \\ + 1\frac{2}{5} \\ \hline \end{array}$ *The LCM of 4 and 5 is 20. So, 20 is the LCD.*	$3\frac{3}{4} = 3\frac{15}{20}$ $+ 1\frac{2}{5} = 1\frac{8}{20}$	$\begin{array}{r} 3\frac{15}{20} \\ + 1\frac{8}{20} \\ \hline 4\frac{23}{20} = 5\frac{3}{20} \end{array}$

Another way to compute with mixed numbers is with a calculator. Since you cannot input fractions into many calculators, you use decimals instead.

● Use your calculator to find equivalent decimals for each fraction part.

● Rewrite each mixed number as a decimal. Add.

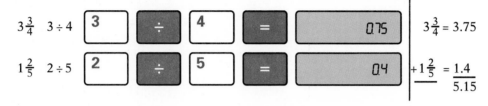

$3\frac{3}{4}$ $3 \div 4$ | 3 | | ÷ | | 4 | | = | | 0.75 | $3\frac{3}{4} = 3.75$

$1\frac{2}{5}$ $2 \div 5$ | 2 | | ÷ | | 5 | | = | | 0.4 | $+1\frac{2}{5} = \underline{1.4}$
                                                                              5.15

7. Are $5\frac{3}{20}$ and 5.15 equal? Explain.

8. Use a calculator to compute $6\frac{5}{8} - 3\frac{2}{5}$. How do the steps change when you subtract instead of add?

Write the answer as a mixed number in simplest form.

9. $3\frac{3}{5} + 1\frac{1}{5}$ **10.** $7\frac{11}{25} - 4\frac{1}{8}$ **11.** $5\frac{4}{5} + 7\frac{3}{8}$

12. Use a calculator to write each answer in exercises 9–11 as a decimal.

13. Which of the exercises in 9–11 would you rather compute as fractions? As decimals? Explain.

Write the answer as either a mixed number in simplest form or a decimal.

14. $\quad 2\frac{3}{25}$ **15.** $\quad 16\frac{7}{8}$ **16.** $\quad 4\frac{3}{8}$ **17.** $\quad 8\frac{2}{5}$
$\quad + 5\frac{2}{25}$ $\quad - 4\frac{13}{20}$ $\quad + 7\frac{9}{10}$ $\quad - 3\frac{1}{4}$

18. $20\frac{3}{25} - 9\frac{1}{10}$ **19.** $6\frac{5}{8} + 3\frac{2}{5}$ **20.** $2\frac{6}{25} + 3\frac{1}{4}$

MULTIPLICATION AND DIVISION OF FRACTIONS

Food Science

Pancake Breakfast Imagine you are planning a pancake breakfast for your class. The recipe below makes 24 pancakes. Since most people can eat more than one pancake, you may not have enough batter. You can use your knowledge of fractions to double or even triple the recipe.

Suppose you want to make a double batch. Copy down the list of ingredients. Then double the amount of each item. How much of each ingredient do you need for a double batch?

Suppose you wanted to make half a batch of pancakes. Copy the list as you did above, and then divide the amount of each item in half. How much of each ingredient would you need?

Buttermilk Pancakes

Ingredients:

$\frac{1}{2}$ cup whole wheat flour
$\frac{1}{2}$ cup unbleached white flour
$\frac{1}{2}$ teaspoon baking soda
$\frac{1}{4}$ teaspoon salt
2 eggs
1 cup buttermilk
3 tablespoons melted butter

Directions:

- sift the flour with the salt and soda.
- Beat the eggs slightly and then mix in buttermilk and melted butter.
- Add the liquids to the dry ingredients and stir to combine.
- Ladle onto a moderately hot griddle or frying pan and take it from there.

FRACTION FACTORS

STRAWBERRY SOUP
(makes 1 serving)
$\frac{1}{4}$ teaspoon of brown sugar
$\frac{1}{8}$ teaspoon of vanilla extract
$\frac{1}{2}$ cup of cream
$\frac{1}{3}$ pint of strawberries

In this lesson, you will discover a way to multiply fractions and whole numbers. You will need the recording sheet.

Jerry is going to make Strawberry Soup. The recipe makes 1 serving, but Jerry wants 6 servings. He wants to know how much brown sugar he needs.

Jerry needs $\frac{1}{4}$ teaspoon (tsp) of sugar for 1 serving. How much does he need for 6 servings?

He can solve the problem by using a model or repeated addition.

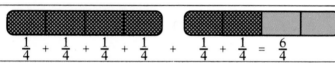

$$\frac{1}{4} + \frac{1}{4} + \frac{1}{4} + \frac{1}{4} + \frac{1}{4} + \frac{1}{4} = \frac{6}{4}$$

Since you can represent the problem with a repeated-addition sentence, you can also represent it with a multiplication sentence.

$6 = \frac{6}{1}$ $\frac{6}{1} \times \frac{1}{4}$ tsp $= \frac{6}{4}$ tsp

Jerry needs $\frac{6}{4}$, or $1\frac{2}{4}$, or $1\frac{1}{2}$ teaspoons of sugar.

1. Find how much of each of the other three ingredients Jerry needs for the soup. Complete the chart on your recording sheet.

Ingredient	Quantity (1 serving)	Addition Sentence (6 servings)	Multiplication Sentence (6 servings)	Quantity (6 servings)
brown sugar	$\frac{1}{4}$ teaspoon	$\frac{1}{4}+\frac{1}{4}+\frac{1}{4}+\frac{1}{4}+\frac{1}{4}+\frac{1}{4}=\frac{6}{4}$	$\frac{6}{1} \times \frac{1}{4} = \frac{6}{4}$	$\frac{6}{4}$ or $1\frac{2}{4}$ or $1\frac{1}{2}$ teaspoons
vanilla extract	$\frac{1}{8}$ teaspoon			
cream	$\frac{1}{2}$ cup			
strawberries	$\frac{1}{3}$ pint			

2. Look at the numerators in the multiplication sentences on the chart. How can you find the numerator in each product?

3. Look at the denominators in the multiplication sentences on the chart. How can you find the denominator in each product?

Predict the product for each multiplication sentence. Write repeated-addition sentences to check your predictions.

4. $\frac{3}{1} \times \frac{1}{6} = $ ▨

5. $8 \times \frac{1}{4} = $ ▨

6. $2 \times \frac{7}{8} = $ ▨

7. $5 \times \frac{2}{5} = $ ▨

From exercise 5 above, you know that $8 \times \frac{1}{4} = 2$. What is $\frac{1}{4} \times 8$? Again, you can use a model. Arrange 8 into 4 equal groups.

One of the four groups, or $\frac{1}{4}$ of 8, is 2. So, $\frac{1}{4} \times 8 = 2$, and $8 \times \frac{1}{4} = 2$.

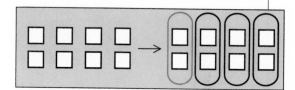

SUMMING IT UP

8. Write a rule for multiplying a fraction and a whole number.

9. Use your rule to write the product.

a. $3 \times \frac{3}{4}$

b. $\frac{3}{12} \times 2$

c. $6 \times \frac{1}{3}$

d. $\frac{4}{5} \times 4$

10. Discuss your rule with the class.

PROJECT • Critical Thinking

Work in small groups. Use the recipe for apple bran muffins in the General Information section of your Data Book.

• Find the number of batches you would need to make so that everyone in your class would get at least one muffin.

• Find the amount of each ingredient you would need. Make up your own recording sheet to show your answers.

MULTIPLYING WITH FRACTIONS

▶ Ethan's class is having a pizza party. The students are sitting in 8 groups. Each group eats $\frac{3}{4}$ of a pizza. How many entire pizzas do the students eat?

Multiply: $8 \times \frac{3}{4}$

You can solve this problem using repeated addition or a model.

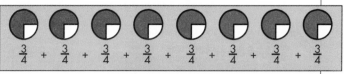

$$\frac{3}{4} + \frac{3}{4} + \frac{3}{4} + \frac{3}{4} + \frac{3}{4} + \frac{3}{4} + \frac{3}{4} + \frac{3}{4}$$

The students eat $\frac{24}{4}$, or 6, pizzas.

▶ The teacher brings in 8 boxes of craft sticks for a project. The class uses $\frac{3}{4}$ of the boxes. How many boxes do they use?

To find $\frac{3}{4}$ of 8, you can multiply: $\frac{3}{4} \times 8$

Again, you can use a model.

They use 6 boxes.

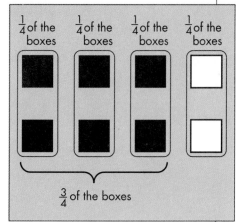

$\frac{1}{4}$ of the boxes $\frac{1}{4}$ of the boxes $\frac{1}{4}$ of the boxes $\frac{1}{4}$ of the boxes

$\frac{3}{4}$ of the boxes

▶ You can also multiply to find products.

● Write the whole number as a fraction.	● Multiply numerators. Multiply denominators.	● Simplify if you can.
$\frac{3}{4} \times 8 = \frac{3}{4} \times \frac{8}{1}$	$\frac{3}{4} \times \frac{8}{1} = \frac{24}{4}$	$\frac{24}{4} = 6$

Think

• When you multiply a whole number by a fraction less than 1, is the product greater than or less than the whole number?

Write the product in simplest form.

1. $\frac{1}{4}$ of 8
2. $\frac{2}{3}$ of 9
3. $\frac{1}{2}$ of 5
4. $\frac{3}{4}$ of 12
5. $\frac{3}{8}$ of 2

6. $20 \times \frac{6}{5}$
7. $10 \times \frac{2}{5}$
8. $\frac{1}{3} \times 9$
9. $\frac{3}{2} \times 6$
10. $\frac{1}{4} \times 7$

11. Look at exercises 6 and 9. What kind of fraction in used in each? How does the product compare with the whole number?

INDEPENDENT PRACTICE

Write the product in simplest form.

12. $\frac{1}{2}$ of 10
13. $\frac{1}{5}$ of 30
14. $\frac{1}{6}$ of 42
15. $\frac{1}{2}$ of 22
16. $\frac{3}{5}$ of 15

17. $\frac{3}{5} \times 15$
18. $4 \times \frac{2}{3}$
19. $4 \times \frac{4}{5}$
20. $\frac{3}{8} \times 8$
21. $8 \times \frac{3}{8}$

Problem Solving Remember: some problems may not have enough information.

22. There are 24 children in Ethan's class. If $\frac{3}{8}$ of them are in the band, how many children in his class are in the band?

23. Every day, 12 students each get 15 minutes of computer time. How many hours of computer time do the students get altogether?

24. There are 8 students working on the class science project, and $\frac{3}{4}$ of them are girls. How many of them are boys?

25. In gym class, $\frac{1}{4}$ of the students are running laps, $\frac{1}{3}$ of them are practicing the broad jump, and the rest are climbing ropes. How many students are climbing ropes?

CHALLENGE • Number Sense

A number is a **perfect number** if it is one half the sum of its factors. For example, the number 6 is a perfect number.

Factors of 6: 1, 2, 3, 6 $1 + 2 + 3 + 6 = 12$ $\frac{1}{2}$ of $12 = 6$

What perfect number is between 20 and 30?

FINDING A FRACTION OF A NUMBER

▶ How much money will you save by buying this game on sale?

Find $\frac{1}{4}$ of $24.

SALE!
$\frac{1}{4}$ off

$24.⁰⁰

You could use pencil and paper:

$\frac{1}{4} \times \$24 = \frac{1}{4} \times \frac{\$24}{1} = \frac{\$24}{4} = \$6$

But this problem is easier to do mentally. The fraction $\frac{1}{4}$ means "1 of 4 equal parts." Divide $24 into 4 equal parts.

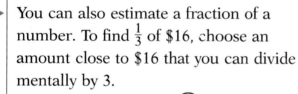

One of 4 equal parts is $6. So, $\frac{1}{4}$ of $24 is $6. You will save $6.

▶ You can also estimate a fraction of a number. To find $\frac{1}{3}$ of $16, choose an amount close to $16 that you can divide mentally by 3.

Estimate: $\frac{1}{3}$ of $16 ⚬ ⚬ ($\frac{1}{3}$ of $15 = $5)

So, $\frac{1}{3}$ of $16 is about $5.

Think

≋ • What are two reasonable estimates for $\frac{1}{6}$ of $39?

$16.⁰⁰

WORD WIGGLE

SALE!
$\frac{1}{3}$ off

Other Examples

Find $\frac{1}{5}$ of 3500 mentally.

(3500 ÷ 5 = 700)

So, $\frac{1}{5}$ of 3500 is 700.

Estimate: $\frac{1}{4}$ of 142

($\frac{1}{4}$ of 120 = 30) ($\frac{1}{4}$ of 160 = 40)

Both 30 and 40 are reasonable estimates.

Use mental math to solve.

1. $\frac{1}{3}$ of 18   2. $\frac{1}{2}$ of 50   3. $\frac{1}{6}$ of $360   4. $\frac{1}{4}$ of 2800

Estimate.

5. $\frac{1}{5}$ of 17   6. $\frac{1}{8}$ of $59   7. $\frac{1}{4}$ of 101   8. $\frac{1}{3}$ of 1386

9. What is another reasonable estimate for exercise 6?

INDEPENDENT PRACTICE

Use mental math to solve.

10. $\frac{1}{4}$ of 32   11. $\frac{1}{6}$ of $48   12. $\frac{1}{8}$ of 64   13. $\frac{1}{5}$ of 300

14. $\frac{1}{10}$ of 900   15. $\frac{1}{2}$ of 220   16. $\frac{1}{6}$ of $4200   17. $\frac{1}{5}$ of 2500

Estimate.

18. $\frac{1}{5}$ of 27   19. $\frac{1}{3}$ of 20   20. $\frac{1}{4}$ of 83   21. $\frac{1}{6}$ of $202

22. $\frac{1}{8}$ of $339   23. $\frac{1}{4}$ of 856   24. $\frac{1}{5}$ of $3624   25. $\frac{1}{7}$ of 1386

Estimate the amount saved on each item.

26.

$107.00 $\frac{1}{3}$ off

27.
$27.00 $\frac{1}{4}$ off   BLASTER

28.
$69.00 $\frac{1}{4}$ off   VIDEO GAME

29.
$245.00 $\frac{1}{5}$ off

CHALLENGE • Consumer Math

About how much will you pay for the bike lock that is on sale?

$19.49 $\frac{1}{4}$ off

GUESS AND CHECK, MAKE A TABLE

Often, people combine strategies to solve a problem.

One time, we made a table and used guess and check to help us run our ice cream stand.

OUR PROBLEM

We had no pint containers one day. When customers wanted a pint of ice cream, we gave them a quart container filled halfway. By closing time, we had used 20 containers and had sold $72 worth of ice cream. We wanted to know how many pints and how many quarts we had sold.

OUR SOLUTION

We decided to try guessing and checking. We kept guessing combinations of pints and quarts that added up to 20 containers. We made a table to keep track of our guesses and checks.

Guesses	Checks		
	Money from pints	Money from quarts	Total Sales
10 pt + 10 qt	10 × $3 = $30	10 × $5 = $50	$30 + $50 = $80 (too high)
15 pt + 5 qt	15 × $3 = $45	5 × $5 = $25	$45 + $25 = $70 (too low)

Soon, we had our answer. Can you figure out what it was?

GUIDED PRACTICE

Use guess and check and make a table, or use other strategies you think will help.

1. Toni is the coin guesser at the school fair. People tell Toni the number of coins they have, the type of coins, and the total value. Then Toni tells them exactly what coins they have. What would Toni tell Jenni and Greg?

   a. Jenni says, "I have 12 coins, all nickels and dimes. The coins are worth $1.00."

   b. Greg says, "I have 12 coins, all nickels, dimes, and quarters. The coins are worth $1.50."

....

APPLICATION

Work in pairs to solve each problem.

2. Joe and Chang are making a 70-foot walkway to their front door. They have 3 lengths of tile: 2-foot-long tiles, 3-foot-long tiles, and 5-foot-long tiles. They want to use the same number of each tile. How many of each should they use?

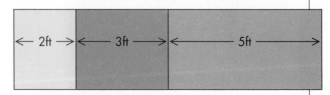

3. Stephanie sells tour booklets for $3.15 each and maps for $2.75 each. Today her sales totaled $20.45. How many booklets and maps did Stephanie sell?

4. The ink on three of Billy's test scores smudged so they couldn't be read. What were the three scores?

5. A rectangle has a perimeter of 38 inches. The product of its length in inches and its width in inches is 48. How long and how wide is the rectangle?

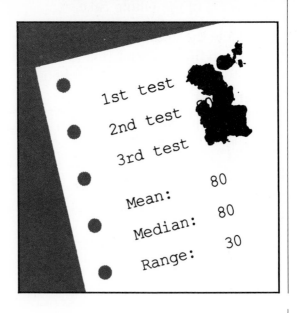

1st test
2nd test
3rd test
Mean: 80
Median: 80
Range: 30

FRACTIONS AND MULTIPLICATION

In this lesson, you will discover a way to multiply a fraction by a fraction. You will need the recording sheet, a red crayon, and a blue crayon.

The Alvarado family had $\frac{3}{4}$ of a cake left over.

Today, they ate $\frac{1}{2}$ of the leftover cake. How much of a whole cake did they eat today?

We need to find $\frac{1}{2}$ of $\frac{3}{4}$ of the cake, or $\frac{1}{2} \times \frac{3}{4}$.

1. Do you think the product will be greater than or less than 1? Explain.

You can solve the problem by using a model.

The square model represents the cake. Three of the four parts have red stripes to represent the amount of leftover cake.

The bottom half has blue stripes to represent half of the cake.

2. How many sections is the model divided into altogether?

3. How many parts have both red and blue stripes? Write this as a fraction. This is your product for $\frac{1}{2} \times \frac{3}{4}$.

They ate $\frac{3}{8}$ of the whole cake.

Complete the chart on your recording sheet. Draw models to find each product. Directions for drawing models are on the recording sheet.

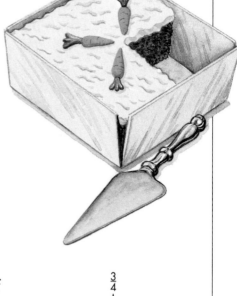

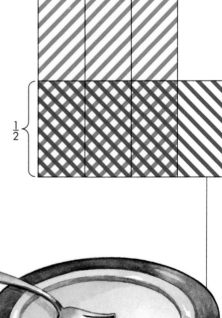

CHART

Problem	Multiplication Problem	Product
$\frac{1}{2}$ of $\frac{3}{4}$	$\frac{1}{2} \times \frac{3}{4}$	$\frac{3}{8}$
$\frac{1}{2}$ of $\frac{2}{3}$		
$\frac{1}{3}$ of $\frac{1}{4}$		
$\frac{3}{4}$ of $\frac{2}{5}$		
$\frac{1}{2}$ of $\frac{4}{5}$		

4. Look for patterns in each multiplication problem and product in the chart.

   a. How can you find the numerator in each product? $\frac{1}{2} \times \frac{3}{4} = \frac{3}{8}$

   b. How can you find the denominator in each product? $\frac{1}{2} \times \frac{3}{4} = \frac{3}{8}$

5. Write the product for each multiplication sentence.

   a. $\frac{1}{4} \times \frac{2}{3} = \blacksquare$ **b.** $\frac{2}{5} \times \frac{1}{4} = \blacksquare$ **c.** $\frac{3}{8} \times \frac{1}{2} = \blacksquare$ **d.** $\frac{1}{8} \times \frac{3}{4} = \blacksquare$

   Check your answers by drawing models.

6. Is each product in exercise 5 greater than or less than 1?

7. From exercise 5b above, you know that $\frac{2}{5} \times \frac{1}{4} = \frac{2}{20}$, or $\frac{1}{10}$.

   a. Draw a model to find $\frac{1}{4} \times \frac{2}{5}$. Write the product.

   b. Compare the products of $\frac{2}{5} \times \frac{1}{4}$ and $\frac{1}{4} \times \frac{2}{5}$. What do you notice?

SUMMING IT UP

8. Write a rule for multiplying fractions by fractions.

9. How is this rule different from the rule for multiplying whole numbers and fractions? How is it the same?

10. Discuss your rule for multiplying fractions by fractions with the class.

 **• Mixed Practice**

Write each answer in simplest form.

1. $5\frac{5}{12} + 5\frac{1}{2}$ **2.** $1\frac{5}{6} - \frac{1}{3}$ **3.** $4\frac{5}{8} - 3\frac{7}{8}$ **4.** $2 - 1\frac{3}{10}$ **5.** $\frac{4}{7} + \frac{4}{5}$

MULTIPLYING FRACTIONS

Gloria's science class lasts $\frac{3}{4}$ of an hour. On Thursday, they spent $\frac{2}{3}$ of the class time watching a movie about whales. How long did they watch the movie?

Multiply: $\frac{2}{3} \times \frac{3}{4}$ h

You can use a model to help you multiply.

Think

• How many parts is the model divided into?

• How many parts are shaded twice?

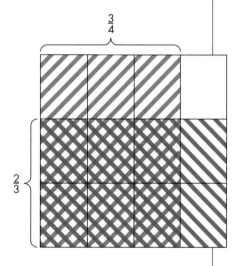

They watched the movie for $\frac{6}{12}$, or $\frac{1}{2}$, of an hour.

You can also find the product without using a model.

● **Multiply numerators.**

$\frac{2}{3} \times \frac{3}{4}$ h $= \frac{6}{}$ h

● **Multiply denominators.**

$\frac{2}{3} \times \frac{3}{4}$ h $= \frac{6}{12}$ h

● **Simplify if you can.**

$\frac{2}{3} \times \frac{3}{4}$ h $= \frac{6}{12}$ h $= \frac{1}{2}$ h

Think

• Can you solve the problem above by changing $\frac{3}{4}$ hour to minutes? Explain.

GUIDED PRACTICE

Write the product in simplest form. Use the model if it helps.

1. $\frac{1}{2} \times \frac{1}{3}$

2. $\frac{3}{4} \times \frac{4}{5}$

3. $\frac{2}{7} \times \frac{2}{3}$

4. $\frac{3}{4} \times \frac{1}{3}$

5. $6 \times \frac{2}{5}$

6. $\frac{1}{5} \times \frac{2}{5}$

7. $\frac{4}{5} \times \frac{2}{3}$

8. $\frac{1}{3} \times \frac{12}{5}$

9. In exercises 1–3, did you find it easier to use models or to multiply? Explain.

....

INDEPENDENT PRACTICE

Write the product in simplest form. Use the model if it helps.

10. $\frac{3}{4} \times \frac{3}{4}$

11. $\frac{2}{3} \times \frac{1}{4}$

12. $\frac{1}{3} \times \frac{3}{4}$

13. $\frac{3}{4} \times 12$

14. $\frac{1}{6} \times 8$

15. $8 \times \frac{3}{5}$

16. $\frac{1}{4} \times \frac{1}{2}$

17. $\frac{4}{5} \times \frac{2}{8}$

18. $\frac{2}{7} \times \frac{1}{2}$

19. $5 \times \frac{3}{4}$

20. $\frac{4}{5} \times \frac{1}{5}$

21. $\frac{1}{3} \times 6$

22. $4 \times \frac{1}{8}$

23. $\frac{1}{4} \times 4$

24. $\frac{5}{4} \times \frac{1}{2}$

25. $\frac{5}{12} \times \frac{1}{3}$

26. $\frac{4}{3} \times \frac{5}{6}$

27. $\frac{2}{3} \times \frac{7}{8}$

Problem Solving

28. Today Gloria spent $\frac{1}{2}$ of her $\frac{3}{4}$-hour science class outdoors. She also spent $\frac{3}{4}$ of her $\frac{1}{2}$-hour gym class outdoors. How much time did she spend outdoors during the school day?

29. During April, Gloria went to school on all 18 school days. It takes her 15 minutes to walk to school and 15 minutes to walk home. How many hours did she spend walking to and from school that month?

This week, Mr. Daly bought 12 crates of melons for his market. Each crate cost $5.00 and contained 8 melons.

Each melon weighs about $2\frac{1}{2}$ pounds. He will sell them for $0.70 per pound through Thursday. After that, he will drop the price to $0.50 per pound.

UNIT PRICE $0.70 PER POUND F R E S H MELONS

Solve each problem. You may use a calculator.

1. How much did Mr. Daly pay for melons this week?

2. About how many pounds of melons were in each crate?

3. On Monday, he sells 1 crate of melons. About how much money does he take in?

4. If Mr. Daly sells all the melons by Thursday, about how much money will he take in?

5. If Mr. Daly sells all the melons in 3 crates by Thursday, will he have gotten back the money he spent buying them? Explain.

6. What is the fewest number of melons Mr. Daly can sell and still make back the money he spent buying them?

7. Study the possibilities below. Write the letter of the one that will make the most money for Mr. Daly and the one that will make the least.

a. He sells $\frac{1}{3}$ of the melons by Thursday, $\frac{1}{3}$ after that, and the rest spoil.

b. He sells $\frac{1}{2}$ the melons by Thursday and none after that.

c. He sells $\frac{1}{4}$ of the melons by Thursday, $\frac{1}{2}$ after that, and the rest spoil.

SECTION REVIEW

for pages 322–334

Solve each problem.

1. Sergio has $30 to buy sneakers. The sale price of the sneakers is $\frac{1}{4}$ off the regular price of $32. How much money will he save by buying the sneakers on sale?

2. Mrs. Peabody makes $\frac{2}{3}$ of her backyard into a garden. She plants tomatoes in $\frac{1}{4}$ of the garden. What fraction of her backyard does she use to grow tomatoes?

Write the letter of the answer that is in simplest form.

3. $\frac{1}{8} \times 16$
   a. $\frac{16}{9}$
   b. $\frac{4}{2}$
   c. $\frac{16}{8}$
   d. 2

4. $7 \times \frac{3}{5}$
   a. $1\frac{2}{3}$
   b. $\frac{21}{5}$
   c. $4\frac{1}{5}$
   d. $\frac{3}{35}$

5. $9 \times \frac{2}{3}$
   a. $\frac{18}{3}$
   b. 6
   c. $1\frac{3}{4}$
   d. $\frac{2}{27}$

6. $\frac{1}{4} \times 5$
   a. $\frac{1}{20}$
   b. $1\frac{1}{4}$
   c. $1\frac{1}{5}$
   d. $\frac{5}{4}$

7. $\frac{3}{4} \times \frac{1}{6}$
   a. $\frac{3}{24}$
   b. $\frac{1}{3}$
   c. $\frac{1}{8}$
   d. $\frac{1}{6}$

8. $\frac{9}{10} \times \frac{2}{3}$
   a. $\frac{3}{5}$
   b. $\frac{18}{30}$
   c. $\frac{6}{10}$
   d. $\frac{11}{13}$

9. $\frac{3}{4} \times \frac{1}{12}$
   a. $\frac{1}{16}$
   b. $\frac{3}{48}$
   c. $\frac{1}{4}$
   d. 9

10. $\frac{4}{5} \times \frac{5}{6}$
   a. $\frac{9}{11}$
   b. $\frac{24}{25}$
   c. $\frac{4}{6}$
   d. $\frac{2}{3}$

11. $\frac{3}{8} \times \frac{4}{3}$
   a. $\frac{12}{24}$
   b. $\frac{9}{32}$
   c. $\frac{1}{2}$
   d. $\frac{7}{11}$

12. $\frac{1}{3} \times \frac{1}{3}$
   a. $\frac{2}{6}$
   b. 1
   c. $\frac{1}{9}$
   d. $\frac{2}{3}$

13. $\frac{7}{8} \times \frac{3}{4}$
   a. $\frac{21}{32}$
   b. $\frac{10}{12}$
   c. $\frac{5}{6}$
   d. $\frac{6}{7}$

14. $\frac{7}{5} \times \frac{5}{7}$
   a. $\frac{12}{12}$
   b. $\frac{25}{49}$
   c. $\frac{35}{35}$
   d. 1

EXPLORING FRACTIONS AND DIVISION

In this lesson, you will explore dividing by fractions. Work in pairs. You will need the recording sheet.

▶ You can show division by fractions by using a number line. Start with the example $1 \div \frac{1}{2}$. How many halves are there in 1?

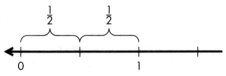

The number line shows there are 2 halves in 1.

What is $2 \div \frac{1}{2}$? How many halves are there in 2?

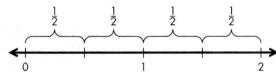

The number line shows there are 4 halves in 2.

1. Use your recording sheet. Use the number line marked in halves to complete Chart A.

2. Look at Chart A. Do you think the quotient of $6 \div \frac{1}{2}$ is greater than or less than 6? Greater than or less than 10?

CHART A

How Many Halves in:	Division Sentence
1	$1 \div \frac{1}{2} = 2$
2	$2 \div \frac{1}{2} = \blacksquare$
3	$3 \div \frac{1}{2} = \blacksquare$
4	$\blacksquare \div \blacksquare = \blacksquare$
5	$\blacksquare \div \blacksquare = \blacksquare$

▶ Now use the number line to find the quotient for $1 \div \frac{1}{3}$. How many thirds are there in 1?

The number line shows there are 3 thirds in 1.

What is $2 \div \frac{1}{3}$? How many thirds are there in 2?

The number line shows there are 6 thirds in 2.

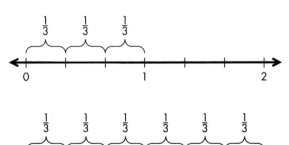

336

3. Use your recording sheet. Use the number line marked in thirds to complete Chart B.

4. Look at Chart B. Do you think the quotient of $6 \div \frac{1}{3}$ is greater than or less than 6? Greater than or less than 15?

▶ $2 \div \frac{1}{3} = 6$. What is $2 \div \frac{2}{3}$? How many two thirds are there in 2? You can use a number line to show this division also.

CHART B

How Many Thirds in:	Division Sentence
1	$1 \div \frac{1}{3} = 3$
2	$2 \div \frac{1}{3} = \blacksquare$
3	$\blacksquare \div \blacksquare = \blacksquare$
4	$\blacksquare \div \blacksquare = \blacksquare$
5	$\blacksquare \div \blacksquare = \blacksquare$

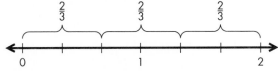

There are 3 two thirds in 2.

Use the number line to write each quotient.

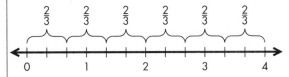

5. How many two thirds in 4?

$4 \div \frac{2}{3} = \blacksquare$

6. How many three fourths in 3?

$3 \div \frac{3}{4} = \blacksquare$

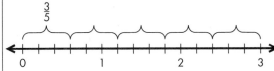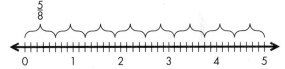

7. How many three fifths in 3?

$3 \div \frac{3}{5} = \blacksquare$

8. How many five eighths in 5?

$5 \div \frac{5}{8} = \blacksquare$

Complete each pair of sentences. Use a number line if you need to.

9. $4 \div \frac{1}{3} = \blacksquare$
$4 \div \frac{2}{3} = \blacksquare$

10. $3 \div \frac{1}{4} = \blacksquare$
$3 \div \frac{3}{4} = \blacksquare$

11. $6 \div \frac{1}{3} = \blacksquare$
$6 \div \frac{2}{3} = \blacksquare$

12. $5 \div \frac{1}{8} = \blacksquare$
$5 \div \frac{5}{8} = \blacksquare$

SUMMING IT UP

Use what you have learned about dividing by fractions to answer each question.

13. Is the quotient of $4 \div \frac{1}{12}$ greater than or less than 4?

14. Which quotient is greater, $4 \div \frac{1}{12}$ or $4 \div \frac{3}{12}$?

RECIPROCALS

In this lesson, you will discover patterns in fractions that have a product of 1.

The number 1 can be written as a fraction many different ways.

Here are some fractions that represent 1.

 $\frac{2}{2} = 1$ $\frac{5}{5} = 1$ 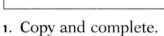 $\frac{8}{8} = 1$

1. Copy and complete.

a. $\frac{4}{\blacksquare} = 1$ b. $\frac{\blacksquare}{75} = 1$ c. $\frac{1}{\blacksquare} = 1$ d. $\frac{\blacksquare}{23} = 1$

You can multiply two factors and get a product of 1.

$\frac{2}{3} \times \frac{3}{2} = \frac{6}{6} = 1$ $\frac{5}{8} \times \frac{8}{5} = \frac{40}{40} = 1$ $\frac{1}{4} \times \frac{4}{1} = \frac{4}{4} = 1$

2. Copy and complete.

a. $\frac{3}{5} \times \frac{\blacksquare}{3} = \frac{15}{15} = 1$ b. $\frac{7}{2} \times \frac{2}{\blacksquare} = \frac{14}{14} = 1$ c. $\frac{\blacksquare}{3} \times \frac{3}{2} = \frac{6}{6} = 1$

d. $\frac{3}{4} \times \frac{4}{\blacksquare} = \frac{\blacksquare}{\blacksquare} = 1$ e. $\frac{\blacksquare}{2} \times \frac{2}{5} = \frac{\blacksquare}{\blacksquare} = 1$ f. $7 \times \frac{1}{7} = \frac{\blacksquare}{\blacksquare} = 1$

g. $\frac{5}{6} \times \frac{\blacksquare}{\blacksquare} = 1$ h. $\frac{1}{3} \times \blacksquare = 1$ i. $5 \times \frac{\blacksquare}{\blacksquare} = 1$

3. What do you notice about two fractions whose product equals 1?

Two numbers with a product of 1 are called **reciprocals** of each other. For example:

$\frac{4}{9} \times \frac{9}{4} = 1$ So, $\frac{9}{4}$ and $\frac{4}{9}$ are reciprocals.

4. Look at the fractions in the box at the right. Write the fractions that are greater than 1. Write the reciprocal of each. Are the reciprocals greater than or less than 1?

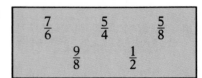

$\frac{7}{6}$ $\frac{5}{4}$ $\frac{5}{8}$
$\frac{9}{8}$ $\frac{1}{2}$

5. Write the fractions that are less than 1. Write the reciprocal of each. Are the reciprocals greater than or less than 1?

6. How do you write the whole number 6 as a fraction? What is its reciprocal?

7. How do you write the mixed number $2\frac{3}{4}$ as a fraction? What is its reciprocal?

8. Write each whole number or mixed number as a fraction. Then write its reciprocal.

a. $1\frac{2}{3}$ b. 4   c. $2\frac{3}{10}$ d. 7

9. Is the reciprocal of a whole number greater than or less than 1?

10. Is the reciprocal of a mixed number greater than or less than 1?

....

SUMMING IT UP

11. Use what you have learned about reciprocals to answer the following questions about these numbers: $\frac{10}{9}$, $1\frac{1}{2}$, $\frac{7}{8}$, $\frac{1}{3}$, and 5.

   a. Which numbers have reciprocals less than 1?

   b. Which number has the reciprocal closest to 0?

   c. Which number has the reciprocal closest to 1?

   d. Which number has a whole number as its reciprocal?

12. Write a rule for finding the reciprocal of a number.

13. What numbers have reciprocals less than 1? Greater than 1?

MATH LOG

What are two ways you can check to see if two numbers are reciprocals?

DIVIDING BY FRACTIONS

In this lesson, you will discover a way to divide a whole number by a fraction. Work in pairs. You will need the recording sheet.

You can use a number line to show division of a whole number by a fraction. Start with the example $4 \div \frac{1}{3}$. How many thirds are there in 4? Use the number line below to find the answer.

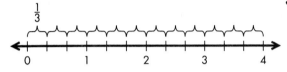

There are 12 thirds in 4. So, $4 \div \frac{1}{3} = 12$.

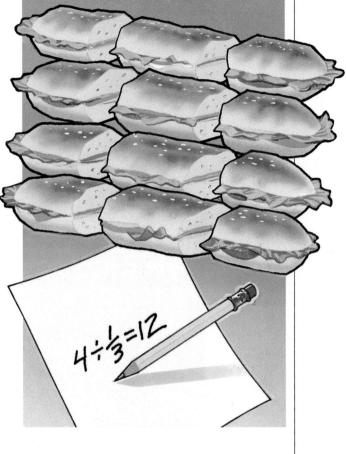

1. Compare the two number sentences $4 \div \frac{1}{3} = 12$ and $4 \times 3 = 12$. What is similar about the two sentences? What is different?

2. Use a number line to show $8 \div \frac{1}{2}$. How many halves are there in 8?

3. What is $8 \div \frac{1}{2}$? What is 8×2? What is the relationship between $\frac{1}{2}$ and 2?

Complete Chart A on your recording sheet. Use a number line when you need to.

4. Look at Chart A. Compare the answers to each set of multiplication and division sentences. What do you notice?

5. Use what you have learned so far to predict each quotient.

   a. $3 \div \frac{1}{5}$ b. $5 \div \frac{1}{4}$ c. $4 \div \frac{1}{2}$ d. $7 \div \frac{1}{8}$

Use a number line to check your predictions.

CHART A

Division Sentence	Reciprocal of Fraction	Multiplication Sentence
$4 \div \frac{1}{3} = 12$	$\frac{3}{1}$, or 3	$4 \times 3 = 12$
$8 \div \frac{1}{2} =$		$8 \times 2 =$
$3 \div \frac{1}{2} =$		$3 \times 2 =$
$2 \div \frac{1}{4} =$		
$5 \div \frac{1}{5} =$		
$1 \div \frac{1}{9} =$		

Now find the quotient of $4 \div \frac{2}{3}$. Notice that the numerator of the fraction is greater than 1. You can also show this division on a number line. How many two thirds are there in 4?

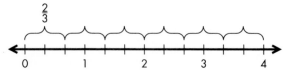

There are 6 two thirds in 4. So, $4 \div \frac{2}{3} = 6$.

6. Compare the two number sentences $4 \div \frac{2}{3} = 6$ and $4 \times \frac{3}{2} = 6$. What is similar about the two sentences? What is different?

7. Use a number line to show $3 \div \frac{3}{4}$. How many three fourths are there in 3?

8. What is $3 \div \frac{3}{4}$? What is $3 \times \frac{4}{3}$? What is the relationship between $\frac{3}{4}$ and $\frac{4}{3}$?

CHART B

Division Sentence	Reciprocal of Fraction	Multiplication Sentence
$4 \div \frac{2}{3} = 6$	$\frac{3}{2}$	$4 \times \frac{3}{2} = 6$
$3 \div \frac{3}{4} =$		$3 \times \frac{4}{3} =$
$2 \div \frac{2}{5} =$		$2 \times \frac{5}{2} =$
$6 \div \frac{2}{3} =$		
$5 \div \frac{5}{6} =$		
$1 \div \frac{2}{4} =$		

Complete Chart B on your recording sheet. Use a number line when you need to.

9. Look at Chart B. Compare the answers of each set of multiplication and division sentences. What do you notice?

10. Write your prediction for each quotient.

   a. $2 \div \frac{2}{3}$ b. $4 \div \frac{2}{5}$ c. $6 \div \frac{3}{8}$ d. $4 \div \frac{2}{7}$

   Use a number line to check your predictions.

....
SUMMING IT UP

11. Write a rule for dividing whole numbers by fractions.

12. Use your rule to write the quotient.

   a. $5 \div \frac{1}{3}$ b. $3 \div \frac{3}{5}$ c. $8 \div \frac{1}{4}$ d. $8 \div \frac{2}{3}$ e. $6 \div \frac{3}{4}$

13. Discuss your rule with the class.

CALCULATOR OR PENCIL AND PAPER

There are 125 students who have signed up to take dance lessons. A full dance class has 16 students. How many students will be in the class that is not filled?

You could use a calculator or pencil and paper to find $125 \div 16$.

The calculator can be used to find the number of people in the class that is not filled, but it requires more steps. Because of this, you might find paper and pencil easier to use when a remainder is needed.

> By using pencil and paper, you can tell that the remainder is 13. The class that is not filled will have 13 students.

> The calculator tells you that $125 \div 16 = 7.8125$. This means that there will be 7 full classes. However, 8125 or 0.8125 is not the number of people in the class that is not filled.

$$\begin{array}{r} 7 \text{ R}13 \\ 16 \overline{\smash{)}125} \\ -112 \\ \hline 13 \end{array}$$

....

INDEPENDENT PRACTICE

Solve each problem. Write whether you used pencil and paper or a calculator.

1. Suppose the dance teacher divides the 125 students into groups of 9 instead of 16. Now how many students will be in the class that is not full?

2. The 81 girls taking dance lessons need sequined headbands for a recital. The headbands come in packages of 12. How many packages does the teacher need to order?

3. For the opening number, the teacher places the 125 students in rows of 15.
   a. How many full rows will there be?
   b. How many students will be in the row that has less than 15?

4. At the end of the year, the students will have their pictures taken in their dance outfits. The teacher places the students in groups of 10 for the pictures. How many students will be in the picture that has fewer than 10 students?

SECTION REVIEW

for pages 336–342

Copy and complete. Write each sentence.

1. $\frac{2}{4} \times \frac{\blacksquare}{2} = \frac{8}{8} = 1$

2. $\frac{5}{\blacksquare} \times \frac{8}{5} = \frac{40}{40} = 1$

3. $\frac{5}{2} \times \frac{2}{5} = \frac{\blacksquare}{\blacksquare} = 1$

4. $\frac{2}{3} \times \frac{\blacksquare}{\blacksquare} = \frac{6}{6} = 1$

5. $9 \times \frac{\blacksquare}{9} = \frac{9}{9} = 1$

6. $4 \times \frac{\blacksquare}{\blacksquare} = \frac{4}{4} = 1$

Write the reciprocal of each number.

7. $\frac{1}{3}$

8. $\frac{3}{4}$

9. $\frac{5}{4}$

10. 3

11. 7

12. $1\frac{2}{3}$

13. $2\frac{3}{10}$

14. $5\frac{4}{5}$

Use the number line to find each quotient.

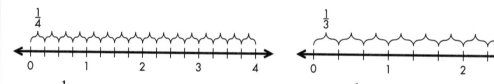

15. $4 \div \frac{1}{4} = \blacksquare$

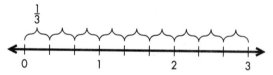

16. $3 \div \frac{1}{3} = \blacksquare$

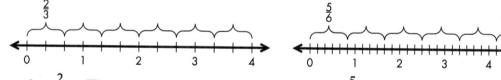

17. $4 \div \frac{2}{3} = \blacksquare$

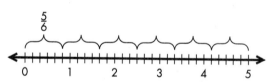

18. $5 \div \frac{5}{6} = \blacksquare$

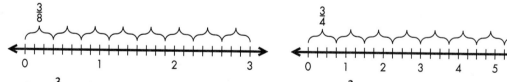

19. $3 \div \frac{3}{8} = \blacksquare$

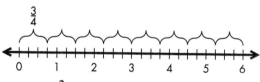

20. $6 \div \frac{3}{4} = \blacksquare$

Write each quotient. Use a number line if you need to.

21. $2 \div \frac{1}{4}$

22. $3 \div \frac{1}{8}$

23. $3 \div \frac{3}{4}$

24. $6 \div \frac{3}{5}$

CHAPTER REVIEW

Language Connection

In this chapter you learned to multiply and divide fractions several ways. You used repeated-addition sentences, models, and a number line.

What else could you have used if you were teaching someone to multiply and divide fractions? Suppose you could use any objects. What would you choose and why?

Test ●●●●●●●

Write the product in simplest form.

1. $\frac{2}{5} \times 9$

2. $\frac{1}{4} \times \frac{2}{3}$

3. $17 \times \frac{1}{8}$

4. $\frac{3}{4} \times \frac{1}{3}$

5. $\frac{1}{6}$ of 24

6. $\frac{3}{5} \times \frac{5}{8}$

7. $\frac{1}{2}$ of 30

8. $\frac{7}{8} \times \frac{1}{2}$

9. $\frac{1}{3}$ of 9

10. $\frac{4}{5} \times \frac{1}{5}$

11. $\frac{7}{12} \times 1$

12. $\frac{7}{8} \times \frac{1}{3}$

13. $8 \times \frac{6}{5}$

14. $\frac{2}{3} \times \frac{5}{6}$

15. $\frac{7}{10}$ of 10

16. $\frac{3}{4} \times \frac{1}{4}$

Write the reciprocal of the number.

17. $\frac{3}{10}$

18. $\frac{7}{8}$

19. $\frac{5}{2}$

20. $\frac{2}{3}$

21. 3

22. 5

23. 7

24. 10

25. $5\frac{3}{10}$

26. $3\frac{2}{3}$

27. $4\frac{4}{5}$

28. $7\frac{1}{12}$

Write the quotient. Use a number line if you need to.

29. $4 \div \frac{1}{3}$ **30.** $2 \div \frac{1}{5}$ **31.** $3 \div \frac{3}{5}$ **32.** $3 \div \frac{3}{8}$

33. $2 \div \frac{1}{3}$ **34.** $4 \div \frac{1}{5}$ **35.** $6 \div \frac{3}{5}$ **36.** $6 \div \frac{3}{8}$

PROBLEM SOLVING

Solve each problem.

37. There are 18 girls and 12 boys in Raoul's class. One third of the students take gymnastics. How many students in Raoul's class take gymnastics?

38. There are 9 students working on the class mural. Two thirds of them are boys. How many girls are working on the mural?

39. Elijah's science teacher wants the class to spend $\frac{1}{3}$ of the $\frac{3}{4}$-hour science period outdoors. If the class goes outdoors at 8:30, at what time should they come back in?

40. Brittany is buying a new pair of socks for the Fourth of July. The sale price is $\frac{3}{4}$ off the regular price of $4. How much money will Brittany save by buying the socks on sale?

CUMULATIVE REVIEW

Compare. Write >, <, or =.

41. $\frac{1}{2} \bullet \frac{5}{11}$ **42.** $1\frac{7}{9} \bullet 1\frac{7}{8}$ **43.** $2\frac{3}{5} \bullet 2\frac{6}{10}$ **44.** $\frac{1}{4} \bullet \frac{4}{20}$

Write the answer in simplest form.

45. $\frac{9}{10} - \frac{2}{3}$ **46.** $\frac{4}{5} + \frac{2}{7}$ **47.** $\frac{5}{6} - \frac{3}{8}$ **48.** $\frac{3}{10} + \frac{3}{4}$

EXCURSION
USING TECHNOLOGY

MULTIPLYING FRACTIONS

Sometimes, the answers you get on a calculator are not exactly right, especially when you compute with fractions.

Multiply: $\frac{1}{4} \times 4$

Using mental math, you know that:

$$\frac{1}{4} \times 4 = 1$$

Many calculators do not allow you to input fractions. You can calculate with fractions by writing them as decimals and then computing.

● Use a calculator to find an equivalent decimal for the fraction

$\frac{1}{4} \times 4$

$\frac{1}{4} = $ ⬚1⬚ ⬚÷⬚ ⬚4⬚ ⬚=⬚ ⬚0.25⬚

● Multiply.

$0.25 \times 4 = 1$

1. Compare the answers found using mental math and using a calculator. What do you notice?

2. Use mental math to find each answer.

   a. $\frac{1}{5} \times 5$ b. $\frac{1}{3} \times 3$

3. Use a calculator to find each answer in exercise 2.

4. Compare the answers to exercises 2 and 3. What do you notice?

5. First use paper and pencil or mental math to find each product. Then use a calculator.

   a. $\frac{2}{5} \times 5$ b. $\frac{2}{3} \times 3$

6. Copy and complete the chart.

Multiply	Product	
	Paper and Pencil or Mental Math	Calculator
$\frac{2}{4} \times 4$		
$\frac{5}{6} \times 6$		
$\frac{2}{7} \times 7$		
$\frac{3}{8} \times 8$		
$\frac{8}{9} \times 9$		
$\frac{7}{10} \times 10$		
$\frac{1}{11} \times 11$		

7. Predict which problems a calculator will give the exact answers for.

   a. $\frac{3}{4} \times 4$ b. $\frac{2}{6} \times 3$ c. $\frac{4}{7} \times 7$ d. $\frac{7}{8} \times 8$

8. Write each product in exercise 7, using mental math or paper and pencil and then using a calculator. Check your predictions.

9. Write two multiplication problems that the calculator will give an exact answer for. One of the factors should be a fraction.

10. Write two multiplication problems that the calculator will not give an exact answer for. One of the factors should be a fraction.

RATIO, PERCENT, AND PROBABILITY

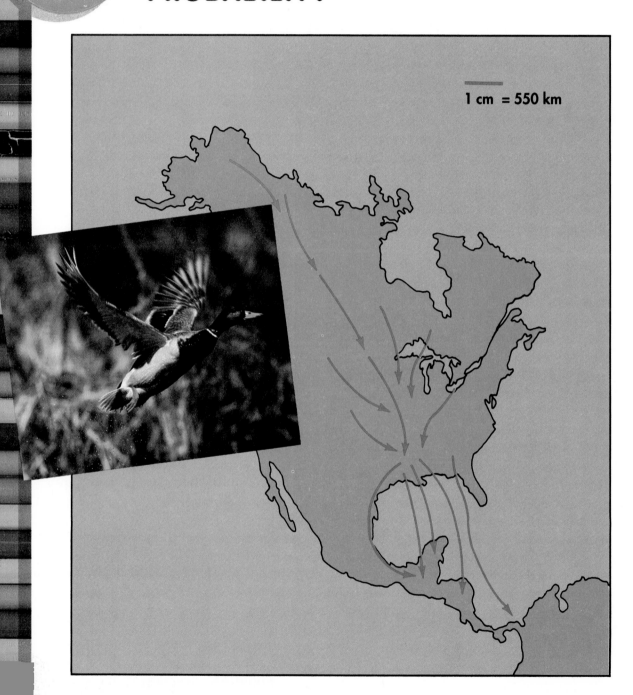

1 cm = 550 km

Connections

Science

Migration During the year, many animals move, or **migrate**, from one place to another. Some animals move to find food or water. Others migrate to escape cold winter weather. Many birds fly from north to south each year. Perhaps you have seen a V-shaped flock of Canada geese flying high overhead during the fall season.

Another bird that migrates is the Mallard duck. You may be surprised to learn how far these ducks will fly to find warm weather. Use a metric ruler to measure the length of the arrows on the map below. According to the map scale, 1 centimeter is equal to 550 kilometers. Therefore, 2 cm is equal to 1100 km, 3 cm is equal to 1650 km, and so on. How far do some of these ducks fly?

Find out about other animals that migrate a great distance. Use a map to describe how far they travel. Be sure to include a map scale.

EXPLORING RATIO

The Color Counter Game is played with two jars of counters like the ones shown. If you pick a blue counter, you get a point. Of course, you must pick without looking. But you do get to decide which jar you will pick from.

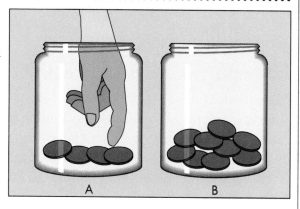

1. Which jar has more blue counters?

▶ To compare the number of blue and red counters in a jar, you can subtract:

Jar A: 3 − 1 = 2   Jar B: 6 − 3 = 3

There are 2 more blue counters than red counters in Jar A.

There are 3 more blue counters than red counters in Jar B.

2. Suppose you decided to pick from the jar with the greater difference between blue and red counters. Which jar would you choose?

▶ Another way to compare blue and red counters is with a **ratio**. A ratio is used to compare two quantities.

In Jar A, the ratio of blue counters to red counters is 3 to 1.

In Jar B, the ratio of blue counters to red counters is 6 to 3.

You can also describe the ratios in this way:

In Jar A, there are 3 blue counters for every red one.

In Jar B, there are two blue counters for every red one.

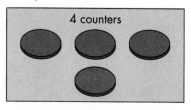
4 counters

9 counters

3. If you were deciding which jar to choose from based on ratios, which jar would you choose?

4. Does comparing by subtracting or by ratios give you the information you need for choosing jars?

Tell which jar of each pair gives you a better chance of
picking a blue counter. Use ratios to explain your choice.

5.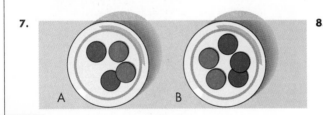

6.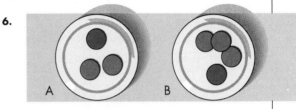

7.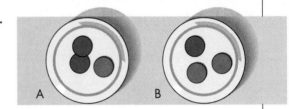

8.

SUMMING IT UP

Select the information that will help you decide. Write *a* or *b*. Explain.

9. You have to decide how many red
counters to add to a jar so that the
number of red counters will equal
the number of blue counters.
  a. The jar has 3 more blue counters
  than red ones.
  b. The jar has 3 blue counters for
  every red counter.

10. You have to decide if you have a
very good chance of picking a
blue counter.
  a. The jar has 3 more blue
  counters than red ones.
  b. The jar has 3 blue counters for
  every red counter.

PROJECT • Game

Play in pairs. You will need 8 blue counters,
8 red counters, and 2 bags.
  a. Partner A puts some counters of each color
  in each bag.
  b. Partner B looks in each bag and chooses
  one to pick a counter from.
  c. Partner A shakes the bag, and partner B picks
  a counter from it without looking. If the
  counter is blue, partner B gets one point.
  d. Repeat with partner B setting up the
  counters in each bag and partner A picking.
  e. The first person to score 5 points wins.

351

RATIOS

Sam likes to look at the fish tank in the pet store. He sees there are 5 Calico Goldfish and 2 Fantail Goldfish.

Remember: you can use a ratio to compare quantities. The ratio of Calico Goldfish to Fantail Goldfish is 5 to 2.

There are three ways to write a ratio:

5 to 2   5:2 $\frac{5}{2}$

In this form, the ratio looks like a fraction.

For each of these you say, "5 to 2."

The order of numbers in a ratio is very important. Just as $\frac{5}{2}$ is not the same fraction as $\frac{2}{5}$, the ratio 5 to 2 is not the same ratio as 2 to 5.

Think

- What would you write for the ratio of Fantail Goldfish to Calico Goldfish? The ratio of Fantail Goldfish to the total number of fish?

GUIDED PRACTICE

Decide whether the ratio is correct. Write *yes* or *no*. If it is not correct, tell why not.

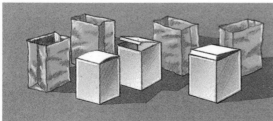

1. bags to boxes   4:3

2. compact disks to tapes   8 to 4

Use the picture below. Write each ratio three different ways.

3. dogs:cats

4. guinea pigs:dogs

5. cats:pets

INDEPENDENT PRACTICE

Write each ratio three different ways.

6.

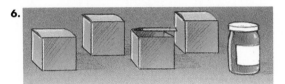

6. **a.** boxes to jars

  b. jars to boxes

8. 9 flutes to 12 clarinets

7.

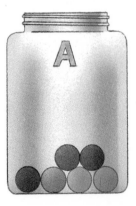

7. **a.** red marbles to green marbles

  b. green marbles to yellow marbles

9. 40 altos to 12 sopranos

Write each ratio using the word *to*.

10. $\frac{7}{11}$

11. $\frac{21}{7}$

12. $\frac{14}{29}$

Problem Solving

13. Suppose you need a red counter. Which jar should you pick from if you have to pick without looking?

14. John mixed 2 cans of frozen juice with 8 cans of water. Jim mixed 1 can of frozen juice with 2 cans of water. Whose juice had a stronger flavor?

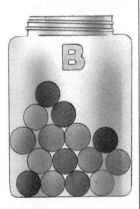

CHALLENGE • Language Arts

Write two words that have a ratio of:
a. vowels to consonants of 2:3.
b. *e*'s to *r*'s of 2:1.

UNDERSTANDING EQUAL RATIOS

Joan and Phil are making lemonade. They use a mixture of juice from 2 lemons and 3 tablespoons (tbsp) of sugar for every quart of water.

1. What is the ratio of lemons to tablespoons of sugar for 1 quart?

2. Joan and Phil make 2 quarts of lemonade.
   a. How many lemons do they use?
   b. How many tablespoons of sugar do they use?

3. Should the 2-quart mixture of lemonade taste the same as the 1-quart mixture?

4. Copy and complete the table. Draw pictures if you need to.

Quarts of Lemonade	1	2	3	4	5	6
Lemons	2	4				
Tbsp of sugar	3	6				

5. What is the ratio of lemons to tablespoons of sugar for 2 quarts?

6. What is the ratio of lemons to tablespoons of sugar for 5 quarts?

Joan and Phil are using the same recipe for different amounts of lemonade. Look at the numbers in your table. For the taste to stay the same, the ratio of lemons to tablespoons of sugar stays the same.

$$\text{So, } \frac{2}{3} = \frac{4}{6} = \frac{6}{9} = \frac{8}{12} = \frac{10}{15} = \frac{12}{18}$$

These are **equal ratios**.

7. You know that to find equivalent fractions you multiply the numerator and denominator by the same number. Would this help you find equal ratios for $\frac{2}{3}$?

354

8. Write two more equal ratios for $\frac{2}{3}$.

After tasting the first batch of lemonade, Joan and Phil thought it needed more lemon juice. They decided to keep the amount of sugar the same but to double the number of lemons used for each quart of water.

9. How many lemons would they now use for 1 quart of water?

10. What is the ratio of lemons to tablespoons of sugar for this new recipe?

11. Is the ratio for the new recipe equal to the ratio for the old recipe?

12. If this new recipe were doubled to make 2 quarts of lemonade, what would be the ratio of lemons to tablespoons of sugar?

13. Is $\frac{4}{3}$ equal to $\frac{8}{6}$? Explain.

14. Suppose Bonnie looked at the new recipe and said, "There is 1 more lemon than tablespoon of sugar. For 5 quarts, I will use 20 lemons and 19 tablespoons of sugar." Would Bonnie's lemonade be the same as Joan and Phil's? Explain.

....

SUMMING IT UP

15. A bowl of fruit punch contains 3 cups of pineapple juice and 2 cups of cranberry juice. How many cups of each juice would you need to make 4 bowls of punch? What is the ratio of juices for 1 bowl? For 4 bowls?

16. Write the letter of each ratio that is equal to $\frac{4}{5}$.

   a. $\frac{9}{10}$ b. $\frac{8}{10}$ c. $\frac{4}{10}$ d. $\frac{12}{15}$ e. $\frac{16}{20}$

17. Write two equal ratios for each.

   a. $\frac{1}{3}$ b. $\frac{2}{5}$ c. $\frac{3}{10}$ d. $\frac{5}{16}$ e. $\frac{6}{5}$

EQUAL RATIOS

Soup to Nuts is a specialty shop that makes many different mixtures of nuts.

The ratio of pecans to almonds in the Special Mix is 3 to 5, or $\frac{3}{5}$. The ratio of pecans to almonds in the Deluxe Mix is 6 to 10, or $\frac{6}{10}$.

Are the ratios of pecans to almonds the same for each mix?

To find if ratios are the same, or equal, you can multiply or divide.

● **Multiply.**

$$\frac{3}{5} \overset{\times\,2}{\underset{\times\,2}{=}} \frac{6}{10}$$

● **Divide.**

$$\frac{6}{10} \overset{\div\,2}{\underset{\div\,2}{=}} \frac{3}{5}$$

Since $\frac{6}{10} = \frac{3}{5}$, we say they are equal ratios. So, the ratio of pecans to almonds is the same for each mix.

Think

● How is finding equal ratios like finding equivalent fractions?

Other Examples

The ratio 1 to 4 is equal to the ratio 4 to 16.

$$\frac{1}{4} \overset{\times\,4}{\underset{\times\,4}{=}} \frac{4}{16}$$

15:12 is equal to 5:4

$$\frac{15}{12} \overset{\div\,3}{\underset{\div\,3}{=}} \frac{5}{4}$$

Decide if the ratios are equal. Write *yes* or *no*.

1. 5 to 3 and 10 to 8   **2.** 4 to 1 and 12 to 3   **3.** 2:5 and 4:10

4. 2:3 and 6:9   **5.** $\frac{6}{3}$ and $\frac{16}{13}$ **6.** $\frac{3}{4}$ and $\frac{30}{40}$

Write the missing number.

7. 4 to 2 is the same as 12 to ▆.   **8.** 3 to 5 is equal to ▆ to 10.

9. $\frac{3}{5} = \frac{▆}{20}$ **10.** $\frac{18}{6} = \frac{▆}{1}$ **11.** $\frac{10}{50} = \frac{2}{▆}$ **12.** $\frac{5}{4} = \frac{15}{▆}$

13. Soup to Nuts mixes almonds and cashews in a ratio of 6 to 5 in its Gourmet Mix. If one batch of this mix has 18 ounces of almonds, how many ounces of cashews does it have?

Write the letter of the equal ratio.

14. 1:4   **a.** 4:1   **b.** 2:8   **c.** 8:4   **d.** 3:6

15. $\frac{1}{7}$ **a.** $\frac{7}{14}$ **b.** $\frac{7}{1}$ **c.** $\frac{8}{56}$ **d.** $\frac{7}{28}$

16. 3 to 2   **a.** $\frac{4}{6}$ **b.** 7:6   **c.** $\frac{3}{4}$ **d.** 15 to 10

Write the missing number.

17. 3 to 1 is the same as 15 to ▆.   **18.** 16 to 8 is equal to ▆ to 2.

19. $\frac{3}{9} = \frac{1}{▆}$ **20.** $\frac{36}{45} = \frac{4}{▆}$ **21.** $\frac{▆}{6} = \frac{4}{24}$ **22.** $\frac{4}{7} = \frac{▆}{21}$

23. $\frac{▆}{9} = \frac{1}{3}$ **24.** $\frac{10}{16} = \frac{5}{▆}$ **25.** $\frac{1}{▆} = \frac{5}{5}$ **26.** $\frac{9}{12} = \frac{▆}{36}$

Problem Solving Use the information on page 356.

27. Soup to Nuts is making a batch of its Special Mix. If it contains 6 ounces of pecans, how many ounces of peanuts should be added?

28. If a batch of the Deluxe Mix contains 3 ounces of pecans, how many ounces of peanuts should it contain?

WRITE A WORD EQUATION

Writing a word equation can help you see how different things are related.

One time, we wrote a word equation to help a director film scenes for a movie . . .

OUR PROBLEM

The movie director used 15 feet of film to shoot the rain scene, which lasted 10 seconds. She wanted to know how many feet of film would be needed to shoot the chase scene, which lasts 60 seconds.

OUR SOLUTION

First, we realized that film always moves at the same speed. So, we wrote two equal ratios.

$$\text{Ratio of film to time for rain scene} = \text{Ratio of film to time for chase scene}$$

Next, we wrote out the ratios in words to get a word equation:

$$\frac{\text{film for rain scene}}{\text{time for rain scene}} = \frac{\text{film for chase scene}}{\text{time for chase scene}}$$

Then, we put in the numbers that we knew:

$$\frac{15 \text{ ft}}{10 \text{ s}} = \frac{\text{film for chase scene}}{60 \text{ s}}$$

We multiplied to find the missing number.

$$\frac{15 \text{ ft}}{10 \text{ s}} \underset{\times 6}{\overset{\times 6}{=}} \frac{?}{60 \text{ s}}$$

15 ft × 6 = 90 ft

We decided that 90 feet of film would be needed for the chase scene.

Complete the word equation. Use it to solve the problem.

1. Joe is making a big batch of Nutty Nut muffins. He plans to use a 32-ounce bag of walnuts. How much flour should he use so the Nutty Nut muffins will taste the way they should?

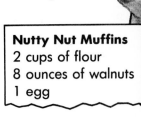

Nutty Nut Muffins
2 cups of flour
8 ounces of walnuts
1 egg

ratio of nuts to flour in recipe $=$ ratio of nuts to flour in Joe's batch

$$\frac{\text{oz of nuts in recipe}}{\text{cups of flour in recipe}} = \frac{\text{oz of nuts in Joe's Batch}}{\blacksquare}$$

Work in pairs. Complete each word equation. Use it to solve the problem.

2. Jack is on a 9-mile canoe trip. He left camp at 1:00 P.M. At 1:20 P.M., he passed the trading post, which is 3 miles down the river. If he keeps going at the same speed, when will the trip end?

ratio of miles to minutes for the first part of the trip $=$ ratio of miles to minutes for the whole trip

$$\frac{\text{miles in first part}}{\text{minutes in first part}} = \frac{\blacksquare}{\blacksquare}$$

3. Sue mixes a paint sample. She mixes 12 drops of blue paint with 8 drops of white to get just the right shade of light blue. She wants to make a bucketful of that same color. If she uses 6 jars of blue paint, how many jars of white paint should she use?

Ratio of drops of blue to drops of white in sample $=$ Ratio of jars of blue to jars of white in bucket

$$\frac{\blacksquare}{\blacksquare} = \frac{\blacksquare}{\blacksquare}$$

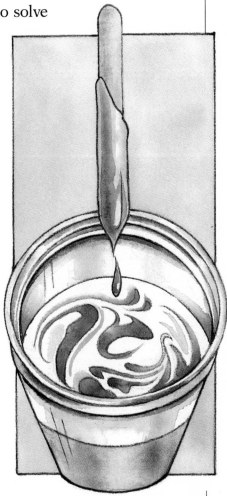

EXPLORING PERCENT

In this lesson, you will explore the meaning of **percent**. Percent is a ratio based on the number 100.

You will need the recording sheet.

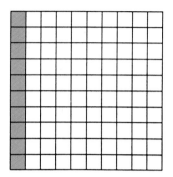 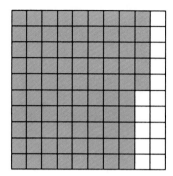

10 out of 100 is $\frac{10}{100}$, or 10 percent.   85 out of 100 is $\frac{85}{100}$, or 85 percent.

You write: 10%   You write: 85%

1. Write each ratio as a percent. Use %.

   a. $\frac{50}{100}$ b. $\frac{30}{100}$ c. $\frac{5}{100}$ d. $\frac{73}{100}$ e. $\frac{0}{100}$

Shade $\frac{1}{2}$ of grid A on your recording sheet.

2. How many squares are shaded? How many squares are in the whole grid?

3. Write the ratio of shaded squares to the total number of squares.

4. What percent of the grid is shaded?

5. How do the shaded and unshaded areas compare? Is one area greater than the other?

Use grid B on your recording sheet. Shade a square area 5 squares long and 5 squares wide. This area represents $\frac{1}{4}$ of the grid.

6. Write the ratio of shaded squares to the total number of squares.

7. What percent of the grid is shaded?

8. On grid A, 50% of the area is shaded. On grid B, 25% of the same-size area is shaded. How does the 25% area compare to the 50% area?

Shade $\frac{3}{4}$ of grid C on your recording sheet.

9. What is the ratio of shaded squares to the total number of squares?

10. What percent of the grid is shaded?

11. Show each ratio by shading the grid on your recording sheet.

a. $\frac{15}{100}$ **b.** $\frac{42}{100}$ **c.** $\frac{60}{100}$

12. Write the percent for each ratio in exercise 11.

....

SUMMING IT UP

13. Look at the grids you have shaded. Complete Chart A on your recording sheet.

Chart A

	Number of Shaded Squares	Total Number of Squares	Ratio of Shaded Squares to Total Squares	Percent Shaded
Grid A	50			50%
Grid B		100		
Grid C			$\frac{75}{100}$	
Grid D	15			
Grid E		100		42%
Grid F			$\frac{60}{100}$	

14. How would you show 100% on a grid?

15. Complete Chart B on your recording sheet.

16. What percent of each circle is shaded?

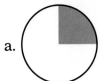

a.   b.   c.

Chart B

	Fraction of Squares Shaded	Percent Shaded
Grid A		
Grid B		
Grid C		

PERCENT

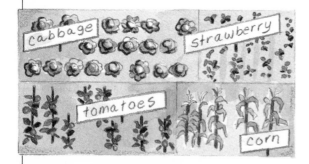

Willie's garden has four different crops. Estimate the percent of the garden that is planted with cabbage.

When you estimate percents, remember the following:

$$\frac{1}{4} = 25\% \qquad \frac{1}{2} = 50\% \qquad \frac{3}{4} = 75\%$$

Try to imagine $\frac{1}{2}$ and then $\frac{1}{4}$ of Willie's garden. The cabbage area is slightly greater than $\frac{1}{4}$, or 25% of the garden.

Since 30% is slightly greater than 25%, 30% is a reasonable estimate.

Think

- What other percent might be a reasonable estimate for the cabbage area?

- Explain how you would estimate what percent of the garden is planted with corn.

Other Examples

About 30% of the corn bread is gone.

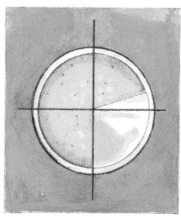

About 40% of the flag of Tanzania is blue.

About 75% of the wall is painted.

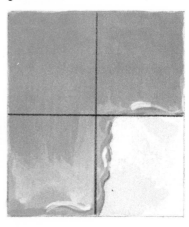

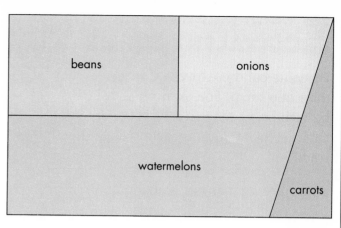

beans

onions

watermelons

carrots

1. Use the diagram. Estimate the percent of the garden that is planted with:
   a. beans.
   b. onions.
   c. watermelons.
   d. watermelons, carrots, or onions.

2. Is 50% a reasonable estimate for watermelons? Why or why not?

INDEPENDENT PRACTICE

Write the letter of the most reasonable estimate for the percent shaded.

3.

   a. 25%
   b. 50%
   c. 70%

4.

   a. 50%
   b. 70%
   c. 95%

5.

   a. 40%
   b. 50%
   c. 60%

6.

   a. 100%
   b. 95%
   c. 75%

Estimate what percent of each flag is blue.

7.

   Burma

8.

   Sweden

9.

   Solomon Islands

PROJECT • Art

Design and draw a garden planted with fruits and vegetables. Make sure your garden has about 25% strawberries, about 15% corn, and about 40% tomatoes. You can decide what to plant in the area left over. Label each area of the garden. Remember: a garden does not have to have a rectangular shape.

EQUIVALENT FORMS

Percents can be expressed in more than one form. For example, 30% can be written as the ratio 30:100. Percents can also be written as decimals and fractions.

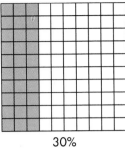

30%

30:100

▶ To write a percent as a decimal: 30% =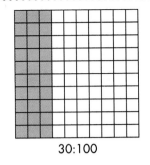

● Write the percent as a fraction with a denominator of 100.

$$30\% = \frac{30}{100}$$

● Write the equivalent decimal.

$$\frac{30}{100} = 0.30$$

So, 30% = 0.30.

▶ To write a decimal as a percent: 0.4 = ▇%

● Write the decimal as hundredths.

0.4 = 0.40 = 40 hundredths

$$40 \text{ hundredths} = \frac{40}{100}$$

$$\frac{40}{100} = 40\%$$

So, 0.4 = 40%.

▶ To write a percent as a fraction: 60% = ▇

● Write the percent as a fraction with a denominator of 100.

$$60\% = \frac{60}{100}$$

● Simplify if you can.

$$\frac{60}{100} \underset{\div\ 20}{\overset{\div\ 20}{=}} \frac{3}{5}$$

So, 60% = $\frac{3}{5}$.

▶ To write a fraction as a percent: $\frac{2}{5}$ = ▇%

● Find an equivalent fraction that has a denominator of 100.

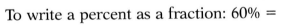

$$\frac{2}{5} \underset{\times\ 20}{\overset{\times\ 20}{=}} \frac{40}{100}$$

● Write the fraction as a percent.

$$\frac{40}{100} = 40\%$$

So, $\frac{2}{5}$ = 40%.

GUIDED PRACTICE

Write each percent as a fraction in simplest form.

1. 10%   **2.** 1%   **3.** 5%   **4.** 50%   **5.** 14%   **6.** 8%

Write each fraction as a percent.

7. $\frac{5}{20}$ **8.** $\frac{1}{5}$ **9.** $\frac{1}{25}$ **10.** $\frac{3}{4}$ **11.** $\frac{3}{5}$ **12.** $\frac{3}{10}$

Write each decimal as a percent.

13. 0.35   **14.** 0.80   **15.** 0.15   **16.** 0.66   **17.** 0.04   **18.** 0.09

19. Write each percent in exercises 1–6 as a decimal.

INDEPENDENT PRACTICE

Write each percent as a decimal and as a fraction in simplest form.

20. 60%   **21.** 4%   **22.** 23%   **23.** 70%   **24.** 20%   **25.** 48%

Copy and complete the table. Write the fractions in simplest form.

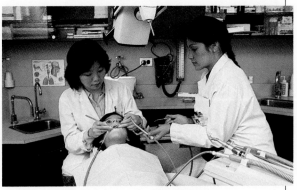

	Fraction	Percent	Decimal
26.	$\frac{4}{5}$	■	0.8
27.	■	15%	■
28.	■	■	0.09
29.	■	70%	■

Problem Solving Use the General Information section of your Data Book.

30. In 1979–1980, what fraction of 13-year-old children in the United States never had had a cavity?

31. In 1986–1987, what percent of 16-year-old children had had a cavity sometime in their life?

32. About half of which age group had been cavity-free in 1979–1980?

CHALLENGE • Visualization

Three views of one cube are shown at the right. Which letter is opposite the *H*?

FINDING PERCENT

Forty people were asked what they bought their fathers for Father's Day. The results are shown in the circle graph at the right. 50% of the people bought ties. How many people bought ties?

Find: 50% of 40

This problem can be done mentally.

50% of 40

$\frac{1}{2}$ of 40 o o o $\left(\ 50\% = \frac{1}{2}\ \right)$

$40 \div 2 = 20$

So, 50% of 40 is 20.

20 of the 40 people bought ties.

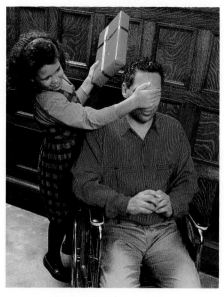

What 40 People Bought Dad for Father's Day

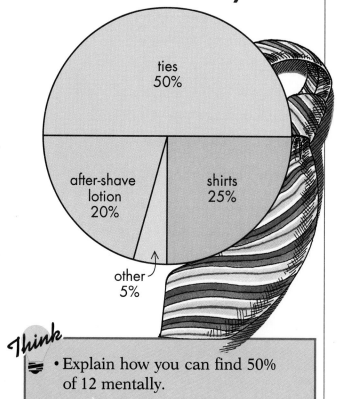

ties
50%

after-shave
lotion
20%

shirts
25%

other
5%

Think

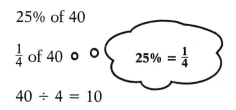

• Explain how you can find 50% of 12 mentally.

▶ How many of the 40 people bought shirts?

25% of 40

$\frac{1}{4}$ of 40 o o $\left(\ 25\% = \frac{1}{4}\ \right)$

$40 \div 4 = 10$

So, 10 people bought shirts.

Other Examples

Find 50% of 120.

$\frac{1}{2}$ of 120

$120 \div 2 = 60$

So, 50% of 120 is 60.

Find 25% of 8.

$\frac{1}{4}$ of 8

$8 \div 4 = 2$

So, 25% of 8 is 2.

GUIDED PRACTICE

Write the answer. Use mental math.

1. 50% of 8
2. 50% of 20
3. 25% of 12

4. 25% of 24
5. 50% of 60
6. 25% of 100

7. 25% of 160
8. 50% of 200
9. 50% of 140

10. How can finding the answer to exercise 3 help you find 75% of 12?

INDENDENT PRACTICE

INDEPENDENT PRACTICE

Write the answer. Use mental math.

11. 25% of 20
12. 25% of 16
13. 50% of 6

14. 50% of 14
15. 25% of 28
16. 25% of 32

17. 50% of 80
18. 50% of 100
19. 25% of 120

20. 25% of 240
21. 50% of 160
22. 50% of 400

Problem Solving Use mental math.

Tony has a job mowing lawns. Last week, he made $20. The circle graph shows what he did with the money.

23. How much money did Tony save?

24. How much money did he spend on movies?

25. How much did Tony spend on food and a gift together?

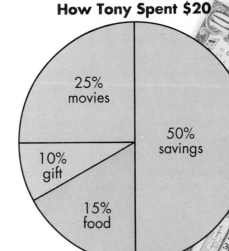

How Tony Spent $20

25% movies

50% savings

10% gift

15% food

MATH LOG

In your own words, tell how you would find 25% of a number.

PERCENT OF A NUMBER

The Madison Stationery Store sold $2750 worth of supplies last week. 10% of their total sales were from notepads. How many dollars worth of notepads did they sell?

Find: 10% of $2750

One way to find a percent of a number is to write the percent as a decimal. Then multiply.

10% = 0.10

0.10 × $2750 = $275

So, the store sold $275 worth of notepads.

Think

• Since 10% of $2750 is $275, what is a quick way to find 20% of $2750? 30% of $2750?

On Sunday, the store sold $550 worth of supplies. 10% of their total sales that day were donated to a shelter for the homeless. How much money did the store donate?

Find: 10% of $550

Another way to find the percent of a number is to write the percent as a fraction. Then multiply.

$10\% = \frac{10}{100}$, or $\frac{1}{10}$

$\frac{1}{10} \times \$550 = \$55$

So, the store donated $55.

Other Examples

Find: 38% of 2650
38% = 0.38
0.38 × 2650 = 1007

Find: 3% of 690

$3\% = \frac{3}{100}$

$\frac{3}{100} \times 690 = 20.7$

Write the percent of the number. Use mental math when you can.

1. 30% of 900   **2.** 50% of 10   **3.** 40% of 50   **4.** 75% of 120

5. 1% of 100   **6.** 20% of 300   **7.** 5% of 528   **8.** 25% of 40

9. When do you find it easier to compute the percent of a number using decimals? Using fractions?

....
INDEPENDENT PRACTICE

Write the percent of the number. Use mental math when you can.

10. 10% of 150   **11.** 20% of 50   **12.** 25% of 16   **13.** 4% of 404

14. 40% of 10   **15.** 90% of 50   **16.** 50% of 200   **17.** 42% of 150

18. 1% of 200   **19.** 25% of 8   **20.** 60% of 600   **21.** 40% of 1000

Problem Solving Use the Almanac section of your Data Book. You may use a calculator.

22. Is 35,000 more than or less than 75% of the seating capacity of Veteran's Stadium?

23. If 88% of the seats in Royals Stadium were filled, what percent of the seats were empty? How many seats were empty?

 **• Multiplying Fractions**

Multiply. Write the product in simplest form.

1. $\frac{5}{6} \times \frac{2}{5}$ **2.** $\frac{3}{5} \times \frac{3}{5}$ **3.** $\frac{7}{12} \times \frac{3}{8}$ **4.** $\frac{3}{4} \times \frac{2}{3}$

5. $\frac{5}{6} \times \frac{1}{2}$ **6.** $\frac{3}{10} \times \frac{1}{2}$ **7.** $\frac{1}{6} \times \frac{5}{8}$ **8.** $\frac{5}{6} \times \frac{2}{3}$

MENTAL MATH OR PAPER AND PENCIL

Beth trains for the marathon for 20 hours each week. Her weekly schedule is shown at the right. How many total hours will she spend doing each activity during one week?

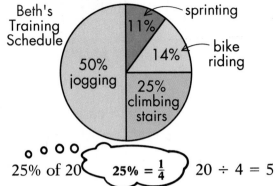

Beth's Training Schedule

sprinting 11%

bike riding 14%

50% jogging

25% climbing stairs

▶ Use mental math to find 50% and 25% of 20.

50% of 20 ⟨**50% = $\frac{1}{2}$**⟩ $20 \div 2 = 10$

So, 50% of 20 is 10. Beth will spend 10 hours jogging.

25% of 20 ⟨**25% = $\frac{1}{4}$**⟩ $20 \div 4 = 5$

So, 25% of 20 is 5. Beth will spend 5 hours climbing stairs.

▶ 11% of 20 and 14% of 20 are difficult to compute mentally. You may need to use paper and pencil to find the answers.

Write each percent as a decimal. Then multiply.

11% of 20 ⟨**11% = 0.11**⟩ $0.11 \times 20 = 2.2$

So, 11% of 20 is 2.2. Beth will spend 2.2 hours sprinting.

14% of 20 ⟨**14% = 0.14**⟩ $0.14 \times 20 = 2.8$

So, 14% of 20 is 2.8. Beth will spend 2.8 hours riding a bike.

Think

• Is it faster to use mental math or paper and pencil to compute 50% of 12? Explain why.

INDEPENDENT PRACTICE

Solve each problem. Write whether you used mental math or paper and pencil.

1. 50% of 16   2. 40% of 35   3. 9% of 100   4. 25% of 40

5. 85% of 20   6. 37% of 100   7. 50% of 50   8. 30% of 180

9. 25% of 80   10. 25% of 14   11. 10% of 30   12. 50% of 7

SECTION REVIEW

for pages 350–370

Write the letter of the correct answer.

1. Jim has 300 comic books in his collection. He has 100 issues of Blue Avenger, 50 issues of Green Cape, and 150 issues of Detective Dan. What is the ratio of issues of Green Cape to issues of Detective Dan?

   a. $\frac{150}{50}$ b. $\frac{50}{150}$ c. $\frac{50}{300}$ d. $\frac{150}{300}$

2. Out of the 200 books in Carolyn's library, 50 are mysteries, 60 are science fiction, and the rest are nonfiction books. What is the ratio of nonfiction books in Carolyn's library to the total number of books?

   a. $\frac{110}{90}$ b. $\frac{110}{200}$ c. $\frac{90}{200}$ d. $\frac{90}{110}$

3. From which jar would you have the best chance of picking a red marble?

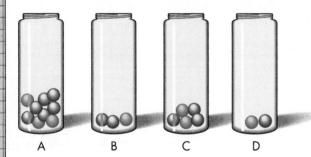

   A   B   C   D

4. Cindy is mixing paint. To get the color she wants, she mixes 1 gallon of red paint with 2 gallons of blue paint. She wants to make a large quantity of the color. If she uses 4 gallons of red paint, how many gallons of blue paint should she use?

   a. 8   b. 5   c. 4   d. 6

Write the missing number.

5. $\frac{2}{4} = \frac{4}{\blacksquare}$ 6. $\frac{4}{2} = \frac{8}{\blacksquare}$ 7. $\frac{\blacksquare}{4} = \frac{5}{20}$ 8. $\frac{9}{36} = \frac{1}{\blacksquare}$

Write each percent as a fraction in simplest form.

9. 18%   10. 24%   11. 40%   12. 80%   13. 65%

Write each percent as a decimal.

14. 20%   15. 75%   16. 80%   17. 97%   18. 2%

Write the percent of the number.

19. 50% of 14   20. 90% of 1000   21. 75% of 400

22. 10% of 1000   23. 50% of 544   24. 25% of 1540

EXPLORING PROBABILITY

At the beginning of this chapter, you used ratios in the Color Counter Game. You decided which jar would give you a better chance of picking a blue counter. In this lesson, you can use what you know about ratios to help you guess the number of counters of each color in a mystery bag.

Work in pairs. You will need a paper bag and counters of at least three different colors.

1. Copy the charts below.

Color	Trial 1	Trial 2	Trial 3	Total

	Prediction		
Color	After Trial 1	After Trial 2	After Trial 3

2. Ask your partner to put four counters into a bag. Your partner should use three different colors. You should not see which colors are used.

Trial 1

3. Without looking into the bag, pick out one counter. Write the color. Record a tally mark in the column marked *Trial 1* on your chart.

4. Return the counter to the bag. Repeat the procedure for a total of four picks. Start a new row if a new color appears. Record each tally mark in the *Trial 1* column.

Look at the tally marks on your chart. Predict what color the counters in the bag are. Predict how many counters of each color are in the bag. Write your prediction in the chart. Maybe you need more data.

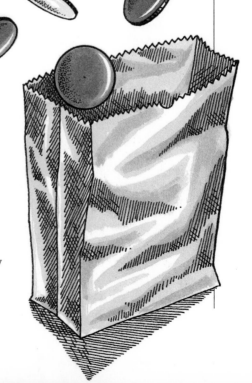

▶ **Trial 2**

5. Pick four more counters from the bag. Record each of these picks in the column marked *Trial 2*. Again, be sure to return the counter to the bag after each pick.

Look at the tally marks again. Now how many counters of each color do you think are in the bag? Write your prediction. Have you changed your mind since your first prediction? Perhaps some more data will help.

▶ **Trial 3**

6. Again, pick four counters from the bag and record your results under *Trial 3*.

7. Now count up the tally marks for all three trials and write the total in the right-hand column.

8. Write your final prediction for the number of counters of each color found in the bag.

9. Ask your partner to show you the counters. Check your final prediction.

10. Repeat the activity. This time, you choose the counters, and let your partner predict the colors and numbers.

SUMMING IT UP

11. How accurate was your first prediction?

12. How accurate was your final prediction?

13. Which color had a ratio of picks to total picks of about 1:2?

14. Which colors had a ratio of picks to total picks of about 1:4?

PROBABILITY AND RATIO

You may have heard people talk about the chance of something happening. **Probability** is a measure of chance. If you spin the spinner at the right, you have an equal chance of landing on green, red, or blue.

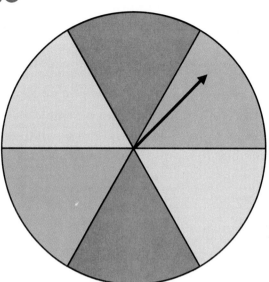

Probability can be written as a ratio. For example, the ratio of green spaces to total spaces on the spinner is 2 to 6. When you spin, you have a 2 out of 6, or a $\frac{2}{6}$, chance of landing on green.

Think

• What is the chance of landing on a color that is not green?

Since there are no orange spaces, the probability of landing on orange is 0 out of 6, or $\frac{0}{6}$. You can say the probability of landing on orange is zero.

Other Examples

If one of these fish is caught, the probability of it being yellow is 2 out of 5, or $\frac{2}{5}$.

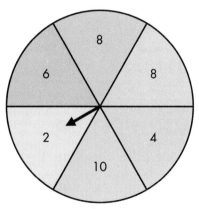

The probability of spinning an even number is 6 out of 6, or $\frac{6}{6}$. You can say the probability of spinning an even number is 1.

GUIDED PRACTICE

Write each probability in the form of a ratio.

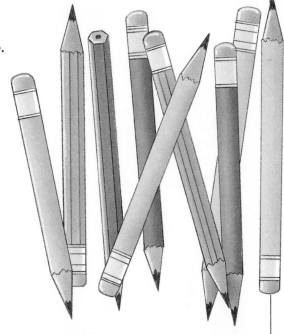

1. If you cover your eyes, what is the probability of choosing a yellow pencil?

2. What is the probability of choosing a red or a yellow pencil?

3. What is the probability of choosing a red pencil with no eraser?

4. What is the chance of choosing a blue pencil with no eraser?

5. Is there a greater chance of choosing a red pencil or a yellow pencil? Explain.

INDEPENDENT PRACTICE

Write each probability in the form of a ratio.

6. If you cover your eyes, what is the chance of choosing an apple?

7. What is the probability of choosing a red apple?

8. What is the chance of choosing a green apple?

9. What is the chance of choosing a wormy apple?

10. Write the probability of choosing a wormy green apple.

CHALLENGE • Critical Thinking

The table shows the results of 50 spins. Draw a spinner divided into 6 equal sections. According to the data, how do you think the spinner was colored? Color your copy of the spinner.

Red	𝍱𝍱𝍱 𝍱𝍱𝍱 𝍱𝍱𝍱 𝍲	$\frac{16}{50}$
Blue	𝍱𝍱𝍱 𝍲𝍲𝍲	$\frac{8}{50}$
Green	𝍱𝍱𝍱 𝍱𝍱𝍱 𝍱𝍱𝍱 𝍲𝍲	$\frac{17}{50}$
Yellow	𝍱𝍱𝍱 𝍲𝍲𝍲𝍲	$\frac{9}{50}$

WRITE A WORD EQUATION

Some word equations use ratios. Some do not. When you write a word equation to help solve a problem, make sure the equation fits the problem.

"Mom, I think some money fell through this hole in my pocket," John said. His mother had given him a $20 bill to buy dog food. John had a $10 bill, a $1 bill, and a quarter left. The dog food had cost $8.45. John and his mother want to know how much money he lost.

Think

• What happened to the $20 John started with?

• Which of the two word equations below would help you find out how much John lost?

A. $\dfrac{\text{Amount left}}{\text{Amount started with}} = \dfrac{\text{Amount lost}}{\text{Amount spent}}$

B. Amount started with − Amount spent − Amount left = Amount lost

Use one of the word equations to find out how much money John lost.

Think

• How can you check your answer?

Read the problem. Use one of the word equations to help solve it.

1. Julio bought a book and a tape. On the way home, he remembered that the book cost $2.69, but he couldn't remember what the tape cost. He had paid with a $10 bill and received $5.50 in change. What did the tape cost?

A. Amount paid − Change received = Cost of book + Cost of tape

B. $\dfrac{\text{Cost of book}}{\text{Cost of tape}} = \dfrac{\text{Change received}}{\text{Amount paid}}$

Solve each problem. Work in pairs. Use a word equation when it helps.

2. Liz's class is having a book sale. This morning they had 163 books. Then Liz brought in 2 dozen more books. At the end of the sale, they had 127 books left. How many books did Liz's class sell today?

3. Jill makes a small jug of fruit punch by mixing 2 cups of orange juice with 5 cups of grape juice. If Jill uses 15 cups of grape juice, how much orange juice should she use?

4. The Fido-Bowl factory makes 450 puppy dishes a day. They have 3 machines to make the dishes. If they buy 2 more machines, how many puppy dishes will they be able to make each day?

CALCULATOR OR MENTAL MATH

A calculator is a useful tool for computing quickly. But sometimes using mental math to solve a problem is quicker than using a calculator. For each problem you should use the method that works best for you.

Questions to consider:

- Will entering the problem into a calculator take too much time?

- Do I know a mental math strategy that will help me solve the problem?

INDEPENDENT PRACTICE

Solve each problem. Write whether you used a calculator or mental math.

1. $80 + 120 + 30$

2. $12.2 + 6.205$

3. 10×530

4. $12 \times \frac{1}{2}$

5. $\frac{3}{4} \times \frac{1}{5}$

6. $6000 \div 8$

7. $63 + 200$

8. 25.1×7.8

9. $240 \div 6$

10. 50% of 12

11. 25% of 160

12. $\$10.00 - \$7.99$

13. $\frac{3}{9} + \frac{2}{9}$

14. 32×56

15. $2 \times 7 \times 5$

16. 25% of 40

Problem Solving

17. Star Video sells 3 cassette tapes for $12.75. Discount Sound sells the same tapes separately for $4.15 each. Which store sells 3 tapes for less?

18. Ted buys a package of video tapes for $13.99. He pays with a $20 bill. How much is his change?

19. Write a word problem of your own that would be easier to do:
    a. with mental math.
    b. with paper and pencil.

Write what the probability would be if the cards were placed face down on the table.

1. What is the probability of picking a vowel?

2. What is the chance of picking the letter *N*?

3. What is the probability of picking the letter *S*?

4. What is the chance of picking a consonant?

5. What is the probability of picking the letter *E*?

6. About how many times out of 50 do you predict you might pick a consonant?

The numbers 1–6 are written on the cube.

7. What numbers have a $\frac{1}{6}$ probability of being rolled?

8. What is the chance of an odd number being rolled?

9. What is the probability of an even number being rolled?

10. Is there a greater chance of rolling a number less than 4 or greater than 4?

11. Write a number that has a 0 probability of being rolled.

CHAPTER REVIEW

Language Connection

Dan wanted a spotted puppy. He called three pet stores. The first pet shop owner said, "Two eighths of our pups have spots." The second one said, "Twenty-five percent of our pups have spots." The third one said, "You have one chance out of four of finding a spotted pup here."

Dan didn't know where to go. His mother drove to the closest store, mumbling "equal ratios." What did she mean?

Test ● ● ● ● ● ● ●

Use the picture below. Write each ratio three different ways.

1. pears: apples

2. fruit: yellow fruit

3. red apples: yellow apples

Decide whether the ratios are equal. Write *yes* or *no*.

4. 3:5 and 5:8   **5.** 2:4 and 8:16   **6.** 12:3 and 20:5   **7.** 6:3 and 7:4

Write the missing number.

8. $\dfrac{6}{8} = \dfrac{\blacksquare}{12}$ **9.** $\dfrac{11}{22} = \dfrac{4}{\blacksquare}$ **10.** $\dfrac{4}{5} = \dfrac{\blacksquare}{15}$ **11.** $\dfrac{12}{10} = \dfrac{6}{\blacksquare}$

Write each percent as a decimal and as a fraction. Write each fraction in simplest form.

12. 8%   **13.** 13%   **14.** 5%   **15.** 55%

Write the percent of the number.

16. 20% of 60   **17.** 75% of 28   **18.** 5% of 80   **19.** 12% of 400

Use the spinner at the right. Write the probability of spinning each color.

20. yellow   **21.** purple

22. blue   **23.** not red

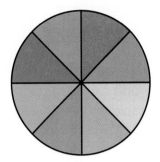

PROBLEM SOLVING

Solve each problem.

24. A store is selling everything at 40% off the regular price. How much will Jordan save if she buys a TV and a VCR that regularly sell for $550 and $350?

25. Ramona bought 3 small model cars, 4 large model cars, and 2 model airplanes at the hobby store. What is the ratio of the number of model airplanes Ramona bought to the number of model cars she bought?

26. Sonya is using a recipe that calls for 5 cups of flour and 2 cups of walnuts. She wants to use 6 cups of walnuts. How many cups of flour does Sonya need?

27. Glen reads that 85% of the people in his town recycle their newspapers. What fraction of the people in town do not recycle?

CUMULATIVE REVIEW

Write the answer in simplest form.

28. $4\frac{5}{8}$
$-\ 3\frac{3}{8}$

29. $12\frac{4}{5}$
$-\ 8\frac{7}{10}$

30. $6\frac{1}{4}$
$+\ 1\frac{5}{12}$

31. $9\frac{1}{3}$
$-\ 2\frac{3}{5}$

Write the product in simplest form.

32. $6 \times \frac{7}{8}$ **33.** $\frac{7}{10}$ of 8   **34.** $\frac{2}{5} \times 6$ **35.** $\frac{3}{4}$ of 9

Excursion

USING TECHNOLOGY

DOING AN EXPERIMENT

When you toss a coin there are two ways it can land. It can land heads up, or it can land tails up. What if you toss it many times? It should land heads up half the time and tails up half the time. Does that mean that if you toss a coin 10 times, you will get 5 heads and 5 tails?

1. Flip a coin 10 times. How many heads did you get? How many tails?

The program below models tossing a coin. The number 1 is considered to be heads, and the number 2 is considered to be tails. There are three parts to the program:

• The program asks you how many tosses you want to model.

• The computer randomly chooses either 1 (heads) or 2 (tails) for each toss.

• The computer prints out the number of heads and tails it got.

Type the BASIC program into your computer.

```
10 REM      DOING AN EXPERIMENT
15 PRINT
20 PRINT "HOW MANY TOSSES"
30 PRINT "WOULD YOU LIKE";
40 INPUT N
45 PRINT
50 FOR X = 1 TO N
60 LET F = INT (RND (1) * 2) + 1
70 IF F = 1 THEN LET H = H + 1
```

```
80 IF F = 2 THEN LET T = T + 1
90 NEXT X
100 PRINT "NUMBER OF HEADS ="; H
110 PRINT "NUMBER OF TAILS ="; T
115 PRINT
999 END
```

2. Use the computer program to model 10 tosses. Repeat for a total of 3 trials. Do you get 5 heads and 5 tails each time?

3. Copy the chart below. Run the program for 10 trials of 10 tosses each. Complete the chart.

Results	Trial Number										Total
	1	2	3	4	5	6	7	8	9	10	
Heads											
Tails											

4. Find the average number of heads for 10 tosses. Remember: average is the total number divided by the number of trials.

5. Find the average number of tails for 10 tosses.

6. If you toss a coin 10 times, will you get 5 heads and 5 tails every time?

7. If you toss a coin 10 times over and over again, will the average number of heads and tails be close to 5?

CHAPTER 13

AREA AND VOLUME

Connections

Estimation

Gift Wrapping Look at the beautiful packages on page 384. Each gift is neatly wrapped and trimmed. Have you ever tried to gift wrap a package? If you have, then you know it's not as easy as it looks.

When you wrap a package, you always seem to have too much or too little paper. Perhaps it would be a good idea to practice your wrapping skills. You will need a small box, a sheet of newspaper, a scissors, and tape.

Look at the size of the box and estimate the amount of paper that will be needed to cover it. HINT: Try to imagine the size of the box when it is completely unfolded. Then, cut out a piece of newspaper, and wrap the box as neatly as possible. Compare your results with others in your class.

AREA OF A RECTANGLE

The number of units needed to cover a surface is called its **area**. Some of the units used to measure area are:

square inches, or in.²

square feet, or ft²

square centimeters, or cm²

square meters, or m²

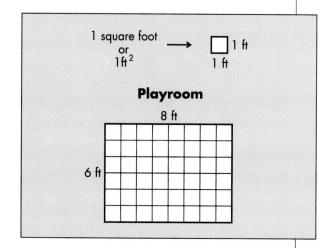

1 square foot
or
1 ft² → ☐ 1 ft
            1 ft

Playroom
8 ft
6 ft

▶ To find the area of the playroom, you need to find how many square feet it takes to cover the room.

You could count all the squares to find the area of the playroom. You could also use the rule:

Area of a rectangle = length × width
$$A = l \times w$$
For the playroom: $A = 8 \text{ ft} \times 6 \text{ ft}$
$$A = 48 \text{ ft}^2$$

The area of the playroom is 48 square feet.

Think

- List the lengths and widths of three other rectangular rooms that would have an area of 48 square feet.

- How is area different from perimeter?

▶ A square is a special kind of rectangle. Since all 4 sides have the same length, you can use a different form of the area rule:

Area of a square = length of side × length of side

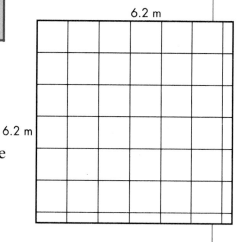

6.2 m

6.2 m

So, for the square shown: $A = s \times s$
$$A = 6.2 \text{ m} \times 6.2 \text{ m}$$
$$A = 38.44 \text{ m}^2$$

The area of the square is 38.44 square meters.

GUIDED PRACTICE

Write the area of each rectangle. Remember to use square units in your answer.

1. length = 7 in.
   width = 6 in.

2. length = 3 cm
   width = 4.5 cm

3. side = 5 yd

4. Which is a larger area, 42 square inches or 25 square feet?

INDEPENDENT PRACTICE

Write the area of each rectangle. Remember to use square units in your answer.

5.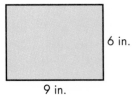
   6 in.
   9 in.

6.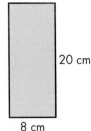
   20 cm
   8 cm

7.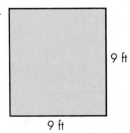
   9 ft
   9 ft

8. side = 1.2 mm

9. length = 4 in.
   width = 9 in.

10. length = 22.5 m
    width = 20.2 m

11. length = 35 mi
    width = 23 mi

12. length = 200 cm
    width = 30 cm

13. side = 40 cm

Problem Solving

14. A 5-inch by 7-inch picture is put in a frame that measures 11 inches long by 8 inches wide. Will the picture take up more than half the area inside the frame?

15. One can of paint covers an area of about 400 square feet. Benjamin used a new can to paint a wall with an area of 90 square feet. About how much area will the leftover paint cover?

16. The area of a square puzzle when it is put together is 4 square feet. How long is each side?

17. Write two word problems of your own, one to find the area of a square and the other to find the area of a rectangle.

AREA

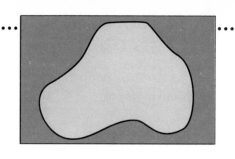

Inez is building a model of a golf course. She needs to design a sand trap with an area between 10 and 20 square units. Will the design at the right fit her model?

She estimates the area of the sand trap by using a grid.

There are 8 whole squares covered by the sand trap. The partly covered squares have a sum of about 5 whole squares.

Altogether, the area of the sand trap is about 8 + 5, or 13 square units.

Yes, this sand-trap design will fit Inez's model.

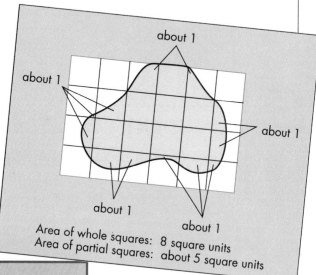

about 1

about 1

about 1

about 1

about 1

Area of whole squares: 8 square units
Area of partial squares: about 5 square units

Think

• How can you tell that the area of the sand trap is greater than 8 square units but less than 24 square units?

GUIDED PRACTICE

Estimate the area. Give your answer in square units.

1.

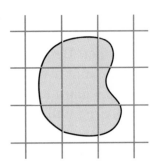

2.

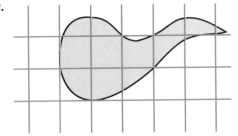

3. Explain why there can be more than one reasonable estimate for exercises 1 and 2.

PROJECT • Problem Solving

Inez has five more sand traps to design. She has decided the areas of the different traps should be as follows:

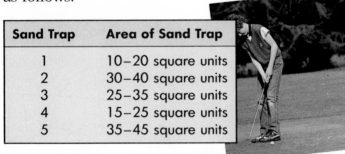

Sand Trap	Area of Sand Trap
1	10–20 square units
2	30–40 square units
3	25–35 square units
4	15–25 square units
5	35–45 square units

Work in pairs to help Inez design the sand traps for the golf course. You will need centimeter squared paper.

• Each sand trap must fit within the designated area.

• Each sand trap must have a different shape.

• Each sand trap must be made up of curves, not line segments.

Label each sand trap with your estimate of its area.

Compare your method for designing the sand traps and your sand-trap designs with those of another pair of students. How are your methods similar? Different? How are your designs similar? Different?

MATH LOG

What method for designing sand traps worked best for you? Explain.

PROBLEM SOLVING
USING STRATEGIES

Work in groups. Use the blueprint of Autumn Waves Theme Park to solve each problem. Each square represents 100 square feet (100 ft²).

If you get stuck, remember....

Tips for Problem Solving

on pages 448–449

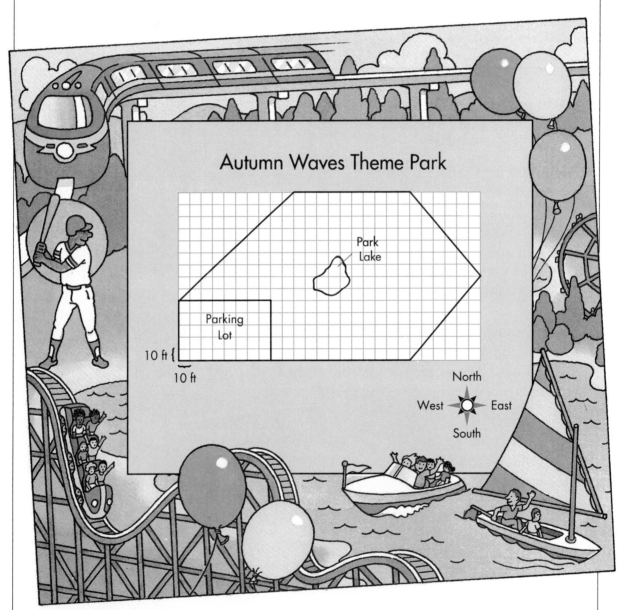

Autumn Waves Theme Park

Park Lake

Parking Lot

10 ft {

10 ft

North

West — East

South

1. Is your classroom larger than or smaller than the area represented by one of the squares in the park?

2. Is the area of Park Lake more than or less than 1000 square feet? Explain.

3. Look at the cover of the booklet about the park shown at the right. What number can they safely put in the statement? Explain.

4. The park owners plan to build a monorail ride from the northeast corner of the parking lot to the most eastern point of the park. Make a sketch to show where the monorail would be. About how long would the monorail be?

5. The owners of the theme park would like to buy the three triangular sections of land around the park so that the park is rectangular. If they buy the land, will the parking lot cover more than $\frac{1}{10}$ of the total park? Explain.

6. The three sections the owners want to buy are about 4500 square feet, 2100 square feet, and 2100 square feet. The sections are for sale at $2.25 per square foot. Will $10,000 be enough to buy all the sections? Explain.

7. A parking lot can hold 1 car for every 50 square feet. How can the present parking lot dimensions be changed so that 100 cars can fit?

PROJECT • Critical Thinking

8. Design your own theme park. Use centimeter squared paper to make a blueprint for a rectangular park 20 cm long and 15 cm wide. Divide your park into at least 3 different sections. Name them. Show where items like these will go:

   • rides   • places to eat

   • parking lot   • paths

   Choose sizes that make sense.

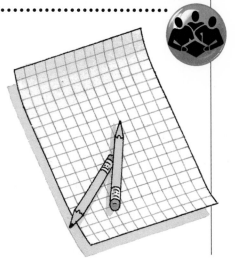

AREA OF A TRIANGLE

In this lesson, you will explore the area of triangles. Work in pairs. You will need geoboard dot paper, a ruler, and tracing paper.

▶ You can use the area of a rectangle to find the area of a right triangle.

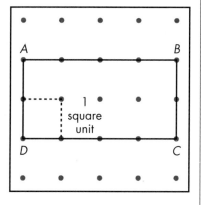

Draw rectangle *ABCD* on your geoboard dot paper.

1. What is the area of rectangle *ABCD*?

Remember: a triangle with an angle of 90° is a right triangle. A diagonal divides a rectangle into two right triangles.

Draw the diagonal shown in rectangle *ABCD*.

2. Use tracing paper. Are the two right triangles congruent?

3. What fraction of the rectangle does each right triangle take up?

4. If the area of rectangle *ABCD* is 8 square units, what is the area of each triangle?

5. Draw each of the rectangles below on your geoboard dot paper. Write the area of each rectangle.

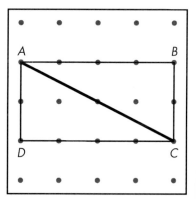

a.
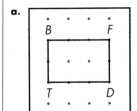

b.
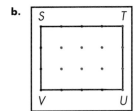

c.
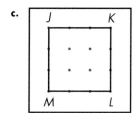

6. Draw a diagonal in each of the rectangles in exercise 5 as shown. Are the two triangles formed in each rectangle congruent?

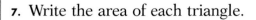

7. Write the area of each triangle.

   a. △*BFD*   **b.** △*SVU*   **c.** △*JKL*

You can also use the area of a rectangle to find the area of triangles that are not right triangles.

To find the area of △CDE, draw two rectangles that have $\overline{CA}$ for one side.

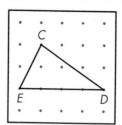

 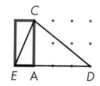

8. What is the area of rectangle CAEF? Rectangle CADB?

9. Use tracing paper. Are the two triangles in rectangle CAEF congruent? Are the two triangles in rectangle CADB congruent?

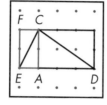 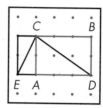

10. What is the area of △CAE? △CAD?

11. How can you use your answers to exercise 10 to find the area of △CDE?

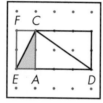 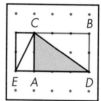

12. What is the area of △CDE?

⋯⋯⋯⋯⋯⋯⋯⋯

SUMMING IT UP

Copy each triangle onto geoboard dot paper. Write the area of each. In exercises 16–18, use the dotted lines to start your rectangles.

13.
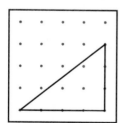

14.
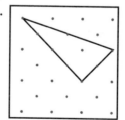

15.
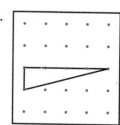

16.
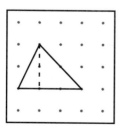

17.
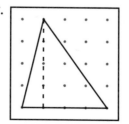

18.
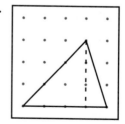

FINDING MORE THAN ONE ANSWER

Some problems have more than one answer. Keep this in mind as you solve each problem. You will need squared paper.

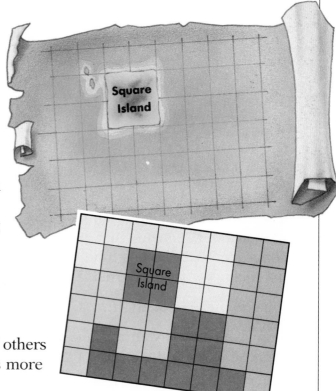

1. Two treasure hunters are looking for a sunken ship in the waters around Square Island. They have 4 days to search the section shown on the map. The diagram to the right shows their plan for covering an equal area each day.

Copy the map, and make a different plan for covering an equal area each day.

Compare your plan with the plans of others in your class. As you can see, there is more than one possible plan.

Find at least two answers for each problem.

2. The treasure hunters need to drive across Square Island from point *A* to point *C*. What is the shortest route they can take?

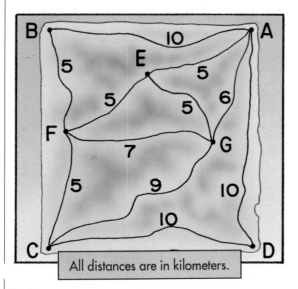

All distances are in kilometers.

3. The two treasure hunters found seven pieces of gold. How can they divide the pieces, without breaking any, so that they each get the same amount of gold? All the pieces are the same thickness. List the pieces each should receive.

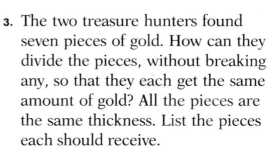

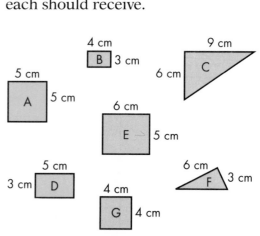

SECTION REVIEW

for pages 386–394

Write the area of each rectangle. Remember to use square
units in your answer.

1.
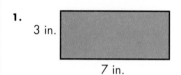
3 in.
7 in.

2.
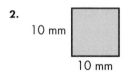
10 mm
10 mm

3.
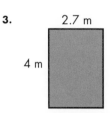
2.7 m
4 m

4.
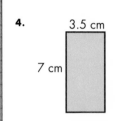
3.5 cm
7 cm

5.
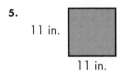
11 in.
11 in.

6.
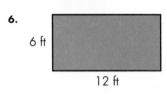
6 ft
12 ft

7.
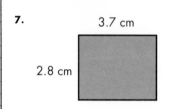
3.7 cm
2.8 cm

8.
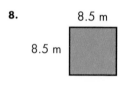
8.5 m
8.5 m

9.
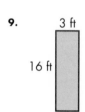
3 ft
16 ft

10. side = 8 cm

11. side = 4 in.

12. side = 21 m

13. length = 18 yd
width = 4 yd

14. length = 27 ft
width = 5 ft

15. length = 25.2 mm
width = 10 mm

Solve each problem.

16. A rectangular stage is 18.5 meters
long and 15 meters wide. What is
the area?

17. A dance floor is square and has an
area of 64 square meters. How
long is each side?

18. Roy's front yard is 55 meters long
and 24 meters wide. His backyard
is 30 meters long and 29 meters
wide. Which yard covers a larger
area?

19. Blair has a space on her wall 32
inches long and 20 inches wide.
Will a poster measuring 28 inches
long and 24 inches wide fit in the
space?

SOLIDS

Here are some solids.

triangular pyramid	pentagonal prism	sphere	cylinder	cone

Think

- Which of the solids above has no surfaces that are flat? One flat surface? Two flat surfaces? More than two flat surfaces?

Two kinds of solids are **pyramids** and **prisms**.

These are pyramids.

These are prisms.

 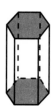

Some parts of pyramids and prisms are labeled below.

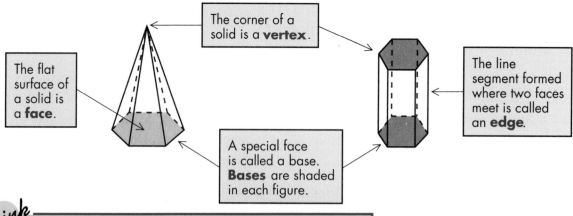

The corner of a solid is a **vertex**.

The flat surface of a solid is a **face**.

The line segment formed where two faces meet is called an **edge**.

A special face is called a base. **Bases** are shaded in each figure.

Think

- How are pyramids and prisms similar? Different?

396

GUIDED PRACTICE

Copy and complete the table below.

Solid	Bases	Other Faces	Edges	Vertices
1. Triangular Prism				
2. Pentagonal Prism				
3. Pentagonal Pyramid				
4. Hexagonal Pyramid				

5. Name the different polygons that are the bases for the solids in exercises 1–4. Remember: the bases are shaded.

....

PROJECT • Critical Thinking

For this project you will need tape, scissors, colored pencils, centimeter squared paper, and a copy of the nets shown at the right.

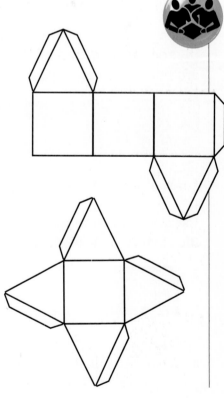

a. On the net for each solid, color one face blue and the edges red. Label the polygons that make up the figure.

b. Cut out and tape each net to form a solid. Make sure the blue and red marks and the polygon labels are on the outside of the finished figure.

c. See if you can make a different net for each of the solids you made.

d. Choose a prism from page 396 or 397 that you would like to make. Use centimeter squared paper to draw a net for the prism. Cut it out and tape it together. Make corrections in your pattern if you need to.

SURFACE AREA AND SOLIDS

In this lesson, you will explore how to measure the surface of a solid. You will need connecting cubes and the recording sheet. Work in small groups.

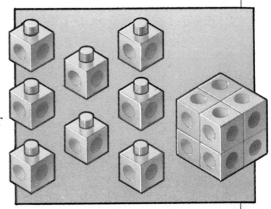

At the right is a solid formed by putting together 8 cubes. Each cube has 6 flat faces. In this lesson we will call the faces unit squares. When a solid is made from the cubes, not all the unit squares of each cube are visible.

Use 8 connecting cubes to make a solid like the one shown.

1. How many unit squares do you see on the top of the solid?

2. Turn the solid so you can see the bottom. How many unit squares are visible on the bottom?

3. How many unit squares do you see on each of the other 4 sides of the solid?

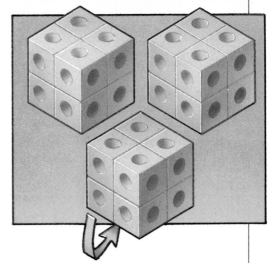

When you find the sum of the unit squares on the top, bottom, and all sides of a figure, you are finding the **surface area** of the solid.

	top	side 1	side 2	side 3	side 4	bottom
square units	4	4	4	4	4	4

4. What is the surface area of the solid you made?

Use your cubes to make each solid below. Then write the surface area of each.

5.   6.   7.

8. What is the least surface area you got for an 8-cube solid? The greatest surface area?

Use 12 cubes. Make a solid figure.

Number of Cubes ___12___

9. What is the surface area of the new solid?

10. Use 12 cubes to make a solid with:
   a. the least surface area.
   b. the greatest surface area.

Record your work in Chart A on your recording sheet.

CHART A

	Surface Area	Sketch of Solid
Least		
Greatest		

Use 13 cubes to make a solid with:
11. the least surface area.
12. the greatest surface area.

Record your work in Chart B on your recording sheet.

Number of Cubes ___13___

CHART B

	Surface Area	Sketch of Solid
Least		
Greatest		

SUMMING IT UP

13. Predict which of the solids below, made with 16 cubes, will have the least surface area. Predict which will have the greatest surface area.

a. 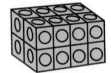   b. 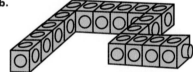   c.

Check your predictions.

14. What kind of shape has the least surface area?

15. What kind of shape has the greatest surface area?

CHALLENGE • Visualization

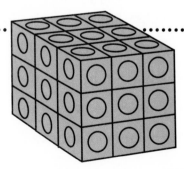

Suppose the solid at the right fell into a bucket of purple paint. How many of the cubes making up the solid would have 3 purple faces? How many would have 2? 1? 0?

399

VOLUME OF A RECTANGULAR PRISM

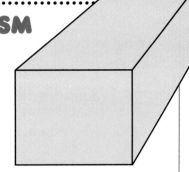

Volume is the amount of space taken up by a solid. To measure the volume of a solid, imagine the solid as a container that can be filled with cubes.

Think

- Why is it better to use a cube to measure volume than a sphere or cylinder?

Some of the units used to measure volume are:

cubic centimeters, cm³

cubic meters, m³

cubic inches, in.³

cubic feet, ft³

1 cubic centimeter (1cm³)

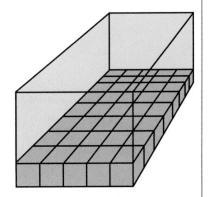

To find the number of cubes in one layer, you can count the cubes or multiply the length by the width.

$$8 \times 5 = 40$$

To find the total number of cubes, or the volume, of a rectangular prism, multiply the number of cubes in the first layer by the number of layers.

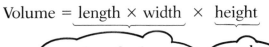

Volume = length × width × height

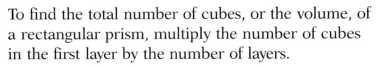

> number of cubes in one layer

> number of layers

Volume =   8 × 5   × 4   = 160

The volume of the solid is 160 cm³.

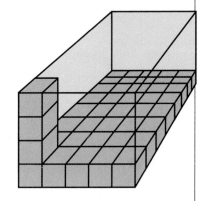

Find the volume of a cracker box that is 8 inches long, 3 inches wide, and 4 inches high.

Volume = length × width × height

Volume = 8 in. × 3 in. × 4 in.

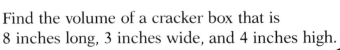

Volume = 24 in.² × 4 in.

The volume of the cracker box is 96 in.³

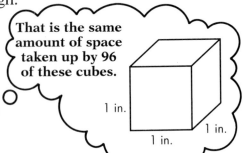

That is the same amount of space taken up by 96 of these cubes.

1 in.

1 in.

1 in.

GUIDED PRACTICE

Write the volume. Give your answer in cubic units.

1.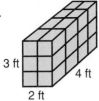

3 ft
4 ft
2 ft

2.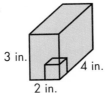

3 in.
4 in.
2 in.

3.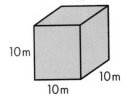

1.25 cm
2 cm
4 cm

4. Name one way you can check your answers to exercises 1–3.

....

INDEPENDENT PRACTICE

Write the volume. Give your answer in cubic units.

5.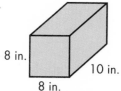

8 in.
10 in.
8 in.

6.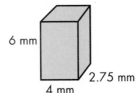

6 mm
2.75 mm
4 mm

7.

10 m
10 m
10 m

Write the missing measurement.

	Length	Width	Height	Volume
8.	4 ft	4 ft	4 ft	
9.	5 m		6 m	90 m³
10.	8 mm	7 mm		560 mm³

Problem Solving

11. Sarah's fish tank measures 20 inches long, 12 inches wide, and 10 inches high. The water line when the tank is filled is 1 inch from the top. What is the volume of the water in a filled tank?

12.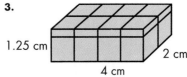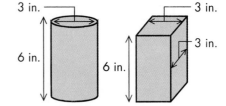

3 in.
6 in.
3 in.
3 in.
6 in.

Which has a greater volume, the cylinder or the prism? Explain.

13. Bill's refrigerator has a volume of 12 cubic feet. If the refrigerator is 2 feet wide and 2 feet long, how tall is it?

14. A box has a volume of 48 cubic centimeters. What could its height, length, and width be? Is there more than one answer? Explain.

VOLUME OF IRREGULAR SOLIDS

In this lesson, you will find the volume of solids with different shapes. You will need centimeter cubes and the recording sheet. Work in pairs.

The three solids at the right are rectangular prisms. Each solid is made of 20 centimeter cubes.

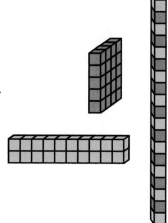

Use 16 centimeter cubes to build three different rectangular prisms.

1. Complete Table A on your recording sheet.
   Remember: volume = length × width × height.

TABLE A

	Length	Width	Height	Volume
Prism 1				
Prism 2				
Prism 3				

2. What do you notice about the volume of each prism?

3. Based on what you've learned so far, what would be the volume of a solid made from 15 centimeter cubes?

You can use the volume of rectangular prisms to help you find the volume of many different solids.

4. What is the volume of prism A below? The volume of prism B? Each small cube is 1 cm³.

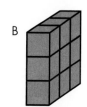

A   B

5. Suppose you combine prism A and prism B to make solid C. How would you find the volume of solid C?

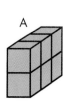
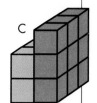

A   B   C

6. Use your cubes to make prisms A and B. Put them together to form a solid that is different from solid C. What is the volume of this new solid?

7. Build a solid from each pair of prisms shown in
Table B on your recording sheet. Sketch solid C.
Complete the table.

TABLE B

Prism A	Prism B	Solid C
Volume:	Volume:	Volume:
Prism A	**Prism B**	**Solid C**
Volume:	Volume:	Volume:

8. Use centimeter cubes to make solid D shown
at the right. Divide the solid into two prisms.
What is the volume of each prism? What is the
volume of solid D?

solid D

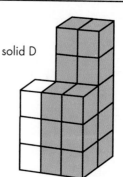

SUMMING IT UP

9. What do you know about the volume of all solids
built using 50 centimeter cubes?

10. How can knowing how to find the volume of a
rectangular prism help you to find the volume of
another solid?

Maintain • Division of Decimals

Write the quotient.

1. $5\overline{)5.05}$

2. $9\overline{)0.063}$

3. $3\overline{)0.606}$

4. $5\overline{)\$2}$

5. $0.7 \div 4$

6. $18.81 \div 9$

7. $0.915 \div 3$

8. $0.16 \div 4$

403

PROBLEM SOLVING

USING STRATEGIES

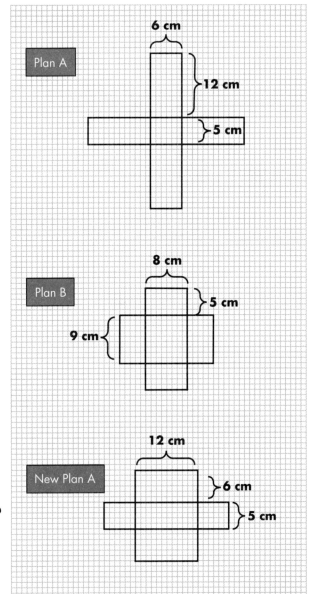

The Xavier Company makes boxes out of sheets of cardboard. A customer asks them to design a box with no top and a volume of 360 cubic centimeters. Two possible designs, Plan A and Plan B are shown.

Solve each problem.

1. How many square centimeters of cardboard does each plan use?

2. What is the volume of the box made from each of the plans?

3. The company wants to use the least possible amount of cardboard. Which plan should they choose? Why?

4. Imagine a new Plan A created by switching two of the dimensions in the original Plan A.
   a. What would be the volume of the box made from the new Plan A?
   b. Should the company choose the new Plan A over the original Plan A? Over Plan B? Explain.

PROJECT • Critical Thinking

Design an open box with the greatest possible volume from a sheet of centimeter squared paper (17 cm x 22 cm).

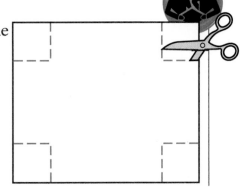

• Cut a square from each corner of the sheet of paper. Fold the remaining paper to make the box.
• Each dimension must be a whole number of centimeters.
• Write the volume of the box you designed.

404

SECTION REVIEW

for pages 396–404

Copy and complete the table.

	Solid		Bases	Other Faces	Edges	Vertices
1.		rectangular pyramid	1			
2.		triangular pyramid		3		
3.		pentagonal prism			15	
4.		hexagonal prism				12

Find the volume of each rectangular prism.
Give your answers in cubic units.

5. length = 8 cm
width = 3 cm
height = 2 cm

6. length = 7 in.
width = 5 in.
height = 1 in.

7. length = 8.8 cm
width = 7.3 cm
height = 2 cm

Write the missing measurement for each
rectangular prism.

	Length	Width	Height	Volume
8.	4 mm		7 mm	56 mm³
9.	20 cm	6 cm		2400 cm³
10.	11 in.		11 in.	968 in.³

Solve the problem.

11. The dolphin tank in the aquarium measures 20 m
long by 15 m wide by 8.25 m high. The water
line is 0.5 m from the top of the tank. What is
the volume of the water in the tank?

CHAPTER REVIEW

Language Connection

Words can be arranged in different ways. The words in this list have been arranged in alphabetical order. However, they could also be classified into two different groups. One group of words has to do with solids. The other group has to do with polygons. Put the words into the correct categories.

ALPHABETICAL ORDER

area	perimeter	side
base	prism	square units
cubic units	pyramid	triangle
face	rectangle	volume

Test •••••••

Find the area of the rectangle or square.

1.

4.9 ft

1.5 ft

2.

13 in.

13 in.

3.

36.5 cm

12.6 cm

4.

17 m

17 m

Use the figure to answer the question.

5. How many edges does the hexagonal prism have?

6. How many vertices does the pentagonal prism have?

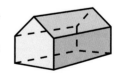

7. How many edges does the cube have?

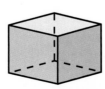

8. How many vertices does the pentagonal pyramid have?

Find the volume of each rectangular prism.

9.

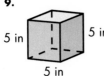
5 in   5 in
5 in

10.

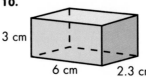
3 cm   6 cm   2.3 cm

11.

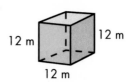
12 m   12 m
12 m

12. length = 7 ft
width = 5 ft
height = 1.3 ft

13. length = 8 in.
height = 8 in.
width = 8 in.

14. width = 10.25 m
height = 10 m
length = 10 m

PROBLEM SOLVING

Solve each problem.

15. A soccer field is 360 feet long and 225 feet wide. What is the area of the field?

16. Judge Kelley grows tomatoes in a square garden plot. The plot has an area of 36 square meters. What is the length of one side of the plot?

17. Box A measures 3 feet long, 2 feet wide, and 3 feet high. Box B measures 4 feet long, 2 feet wide, and 2 feet high. Which box has the greater volume?

18. A 3-inch by 5-inch picture is put in a frame that measures 7 inches long by 5 inches wide. Will the picture take up more than half the area enclosed by the frame?

CUMULATIVE REVIEW

Write each product in simplest form.

19. $\frac{1}{4} \times \frac{4}{5}$ **20.** $\frac{1}{2} \times \frac{2}{3}$ **21.** $\frac{2}{3} \times \frac{2}{3}$ **22.** $\frac{3}{8} \times \frac{1}{3}$

Decide whether the ratios are equal. Write *yes* or *no*.

23. 4:6 and 8:12   **24.** 16:8 and 10:4   **25.** 5:10 and 2:3

Find the percent of the number.

26. 20% of 150   **27.** 5% of 180   **28.** 60% × 200   **29.** 15% of 80

EXCURSION
USING TECHNOLOGY

AREA AND PERIMETER

The rectangles shown on the right all have a perimeter of 16 centimeters. But they all have different areas. Which one has the greatest area? Is there a rule that can help you find the rectangle with the greatest area for a certain perimeter?

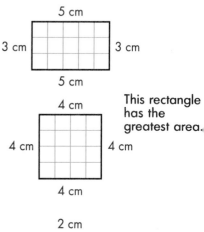

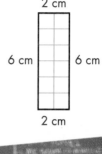

This rectangle has the greatest area.

The program below asks you for the perimeter for a rectangle. Then it asks you to type in the width you think will give you the rectangle with the greatest area. The program will compute the area of that rectangle and tell you whether or not it is the greatest possible area for that perimeter.

Type the BASIC program into your computer.

```
10 REM      AREA AND PERIMETER
20 PRINT "WHAT IS THE PERIMETER";
30 INPUT P: PRINT
40 PRINT "TO HAVE THE GREATEST AREA,"
50 PRINT "HOW WIDE SHOULD THE
RECTANGLE BE";
60 INPUT W: PRINT
70 LET L = (P − 2 * W) /2
80 LET A = W * L
90 IF W = L THEN 160
100 PRINT "WIDTH="; W
110 PRINT "LENGTH="; L
120 PRINT "AREA="; A
130 PRINT
```

140 PRINT "NO, THAT WIDTH DOES NOT GIVE THE"

145 PRINT "GREATEST AREA. TRY AGAIN."

150 PRINT: GOTO 40

160 PRINT "WIDTH="; W

170 PRINT "LENGTH="; L

180 PRINT "AREA="; A

185 PRINT

190 PRINT "YES, THAT'S THE GREATEST"

195 PRINT "POSSIBLE AREA FOR A RECTANGLE"

200 PRINT "WITH A PERIMETER OF "; P

999 END

Write the length and width of the rectangle with the greatest possible area for the perimeter (*P*). Use your computer program to help you.

1. $P = 36$ **2.** $P = 60$ **3.** $P = 28$ **4.** $P = 40$

5. What do you notice about each of these rectangles?

Predict what the width and length will be for the rectangle with the greatest possible area for the given perimeter.

6. $P = 20$ **7.** $P = 88$ **8.** $P = 96$ **9.** $P = 30$

Use your computer program to check your predictions.

SUMMING IT UP

10. Write a rule that can help you find the rectangle with the greatest area for a certain perimeter.

More Practice

CHAPTER 1 USE WITH PAGES 4–5.

Write the number in standard form.

1. 700,000,000 + 60,000 + 400 + 5

2. 392 billion, 474 thousand, 103

3. 508 thousand, 22

4. 81 million, 666 thousand, 10

Write the number in short word form.

5. 9,000,240

6. 14,001

7. 200,000 + 60,000 + 4000 + 300 + 50

8. 606,700,028

9. 20,003,800

10. 1,000,000 + 10,000 + 10

Write the number in expanded form.

11. 500,672,000

12. 3,034,090

13. 207,508,119

14. 9,073,824,035

15. 85,000

16. 4,001,000,763

CHAPTER 1 USE WITH PAGES 10–11.

Write the value of the underlined digit.

1. 7.0<u>3</u>5

2. 4.81<u>5</u>

3. 6.<u>2</u>02

4. 1.89<u>1</u>

5. 21.1<u>2</u>

6. 3.70<u>2</u>

7. <u>5</u>.991

8. 7.3<u>6</u>2

Write the word form of each decimal.

9. 505.55

10. 2.801

11. 3.6

12. 0.035

Write an equivalent decimal.

13. 7.01

14. 3.50

15. 6.020

16. 54.88

17. 5.600

18. 4.9

19. 101.01

20. 1.7

CHAPTER 1 USE WITH PAGES 12–13.

Compare. Write >, <, or =.

1. 379 ● 401   2. 6.02 ● 6.20   3. 5.05 ● 5.050   4. 8279 ● 8218

5. 0.81 ● 0.809   6. 7.5300 ● 7.53   7. 0.406 ● 0.460   8. 0.37 ● 0.37

Order the numbers from least to greatest.

9. 6.06; 6.60; 0.660; 0.606   10. 0.520; 0.502; 0.25; 0.200

11. 470; 469; 407; 469.001   12. 9.82; 2.99; 9.88; 8.92

13. 0.9; 0.851; 0.87; 0.859   14. 3200; 3020; 3002.9; 900

CHAPTER 1 USE WITH PAGES 14–15.

Add or subtract. Use mental math.

1. 30 + 70   2. 2000 + 200   3. 610 + 100   4. 500 − 100

5. 2600 − 300   6. 860 − 400   7. 9000 − 2000   8. 600 + 290

9. 340 − 30   10. 500 + 900   11. 740 + 50   12. 1400 − 500

CHAPTER 1 USE WITH PAGES 24–25.

Write the answer.

1.
$$2067 + 1876$$

2.
$$500{,}005 - 497{,}206$$

3.
$$4603 - 2815$$

4.
$$23{,}061 - 2{,}909$$

5.
$$21{,}117 + 2{,}227$$

6.
$$3004 + 1299$$

7.
$$\$12.70 - 3.59$$

8.
$$6103 - 47$$

9.
$$47{,}192 + 31{,}050$$

10.
$$808{,}615 + 103{,}276$$

11. 46 lb 5 oz + 13 lb 4 oz   12. 18 min 14 s + 14 min 18 s

13. $72.48 + $50.03 + $10.61   14. 6715 + 283 + 14,409

CHAPTER 1 USE WITH PAGES 26–27.

Round each number to the greatest place.

1. 3.81   **2.** 72.63   **3.** 1.47   **4.** 24.09   **5.** 1.609

6. 43   **7.** 375   **8.** 252   **9.** 1099   **10.** 6742

Round each number to the nearest hundred.

11. 415   **12.** 149   **13.** 151   **14.** 6511   **15.** 1448

16. 9185   **17.** 7777   **18.** 4601   **19.** 2138   **20.** 23,380

CHAPTER 1 USE WITH PAGES 30–31.

Write the sum.

1.
$$\begin{array}{r} 0.902 \\ + 0.408 \\ \hline \end{array}$$
2.
$$\begin{array}{r} 1787.35 \\ + 65.31 \\ \hline \end{array}$$
3.
$$\begin{array}{r} \$28.75 \\ + 3.55 \\ \hline \end{array}$$
4.
$$\begin{array}{r} 9.206 \\ + 0.88 \\ \hline \end{array}$$
5.
$$\begin{array}{r} 3.751 \\ + 1.647 \\ \hline \end{array}$$

6. 7.42 mg + 10.071 mg + 58.609 mg   **7.** $2008.42 + $0.97 + $5113.26

8. $412 + $623.50   **9.** 70.5 cm + 56.2 cm + 30.8 cm

CHAPTER 1 USE WITH PAGES 32–33.

Write the difference.

1.
$$\begin{array}{r} 6.711 \\ - 6.007 \\ \hline \end{array}$$
2.
$$\begin{array}{r} 3450.00 \\ - 983.76 \\ \hline \end{array}$$
3.
$$\begin{array}{r} 96.2 \text{ cm} \\ - 70.5 \text{ cm} \\ \hline \end{array}$$
4.
$$\begin{array}{r} \$502.15 \\ - 102.45 \\ \hline \end{array}$$

5.
$$\begin{array}{r} 24.18 \\ - 8.10 \\ \hline \end{array}$$
6.
$$\begin{array}{r} 0.509 \\ - 0.059 \\ \hline \end{array}$$
7.
$$\begin{array}{r} 48.000 \\ - 0.692 \\ \hline \end{array}$$
8.
$$\begin{array}{r} 15.111 \\ - 2.747 \\ \hline \end{array}$$

9.
$$\begin{array}{r} 0.37 \\ - 0.06 \\ \hline \end{array}$$
10.
$$\begin{array}{r} 3.4 \text{ m} \\ - 1.6 \text{ m} \\ \hline \end{array}$$
11.
$$\begin{array}{r} 1536.014 \\ - 827.900 \\ \hline \end{array}$$
12.
$$\begin{array}{r} 0.090 \\ - 0.009 \\ \hline \end{array}$$

13. 0.8 − 0.463   **14.** 270.01 − 53.5   **15.** 6.9 − 4.217

16. 27.095 − 0.095   **17.** $400 − $89.99   **18.** 303.01 − 300.03

CHAPTER 2 USE WITH PAGES 44–45.

Write the value of each expression.

1. What is $r + 4$ if $r = 3$; if $r = 7$?

2. What is $d + 40$ if $d = 10$; if $d = 15$?

3. What is $m - 2$ if $m = 8$; if $m = 12$?

4. What is $y - 0$ if $y = 10$; if $y = 23$?

5. What is $b + \frac{1}{4}$ if $b = 1$; if $b = 13$

6. What is $30 - c$ if $c = 15$; if $c = 20$?

CHAPTER 2 USE WITH PAGES 48–49.

Write the first two common multiples.

1. 3, 12
2. 3, 6
3. 5, 10
4. 7, 4
5. 6, 20
6. 6, 15
7. 2, 6, 21
8. 3, 5, 6

Write the least common multiple.

9. 3, 9
10. 4, 15
11. 2, 12
12. 6, 8
13. 8, 10
14. 2, 17
15. 4, 5, 6
16. 7, 9
17. 12, 18
18. 2, 4, 12
19. 3, 8, 16
20. 10, 15, 40

CHAPTER 2 USE WITH PAGES 50–51.

Write the product. Use mental math.

1. 4×700
2. 300×6
3. 50×80
4. 30×30
5. 20×900
6. 600×90
7. $6 \times 2 \times 5$
8. $5 \times 3 \times 8$
9. $4 \times 5 \times 7$

Solve. Use mental math.

10. $5 \cdot f = 45$
11. $k \times 7 = 21$
12. $v \cdot 6 = 60$
13. $x \cdot 9 = 81$
14. $p \times 9 = 63$
15. $c \times 9 = 54$
16. $l \times 4 = 36$
17. $10 \times s = 70$

CHAPTER 2 USE WITH PAGES 52–53.

Write your estimate.

1. 22×27 2. 8×27 3. 88×3 4. 26×16

5. 909×4 6. 615×6 7. 274×5 8. 7×263

CHAPTER 2 USE WITH PAGES 56–57.

Write the product.

| 1. $\$1.46 \\ \times \quad 4$ | 2. $97 \text{ in.} \\ \times \quad 8$ | 3. $823 \\ \times \quad 5$ | 4. $61 \text{ km} \\ \times \quad 2$ | 5. $46 \\ \times \quad 6$ |

6. 7×321 mL   7. 9×45 8. 3×39 9. 6×125

10. 97×5 11. $\$8.12 \times 3$ 12. 64×9 13. 444×4

Complete.

14. $384 \times 7 = (300 \times \blacksquare) + (84 \times \blacksquare)$ 15. $3 \times 609 = (\blacksquare \times 600) + (\blacksquare \times 9)$

16. $2 \times 1083 = (2 \times \blacksquare) + (\blacksquare \times 83)$ 17. $412 \times 6 = (400 \times \blacksquare) + (12 \times \blacksquare)$

CHAPTER 2 USE WITH PAGES 58–59.

Complete. Write >, <, or =.

1. $40 \times 5 \bullet 70 \times 2$ 2. $70 \times 7 \bullet 50 \times 8$ 3. $4 \times 60 \bullet 90 \times 3$

4. $12 \times 5 \bullet 30 \times 2$ 5. $4 \times 60 \bullet 50 \times 5$ 6. $50 \times 10 \bullet 100 \times 5$

Write the product.

| 7. $38 \\ \times 62$ | 8. $\$4.04 \\ \times \quad 13$ | 9. $20 \text{ m} \\ \times 47$ | 10. $28 \\ \times 51$ | 11. $73 \\ \times 82$ |

| 12. $276 \\ \times \quad 85$ | 13. $79 \\ \times 79$ | 14. $653 \\ \times \quad 48$ | 15. $807 \\ \times \quad 74$ | 16. $119 \\ \times \quad 36$ |

17. 17×384 18. $\$9.50 \times 61$ 19. 19×80 20. 80×19

CHAPTER 2 USE WITH PAGES 62–63.

Write the product.

1. 503
   × 824

2. 716
   × 950

3. 423
   × 324

4. 609
   × 871

5. 250 m
   × 100

6. $2.97
   × 455

7. 805
   × 369

8. 737
   × 104

9. 516
   × 927

10. 467
    × 432

11. 214 × 108

12. 367 × 525

13. 707 × 941

14. 824 × 673

CHAPTER 3 USE WITH PAGES 74–75.

Copy and complete each chart.

1. To write the number of millimeters as centimeters, divide the number of millimeters (t) by 10.

2. To write the number of cups as pints, divide the number of cups (b) by 2.

Millimeters (t)	Number of Centimeters $\left(\frac{t}{10}\right)$
10	$\frac{10}{10}$, or ▨
20	▨, or ▨
40	▨, or ▨

Cups (b)	Number of Pints $\left(\frac{b}{2}\right)$
4	$\frac{4}{2}$, or ▨
12	▨, or ▨
20	▨, or ▨

CHAPTER 3 USE WITH PAGES 78–79.

Write the answer.

1. 4)57

2. 5)57

3. 7)298

4. 3)374

5. 2)44

6. 4)187

7. 9)735

8. 6)52

9. 4)35

10. 8)256

11. 7)301

12. 3)994

13. 5)565

14. 9)382

15. 7)86

16. 688 ÷ 8

17. 69 ÷ 4

18. 57 ÷ 2

19. 434 ÷ 7

20. 87 ÷ 3

21. 608 ÷ 7

CHAPTER 3 USE WITH PAGES 80–81.

Write the answer.

1. $4\overline{)83}$ 2. $5\overline{)530}$ 3. $2\overline{)181}$ 4. $3\overline{)610}$

5. $3\overline{)122}$ 6. $8\overline{)7920}$ 7. $6\overline{)5943}$ 8. $7\overline{)3605}$

9. $5\overline{)2005}$ 10. $3\overline{)4829}$ 11. $9\overline{)46,302}$ 12. $4\overline{)20,206}$

13. $9160 \div 4$ 14. $45,031 \div 6$ 15. $27,090 \div 7$

16. $\frac{95}{3}$ 17. $\frac{98}{4}$ 18. $\frac{130}{5}$

CHAPTER 3 USE WITH PAGES 86–87.

Write the quotient.

1. $30\overline{)90}$ 2. $40\overline{)800}$ 3. $20\overline{)8000}$ 4. $60\overline{)4200}$

5. $3\overline{)21,000}$ 6. $400\overline{)1600}$ 7. $80\overline{)4000}$ 8. $9\overline{)540}$

9. $900 \div 30$ 10. $6300 \div 700$ 11. $12,000 \div 20$ 12. $1000 \div 50$

CHAPTER 3 USE WITH PAGES 92–93.

Write the quotient.

1. $30\overline{)816}$ 2. $15\overline{)467}$ 3. $49\overline{)1000}$ 4. $62\overline{)9052}$

5. $29\overline{)794}$ 6. $56\overline{)8288}$ 7. $90\overline{)277}$ 8. $38\overline{)2651}$

9. $81\overline{)6006}$ 10. $43\overline{)1352}$ 11. $27\overline{)6918}$ 12. $15\overline{)3497}$

13. $67\overline{)5427}$ 14. $39\overline{)40,400}$ 15. $86\overline{)3612}$ 16. $93\overline{)92,535}$

17. $902 \div 22$ 18. $602 \div 74$ 19. $5183 \div 68$

20. $1220 \div 59$ 21. $4212 \div 36$ 22. $38,612 \div 17$

CHAPTER 3 USE WITH PAGES 98–99.

Write the factors of each number.

1. 8   2. 50   3. 27   4. 16   5. 9   6. 24

7. 34   8. 35   9. 49   10. 42   11. 56   12. 17

Write the greatest common factor for each set of numbers.

13. 8, 50   14. 8, 16   15. 9, 24   16. 17, 34

17. 35, 49   18. 50, 56   19. 42, 24   20. 42, 56

CHAPTER 3 USE WITH PAGES 102–103.

Copy and complete each factor tree.

1.
```
      12
     /  \
   6 × 2
  / \    \
 ▧ × ▧ × 2
```

2.
```
        24
       /  \
     4 × 6
    / |  | \
  ▧ × ▧ × ▧ × ▧
```

3.
```
       45
      /  \
    5 × 9
   /  / \
 ▧ × ▧ × ▧
```

4.
```
        54
       /  \
     6 × ▧
    / |  | \
  ▧ × ▧ × ▧ × ▧
```

Write the prime factorization. Use a factor tree.

5. 15   6. 8   7. 32   8. 21   9. 64   10. 42

11. 36   12. 60   13. 56   14. 30   15. 80   16. 28

CHAPTER 4 USE WITH PAGES 114–115.

Write the mean and the range for each. You may use a calculator.

1. Ages: 30 yr, 35 yr, 33 yr, 37 yr, 38 yr, 31 yr

2. January temperatures (°F): 6°, 10°, 8°, 1°, 7°, 10°, 6°, 8°

3. Number of points scored: 12, 17, 10, 1, 20, 13, 25

4. August temperatures (°F): 96°, 98°, 96°, 96°, 99°, 91°

5. Number of students: 25, 25, 27, 26, 27

6. Number of pages read: 101, 51, 44, 39, 103, 111, 59, 44

7. Basketball player heights: 71 in., 71 in., 78 in., 76 in., 79 in.

8. Number of miles driven: 6 mi, 5 mi, 27 mi, 18 mi, 34 mi, 91 mi, 1 mi

CHAPTER 4 USE WITH PAGES 116–117.

Order the numbers from least to greatest. Write the median, mean, and range.

1. Number of people: 106, 114, 149, 125, 101

2. Temperatures across region (°F): 47°, 44°, 43°, 47°, 44°

3. Pet weights: 3 lb, 25 lb, 15 lb, 16 lb, 3 lb, 29 lb, 14 lb

4. Jacket prices: $63, $50, $49, $71, $57, $55, $32, $90, $73

5. Number of kilometers between cities: 2 km, 85 km, 79 km, 85 km, 74 km, 169 km, 2 km, 88 km, 82 km

CHAPTER 4 USE WITH PAGES 120–121.

Write the answer. Use estimation.

1. About how many puppets were sold in 1988? 1990?

2. In which years were more than 300 puppets sold?

3. In which year were about 475 puppets sold?

4. In which years were between 250 and 350 puppets sold?

5. About how many more puppets were sold in 1991 than in 1988?

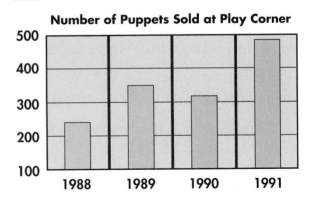

Number of Puppets Sold at Play Corner

CHAPTER 4 USE WITH PAGES 124–125.

Use one of the graphs to answer each question.

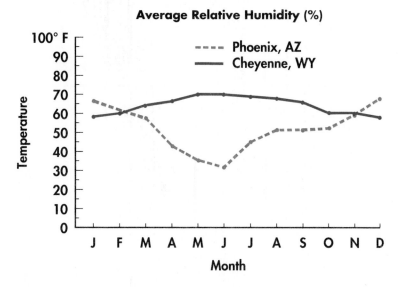

Average Relative Humidity (%)

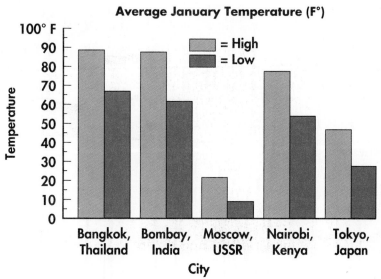

Average January Temperature (F°)

1. Which city has the highest average humidity in December? In April?

2. In which month did Cheyenne and Phoenix have the greatest difference in humidity?

3. In which 2 months did the two cities have about the same amount of humidity?

4. Which city has the highest average temperature in January? The lowest?

5. Which city has the smallest range between high and low temperature in January?

6. Which two cities have about the same high and low temperatures?

CHAPTER 5 USE WITH PAGES 140–141.

Estimate the length of each leaf to the nearest inch and then measure.

1.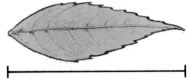

2.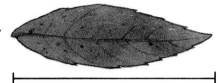

Measure the length of each object to the nearest $\frac{1}{2}$ inch.

3.

4.

Measure each object to the nearest $\frac{1}{4}$ inch and then to the nearest $\frac{1}{8}$ inch.

5.

6.

7.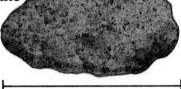

CHAPTER 5 USE WITH PAGES 152–153.

Write the perimeter.

1.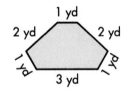
1 yd, 2 yd, 2 yd, 1 yd, 1 yd, 3 yd

2.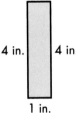
1 in., 4 in., 4 in., 1 in.

3.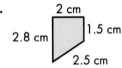
2 cm, 1.5 cm, 2.8 cm, 2.5 cm

4. Rectangular pool:
length = 25 m
width = 10 m

5. Square wrestling mat:
side = 34 ft

6. Rectangle:
length = 15 ft
width = 11 ft

7. Square:
side = 12.5 cm

8. Rectangle:
length = 16.3 m
width = 4.7 m

9. Square:
side = 5.25 m

CHAPTER 5 USE WITH PAGES 158–159.

Write how much time will pass.

1. from 1:15 P.M. to 4:20 P.M.

2. from 7:45 A.M. to 10:12 A.M.

3. from 11:00 A.M. to 4:30 P.M.

4. from 8:10 P.M. to 2:45 A.M.

5. from 10:53 P.M. to 1:05 A.M.

6. from 9:14 A.M. to 2:35 P.M.

7. from 3:30 P.M. to 11:20 P.M.

8. from 9:15 P.M. to 12:47 A.M.

9.
$$\begin{array}{r} 25 \text{ h } 9 \text{ min} \\ - \ 11 \text{ h } 7 \text{ min} \\ \hline \end{array}$$

10.
$$\begin{array}{r} 10 \text{ h } 17 \text{ min} \\ + \ \ 6 \text{ h } 12 \text{ min} \\ \hline \end{array}$$

11.
$$\begin{array}{r} 47 \text{ min } 25 \text{ s} \\ - \ 16 \text{ min } 19 \text{ s} \\ \hline \end{array}$$

12.
$$\begin{array}{r} 17 \text{ h } 8 \text{ min} \\ + \ \ 7 \text{ h } 5 \text{ min} \\ \hline \end{array}$$

13.
$$\begin{array}{r} 30 \text{ min } 45 \text{ s} \\ - \ 18 \text{ min } 31 \text{ s} \\ \hline \end{array}$$

14.
$$\begin{array}{r} 16 \text{ min } 23 \text{ s} \\ + \ 16 \text{ min } 25 \text{ s} \\ \hline \end{array}$$

CHAPTER 5 USE WITH PAGES 162–163.

Copy and complete. What time is it in the other three cities?

	Washington, D.C.	St. Louis	Denver	Portland
	3:30 P.M.	2:30 P.M.	1:30 P.M.	12:30 P.M.
1.	12:45 A.M.			
2.			4:10 A.M.	
3.		1:00 P.M.		
4.				4:18 P.M.

CHAPTER 6 USE WITH PAGES 180–181.

Write the missing number.

1. 4 × $6.25 Estimate: between $24 and $▧

2. 6 × $3.89 Estimate: between $▧ and $24

3. 3 × $9.15 Estimate: between $▧ and $▧

4. 2 × 7.6 Estimate: between ▧ and ▧

5. 5 × 8.2 Estimate: between ▧ and ▧

6. 3 × 4.72 Estimate: between ▧ and ▧

Write the product.

1. $\begin{array}{r} 11.3 \\ \times\quad 5 \\ \hline \end{array}$	**2.** $\begin{array}{r} 46.1 \\ \times\quad 2 \\ \hline \end{array}$	**3.** $\begin{array}{r} 2.9 \\ \times\quad 6 \\ \hline \end{array}$	**4.** $\begin{array}{r} 76.5 \\ \times\quad 3 \\ \hline \end{array}$
5. $\begin{array}{r} 3.8 \\ \times\quad 4 \\ \hline \end{array}$	**6.** $\begin{array}{r} 25.6 \\ \times\quad 8 \\ \hline \end{array}$	**7.** $\begin{array}{r} 55.5 \\ \times\quad 9 \\ \hline \end{array}$	**8.** $\begin{array}{r} 61.2 \\ \times\quad 5 \\ \hline \end{array}$
9. $\begin{array}{r} 89.4 \\ \times\quad 7 \\ \hline \end{array}$	**10.** $\begin{array}{r} 7.3 \\ \times\quad 3 \\ \hline \end{array}$	**11.** $\begin{array}{r} 48.6 \\ \times\quad 4 \\ \hline \end{array}$	**12.** $\begin{array}{r} 37.9 \\ \times\quad 2 \\ \hline \end{array}$
13. $\begin{array}{r} 22.6 \\ \times\quad 5 \\ \hline \end{array}$	**14.** $\begin{array}{r} 54.1 \\ \times\quad 6 \\ \hline \end{array}$	**15.** $\begin{array}{r} 9.1 \\ \times\quad 7 \\ \hline \end{array}$	**16.** $\begin{array}{r} 1.2 \\ \times\quad 8 \\ \hline \end{array}$

17. 6.5×2 **18.** 4.8×3 **19.** 31.3×9

20. 31.7×8 **21.** 94.2×6 **22.** 53.5×4

23. 8.4×5 **24.** 72.6×2 **25.** 28.1×7

Write the product.

1. $\begin{array}{r} 3.06 \\ \times\quad 4 \\ \hline \end{array}$	**2.** $\begin{array}{r} 0.05 \\ \times\quad 9 \\ \hline \end{array}$	**3.** $\begin{array}{r} 1.03 \\ \times\quad 5 \\ \hline \end{array}$	**4.** $\begin{array}{r} 2.07 \\ \times\quad 1 \\ \hline \end{array}$
5. $\begin{array}{r} 0.002 \\ \times\quad 7 \\ \hline \end{array}$	**6.** $\begin{array}{r} 1.08 \\ \times\quad 0 \\ \hline \end{array}$	**7.** $\begin{array}{r} 6 \\ \times\ 0.08 \\ \hline \end{array}$	**8.** $\begin{array}{r} 3.02 \\ \times\quad 5 \\ \hline \end{array}$
9. $\begin{array}{r} 8.09 \\ \times\quad 6 \\ \hline \end{array}$	**10.** $\begin{array}{r} 0.046 \\ \times\quad 2 \\ \hline \end{array}$	**11.** $\begin{array}{r} 7.004 \\ \times\quad 9 \\ \hline \end{array}$	**12.** $\begin{array}{r} 0.05 \\ \times\quad 4 \\ \hline \end{array}$

13. 5.03×4 **14.** 0.09×7 **15.** 12.08×5 **16.** 4.06×3

17. 0.027×5 **18.** 3.01×9 **19.** 0.05×8 **20.** 1.07×2

CHAPTER 6 USE WITH PAGES 192–193.

Write the product. Round dollar amounts to the nearest cent.

1.
$$\begin{array}{r} 5.7 \\ \times\ 2.3 \\ \hline \end{array}$$

2.
$$\begin{array}{r} 4.8 \\ \times\ 9.6 \\ \hline \end{array}$$

3.
$$\begin{array}{r} 25 \\ \times\ 1.2 \\ \hline \end{array}$$

4.
$$\begin{array}{r} \$6.82 \\ \times\ \ \ 3.4 \\ \hline \end{array}$$

5.
$$\begin{array}{r} 8.1 \\ \times\ 10 \\ \hline \end{array}$$

6.
$$\begin{array}{r} 3.7 \\ \times\ 0.04 \\ \hline \end{array}$$

7.
$$\begin{array}{r} 29.3 \\ \times\ \ 6.5 \\ \hline \end{array}$$

8.
$$\begin{array}{r} 0.7 \\ \times\ 1000 \\ \hline \end{array}$$

9.
$$\begin{array}{r} 3.51 \\ \times\ \ \ \ 8 \\ \hline \end{array}$$

10.
$$\begin{array}{r} \$6.42 \\ \times\ \ \ \ 1.3 \\ \hline \end{array}$$

11.
$$\begin{array}{r} 5.09 \\ \times\ \ 0.7 \\ \hline \end{array}$$

12.
$$\begin{array}{r} \$4.28 \\ \times\ \ \ \ 6.3 \\ \hline \end{array}$$

13.
$$\begin{array}{r} 0.94 \\ \times\ \ \ 4.2 \\ \hline \end{array}$$

14.
$$\begin{array}{r} 8.77 \\ \times\ \ \ \ 6 \\ \hline \end{array}$$

15.
$$\begin{array}{r} \$0.15 \\ \times\ \ \ \ 2.9 \\ \hline \end{array}$$

16.
$$\begin{array}{r} 746.9 \\ \times\ \ \ \ 4.5 \\ \hline \end{array}$$

17. 0.35×7.5

18. 0.8×0.1

19. 2.9×41.5

20. 1.75×8

21. 0.75×3.6

22. 2.48×0.2

23. 33.3×100

24. 6.08×7

CHAPTER 7
USE WITH PAGES 208–209.

Equivalent Measures of Length		
1 centimeter (cm) = 10 millimeters	(mm)	
1 meter (m) = 1000 millimeters	(mm)	
1 meter (m) = 100 centimeters	(cm)	
1 kilometer (km) = 1000 meters	(m)	

Use the table. Write the letter of the equivalent measure.

1. 81 km   a. 810,000 m   b. 81,000 m   c. 0.081 m

2. 50.301 m   a. 50,301 cm   b. 503.01 cm   c. 5030.1 cm

3. 426 mm   a. 0.0426 m   b. 4260 m   c. 0.426 m

4. 0.38 cm   a. 0.0038 mm   b. 3800 mm   c. 3.8 mm

Complete.

5. 1000 m = 1▮

6. 37 cm = ▮ mm

7. 56,022 m = ▮ cm

8. 9.88 km = ▮ m

9. 1.497 cm = ▮ mm

10. 15 mm = ▮ m

Complete. Write >, <, or =.

11. 5730 mm ● 573m

12. 741 cm ● 7.41 m

13. 0.7 cm ● 6.2 mm

14. 128 km ● 12,000 m

15. 924 mm ● 0.924 m

16. 0.65 cm ● 0.65 mm

CHAPTER 7 USE WITH PAGES 210–211.

Write the letter of the reasonable estimate. Write a, b, or c.

1. $4.37 ÷ 6 a. $0.07 b. $0.70 c. $7.00

2. $0.68 ÷ 3 a. $0.02 b. $0.20 c. $2.00

3. $9.15 ÷ 4 a. $0.02 b. $0.20 c. $2.00

4. $52.98 ÷ 6 a. $0.09 b. $0.90 c. $9.00

5. $314.05 ÷ 5 a. $0.60 b. $6.00 c. $60.00

CHAPTER 7 USE WITH PAGES 214–215.

Write the quotient.

1. 4)36.04   2. 5)$2.80   3. 7)7.49   4. 2)$105.10

5. 6)28.812   6. 9)0.333   7. 4)82.4   8. 8)1.64

9. 8)15.2   10. 3)42.27   11. 5)28.535   12. 4)69.632

13. 9.06 ÷ 3   14. 2.702 ÷ 2   15. $5.88 ÷ 6

16. 66.69 ÷ 9   17. 0.36 ÷ 8   18. 0.735 ÷ 5

CHAPTER 7 USE WITH PAGES 216–217.

Write the quotient.

1. 6)3   2. 4)11   3. 8)$46   4. 5)92

5. 2)79   6. 5)$2   7. 4)38   8. 4)5

9. 6)15   10. 5)3   11. 2)13   12. 5)97

13. 4)29   14. 2)75   15. 6)$87   16. 4)66

17. 8)$38   18. 8)29   19. 5)9   20. 4)86

21. 36 ÷ 8   22. 75 ÷ 6   23. $11 ÷ 2

24. 4 ÷ 5   25. 9 ÷ 4   26. 63 ÷ 8

CHAPTER 8 USE WITH PAGES 232–233.

For the slide shown, copy and complete each statement.

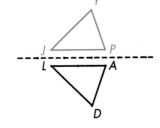

1. $\triangle SZI \cong$
2. $\overline{ZI} \cong$ ▨
3. $\angle ZSI \cong$ ▨
4. $\overline{PR} \cong$ ▨

For the flip shown, copy and complete each statement.

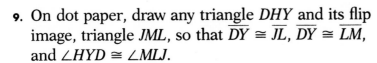

5. $\triangle DLA \cong$ ▨
6. $\overline{LA} \cong$ ▨

7. $\overline{DL} \cong$ ▨
8. ▨ $\cong \angle JYP$

9. On dot paper, draw any triangle DHY and its flip image, triangle JML, so that $\overline{DY} \cong \overline{JL}$, $\overline{DY} \cong \overline{LM}$, and $\angle HYD \cong \angle MLJ$.

10. On dot paper, draw any triangle BFG and its slide image, triangle KNQ, so that $\overline{BF} \cong \overline{KN}$, $\overline{BG} \cong \overline{KQ}$, and $\angle BGF \cong \angle KQN$.

CHAPTER 8 USE WITH PAGES 234–235.

Draw angles with the following measures. Tell what kind of angle each is. Write *acute*, *obtuse*, or *right*.

1. 120°
2. 45°
3. 160°
4. 60°
5. 75°
6. 105°

7. 15°
8. 140°
9. 170°
10. 100°
11. 90°
12. 70°

CHAPTER 8 USE WITH PAGES 236–237.

Copy each figure onto dot paper. Draw the half-turn image for each figure using the turn center given.

1.

2.

3.

Copy each figure onto dot paper. Draw the three-quarter turn image for each using the turn center given.

4.

5.

6.

Write the ordered pair for the vertex.

1. *K*

2. *B*

3. *P*

4. *R*

5. *L*

6. *D*

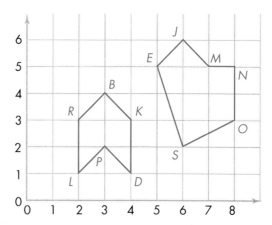

Write the vertex for the ordered pair.

7. (6,2)

8. (8,5)

9. (5,5)

10. (8,3)

11. (7,5)

12. (6,6)

Copy the figure and its grid onto squared paper. Write the ordered pair for each vertex. Multiply the ordered pair of each vertex by 2. Then draw the similar figure.

1.

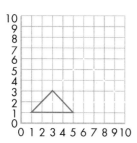

2.

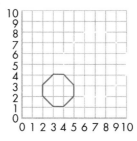

Copy the figure and its grid onto squared paper. Write the ordered pair for each vertex. Divide the numbers in each ordered pair by 2. Then draw the similar figure.

3.

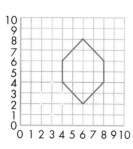

4.

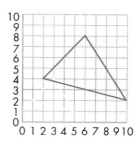

CHAPTER 9 USE WITH PAGES 266–267.

Complete to make equivalent fractions.

1. $\frac{6}{12} = \frac{\blacksquare}{4}$ 5   2. $\frac{1}{3} = \frac{\blacksquare}{30}$ 3. $\frac{7}{42} = \frac{\blacksquare}{6}$ 4. $\frac{5}{5} = \frac{\blacksquare}{15}$

5. $\frac{2}{5} = \frac{8}{\blacksquare}$ 6. $\frac{12}{36} = \frac{1}{\blacksquare}$ 7. $\frac{3}{5} = \frac{\blacksquare}{25}$ 8. $\frac{16}{20} = \frac{\blacksquare}{5}$

Write an equivalent fraction.

9. $\frac{1}{4}$ 10. $\frac{2}{5}$ 11. $\frac{3}{8}$ 12. $\frac{12}{48}$ 13. $\frac{6}{9}$

14. $\frac{32}{36}$ 15. $\frac{7}{8}$ 16. $\frac{4}{2}$ 17. $\frac{5}{50}$ 18. $\frac{15}{20}$

19. $\frac{12}{32}$ 20. $\frac{1}{2}$ 21. $\frac{3}{5}$ 22. $\frac{7}{21}$ 23. $\frac{20}{25}$

CHAPTER 9 USE WITH PAGES 268–269.

List the factors for each number. Circle the greatest common factor.

1. 6, 8   2. 25, 35   3. 12, 42   4. 54, 63

5. 10, 100   6. 30, 50   7. 16, 24   8. 7, 21

Write an equivalent fraction that is in simplest form.

9. $\frac{12}{48}$ 10. $\frac{15}{25}$ 11. $\frac{6}{18}$ 12. $\frac{20}{30}$ 13. $\frac{16}{30}$

14. $\frac{24}{30}$ 15. $\frac{3}{30}$ 16. $\frac{36}{40}$ 17. $\frac{9}{12}$ 18. $\frac{12}{24}$

19. $\frac{10}{15}$ 20. $\frac{7}{21}$ 21. $\frac{7}{35}$ 22. $\frac{20}{24}$ 23. $\frac{10}{100}$

CHAPTER 9 USE WITH PAGES 270–271.

Write whether each fraction is close to 0, $\frac{1}{2}$, or 1.

1. $\frac{1}{10}$ 2. $\frac{7}{12}$ 3. $\frac{13}{12}$ 4. $\frac{21}{100}$ 5. $\frac{6}{25}$

6. $\frac{5}{6}$ 7. $\frac{2}{5}$ 8. $\frac{4}{3}$ 9. $\frac{7}{10}$ 10. $\frac{3}{20}$

11. $\frac{7}{5}$ 12. $\frac{19}{24}$ 13. $\frac{79}{100}$ 14. $\frac{15}{24}$ 15. $\frac{1}{5}$

CHAPTER 9 USE WITH PAGES 276–277.

Write each mixed number as an equivalent fraction.

1. $1\frac{2}{5}$ 2. $6\frac{3}{5}$ 3. $8\frac{1}{2}$ 4. $5\frac{2}{3}$ 5. $3\frac{5}{16}$

6. $4\frac{2}{3}$ 7. $3\frac{1}{8}$ 8. $2\frac{13}{20}$ 9. $6\frac{3}{10}$ 10. $4\frac{1}{4}$

11. $3\frac{3}{8}$ 12. $3\frac{5}{6}$ 13. $5\frac{1}{5}$ 14. $2\frac{1}{12}$ 15. $3\frac{3}{10}$

16. $2\frac{3}{8}$ 17. $6\frac{4}{5}$ 18. $7\frac{2}{3}$ 19. $3\frac{2}{3}$ 20. $3\frac{1}{12}$

CHAPTER 9 USE WITH PAGES 278–279.

Write each fraction as a mixed number or as a whole number in simplest form.

1. $\frac{60}{20}$ 2. $\frac{27}{8}$ 3. $\frac{25}{5}$ 4. $\frac{19}{4}$ 5. $\frac{21}{3}$

6. $\frac{13}{5}$ 7. $\frac{10}{3}$ 8. $\frac{26}{12}$ 9. $\frac{54}{10}$ 10. $\frac{34}{6}$

11. $\frac{52}{5}$ 12. $\frac{48}{6}$ 13. $\frac{16}{12}$ 14. $\frac{7}{4}$ 15. $\frac{55}{25}$

16. $\frac{32}{8}$ 17. $\frac{16}{10}$ 18. $\frac{7}{3}$ 19. $\frac{14}{3}$ 20. $\frac{29}{8}$

CHAPTER 9 USE WITH PAGES 280–281.

Compare. Write >, <, or =.

1. $\frac{1}{4} \bullet \frac{3}{12}$ 2. $\frac{5}{8} \bullet \frac{2}{3}$ 3. $1\frac{1}{10} \bullet 2\frac{7}{8}$ 4. $5\frac{8}{12} \bullet 1\frac{3}{6}$

5. $4\frac{6}{12} \bullet 4\frac{2}{4}$ 6. $\frac{4}{5} \bullet \frac{5}{8}$ 7. $3\frac{3}{10} \bullet 3\frac{1}{4}$ 8. $\frac{7}{12} \bullet \frac{4}{5}$

Write the numbers in order from least to greatest.

9. $\frac{3}{4}; \frac{1}{2}; \frac{1}{3}$ 10. $\frac{3}{10}; \frac{1}{5}; \frac{7}{10}$ 11. $\frac{2}{5}; \frac{1}{6}; \frac{3}{4}$ 12. $\frac{2}{3}; \frac{3}{4}; \frac{1}{3}$

13. $\frac{1}{2}; 1\frac{3}{10}; 1\frac{2}{5}$ 14. $\frac{1}{2}; \frac{5}{8}; \frac{7}{12}$ 15. $1\frac{3}{4}; 1\frac{7}{10}; 1\frac{4}{5}$ 16. $2\frac{1}{4}; 1\frac{5}{12}; 1\frac{1}{6}$

CHAPTER 9 USE WITH PAGES 284–285.

Write each number as a decimal.

1. $\frac{7}{8}$
2. $\frac{1}{4}$
3. $1\frac{3}{5}$
4. $3\frac{9}{10}$

5. $5\frac{63}{100}$
6. $2\frac{6}{12}$
7. $\frac{4}{10}$
8. $\frac{4}{16}$

9. $6\frac{1}{2}$
10. $3\frac{2}{5}$
11. $1\frac{1}{100}$
12. $7\frac{2}{25}$

Write the decimal as a fraction or mixed number in simplest form.

13. 0.83
14. 0.8
15. 2.625
16. 0.45

17. 4.03
18. 0.86
19. 5.875
20. 7.012

CHAPTER 10 USE WITH PAGES 294–295.

Write the answer in simplest form.

1. $\begin{array}{r} \frac{3}{10} \\ + \frac{7}{10} \\ \hline \end{array}$
2. $\begin{array}{r} \frac{5}{12} \\ - \frac{1}{12} \\ \hline \end{array}$
3. $\begin{array}{r} \frac{5}{8} \\ + \frac{1}{8} \\ \hline \end{array}$
4. $\begin{array}{r} \frac{1}{8} \\ + \frac{5}{8} \\ \hline \end{array}$
5. $\begin{array}{r} \frac{7}{8} \\ - \frac{3}{8} \\ \hline \end{array}$

6. $\begin{array}{r} \frac{6}{10} \\ - \frac{2}{10} \\ \hline \end{array}$
7. $\begin{array}{r} \frac{8}{20} \\ - \frac{7}{20} \\ \hline \end{array}$
8. $\begin{array}{r} \frac{5}{6} \\ + \frac{5}{6} \\ \hline \end{array}$
9. $\begin{array}{r} \frac{5}{12} \\ - \frac{3}{12} \\ \hline \end{array}$
10. $\begin{array}{r} \frac{1}{5} \\ + \frac{2}{5} \\ \hline \end{array}$

11. $\frac{13}{16} - \frac{1}{16}$
12. $\frac{3}{6} - \frac{1}{6}$
13. $\frac{8}{15} + \frac{14}{15}$
14. $0 + \frac{1}{4}$

15. $\frac{21}{24} + \frac{3}{24}$
16. $\frac{3}{24} + \frac{21}{24}$
17. $\frac{9}{10} - \frac{3}{10}$
18. $\frac{1}{5} + \frac{1}{5}$

CHAPTER 10 USE WITH PAGES 298–299.

Write the answer in simplest form.

1. $\begin{array}{r} \frac{1}{2} \\ + \frac{2}{3} \\ \hline \end{array}$
2. $\begin{array}{r} \frac{3}{4} \\ - \frac{1}{3} \\ \hline \end{array}$
3. $\begin{array}{r} \frac{7}{12} \\ - \frac{1}{2} \\ \hline \end{array}$
4. $\begin{array}{r} \frac{9}{10} \\ - \frac{2}{5} \\ \hline \end{array}$
5. $\begin{array}{r} \frac{1}{2} \\ + \frac{1}{4} \\ \hline \end{array}$

6. $\begin{array}{r} \frac{5}{8} \\ - \frac{1}{4} \\ \hline \end{array}$
7. $\begin{array}{r} \frac{2}{3} \\ + \frac{5}{18} \\ \hline \end{array}$
8. $\begin{array}{r} \frac{3}{4} \\ + \frac{3}{8} \\ \hline \end{array}$
9. $\begin{array}{r} \frac{11}{12} \\ - \frac{1}{3} \\ \hline \end{array}$
10. $\begin{array}{r} \frac{1}{2} \\ - \frac{1}{8} \\ \hline \end{array}$

11. $\frac{4}{5} - \frac{1}{6}$
12. $\frac{7}{8} - \frac{7}{10}$
13. $\frac{1}{3} + \frac{5}{6}$
14. $\frac{3}{4} + \frac{1}{10}$

CHAPTER 10 USE WITH PAGES 302-303.

Write the answer in simplest form.

1. $\begin{array}{r} 5 \\ + 1\frac{3}{8} \\ \hline \end{array}$

2. $\begin{array}{r} 3\frac{4}{5} \\ - 3\frac{2}{5} \\ \hline \end{array}$

3. $\begin{array}{r} 6\frac{2}{3} \\ - 3\frac{1}{3} \\ \hline \end{array}$

4. $\begin{array}{r} 7\frac{5}{2} \\ + \frac{7}{2} \\ \hline \end{array}$

5. $\begin{array}{r} 9\frac{3}{4} \\ + 8 \\ \hline \end{array}$

6. $\begin{array}{r} 17\frac{2}{3} \\ - 8\frac{1}{3} \\ \hline \end{array}$

7. $\begin{array}{r} 4\frac{3}{12} \\ + 3\frac{7}{12} \\ \hline \end{array}$

8. $\begin{array}{r} 38\frac{5}{6} \\ - 30\frac{1}{6} \\ \hline \end{array}$

9. $\begin{array}{r} 10\frac{1}{4} \\ + 5 \\ \hline \end{array}$

10. $\begin{array}{r} 4\frac{9}{10} \\ - 3\frac{7}{10} \\ \hline \end{array}$

11. $4\frac{21}{24} - 4\frac{7}{24}$

12. $8\frac{2}{3} - 6$

13. $3\frac{1}{10} + 6\frac{9}{10}$

14. $1\frac{7}{8} - \frac{3}{8}$

CHAPTER 10 USE WITH PAGES 306-307.

Write the sum in simplest form.

1. $\begin{array}{r} 4\frac{5}{8} \\ + 5\frac{1}{3} \\ \hline \end{array}$

2. $\begin{array}{r} 1\frac{2}{3} \\ + 7\frac{1}{4} \\ \hline \end{array}$

3. $\begin{array}{r} 3\frac{1}{3} \\ + 2\frac{1}{6} \\ \hline \end{array}$

4. $\begin{array}{r} 8\frac{7}{12} \\ + 1 \\ \hline \end{array}$

5. $\begin{array}{r} 4\frac{3}{4} \\ + \frac{1}{2} \\ \hline \end{array}$

6. $\begin{array}{r} 3\frac{7}{12} \\ + \frac{1}{6} \\ \hline \end{array}$

7. $\begin{array}{r} 4\frac{3}{4} \\ + 4\frac{5}{8} \\ \hline \end{array}$

8. $\begin{array}{r} 11\frac{7}{10} \\ + 6\frac{1}{4} \\ \hline \end{array}$

9. $\begin{array}{r} 1\frac{4}{5} \\ + 1\frac{1}{8} \\ \hline \end{array}$

10. $\begin{array}{r} 2\frac{1}{2} \\ + 5\frac{11}{12} \\ \hline \end{array}$

11. $4\frac{1}{5} + 10$

12. $7\frac{3}{4} + 1\frac{2}{5}$

13. $5\frac{1}{2} + 4\frac{3}{10}$

14. $\frac{3}{4} + 2\frac{2}{3}$

CHAPTER 10 USE WITH PAGES 308-309.

Write the difference in simplest form.

1. $\begin{array}{r} 7\frac{3}{5} \\ - 4\frac{3}{10} \\ \hline \end{array}$

2. $\begin{array}{r} 6\frac{9}{10} \\ - 2\frac{1}{4} \\ \hline \end{array}$

3. $\begin{array}{r} 5\frac{2}{5} \\ - \frac{1}{10} \\ \hline \end{array}$

4. $\begin{array}{r} 1\frac{3}{4} \\ - 1\frac{3}{8} \\ \hline \end{array}$

5. $\begin{array}{r} 3\frac{1}{2} \\ - 2\frac{1}{6} \\ \hline \end{array}$

6. $\begin{array}{r} 5\frac{5}{8} \\ - 1\frac{1}{3} \\ \hline \end{array}$

7. $\begin{array}{r} 3\frac{7}{8} \\ - 1\frac{2}{5} \\ \hline \end{array}$

8. $\begin{array}{r} 9\frac{4}{5} \\ - \frac{7}{12} \\ \hline \end{array}$

9. $\begin{array}{r} 3\frac{5}{6} \\ - 2\frac{1}{3} \\ \hline \end{array}$

10. $\begin{array}{r} 8\frac{7}{8} \\ - 1\frac{2}{3} \\ \hline \end{array}$

11. $8\frac{3}{5} - 2$

12. $14\frac{1}{8} - \frac{1}{6}$

13. $9\frac{5}{12} - 3\frac{1}{4}$

14. $5\frac{3}{4} - 3\frac{7}{12}$

CHAPTER 10 USE WITH PAGES 310–311.

Write the difference in simplest form.

1. $9 - 1\frac{5}{8}$

2. $2\frac{3}{4} - 1\frac{7}{8}$

3. $8\frac{1}{12} - 3\frac{1}{10}$

4. $6\frac{2}{5} - 2\frac{9}{10}$

5. $1\frac{1}{12} - \frac{1}{4}$

6. $5 - \frac{4}{5}$

7. $6\frac{2}{5} - 3\frac{3}{4}$

8. $4 - 3\frac{3}{5}$

9. $7\frac{1}{4} - 6\frac{5}{6}$

10. $8\frac{3}{10} - 5\frac{3}{5}$

11. $6 - 2\frac{16}{100}$

12. $12\frac{1}{2} - 7\frac{11}{12}$

13. $3\frac{2}{3} - 1\frac{9}{10}$

14. $7\frac{2}{5} - 5\frac{7}{8}$

CHAPTER 11 USE WITH PAGES 324–325.

Write the product in simplest form.

1. $\frac{1}{4}$ of 14

2. $\frac{1}{3}$ of 8

3. $\frac{2}{5}$ of 10

4. $\frac{1}{12}$ of 24

5. $\frac{5}{8}$ of 8

6. $\frac{2}{3} \times 3$

7. $5 \times \frac{1}{4}$

8. $\frac{4}{5} \times 9$

9. $\frac{1}{3} \times 6$

10. $7 \times \frac{3}{4}$

11. $16 \times \frac{1}{12}$

12. $\frac{1}{2} \times 5$

13. $\frac{3}{5} \times 10$

14. $8 \times \frac{3}{4}$

15. $\frac{1}{10} \times 4$

CHAPTER 11 USE PAGES 326–327.

Use mental math to solve.

1. $\frac{1}{3}$ of $1500

2. $\frac{1}{2}$ of 40

3. $\frac{1}{5}$ of $200

4. $\frac{1}{6}$ of 30

5. $\frac{1}{4}$ of 28

6. $\frac{1}{3}$ of $120

7. $\frac{1}{8}$ of 6400

8. $\frac{1}{8}$ of 160

9. $\frac{1}{2}$ of 240

10. $\frac{1}{5}$ of 450

11. $\frac{1}{4}$ of $80

12. $\frac{1}{3}$ of 240

Estimate.

13. $\frac{1}{4}$ of 230

14. $\frac{1}{8}$ of 50

15. $\frac{1}{5}$ of $42

16. $\frac{1}{3}$ of 84

17. $\frac{1}{3}$ of 130

18. $\frac{1}{5}$ of 1741

19. $\frac{1}{2}$ of $935

20. $\frac{1}{8}$ of 10

21. $\frac{1}{4}$ of 2108

22. $\frac{1}{3}$ of 789

23. $\frac{1}{2}$ of $5

24. $\frac{1}{8}$ of 111

CHAPTER 11 USE WITH PAGES 332–333.

Write the product in simplest form.

1. $\frac{1}{4} \times 16$ 2. $\frac{2}{3} \times 9$ 3. $12 \times \frac{3}{4}$ 4. $\frac{5}{6} \times \frac{2}{5}$

5. $\frac{2}{3} \times \frac{1}{5}$ 6. $\frac{1}{2} \times \frac{3}{4}$ 7. $\frac{5}{6} \times \frac{3}{10}$ 8. $\frac{4}{5} \times 15$

9. $\frac{1}{2} \times \frac{1}{5}$ 10. $8 \times \frac{1}{5}$ 11. $\frac{3}{4} \times \frac{2}{3}$ 12. $\frac{2}{3} \times \frac{1}{6}$

13. $\frac{3}{10} \times \frac{4}{5}$ 14. $\frac{1}{6} \times \frac{3}{4}$ 15. $\frac{1}{4} \times \frac{3}{5}$ 16. $\frac{2}{3} \times \frac{1}{5}$

17. $\frac{2}{3} \times \frac{3}{5}$ 18. $\frac{3}{5} \times \frac{2}{3}$ 19. $\frac{4}{5} \times \frac{1}{3}$ 20. $\frac{1}{5} \times 3$

CHAPTER 11 USE WITH PAGES 336–337.

Use the number line to write each quotient.

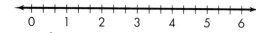

1. $6 \div \frac{1}{3}$

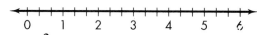

2. $6 \div \frac{2}{3}$

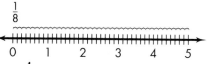

3. $5 \div \frac{1}{8}$

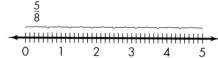

4. $5 \div \frac{5}{8}$

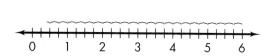

5. $6 \div \frac{1}{4}$

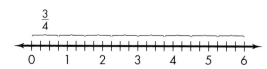

6. $6 \div \frac{3}{4}$

CHAPTER 11 USE WITH PAGES 338–339.

Write the reciprocal of the number.

1. $\frac{3}{8}$ 2. $\frac{1}{5}$ 3. $\frac{2}{3}$ 4. 7 5. 8

6. 50 7. $\frac{5}{2}$ 8. $1\frac{1}{2}$ 9. $2\frac{3}{4}$ 10. $4\frac{1}{5}$

11. 10 12. $\frac{9}{3}$ 13. $6\frac{1}{3}$ 14. $3\frac{2}{10}$ 15. $5\frac{3}{5}$

CHAPTER 12 USE WITH PAGES 352–353.

Write each ratio three different ways

1. marbles to jacks

2. daisies to tulips

3. baseballs to footballs

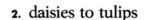

Write each ratio in fraction form.

4. 8 divers to 32 swim-team members.

5. 30 crayons to 3 boxes

6. 53 girls to 50 boys

7. 16 poems to 48 stories

8. 9 chickens to 63 farm animals

Write each ratio using the word *to.*

9. $\frac{3}{20}$

10. $\frac{18}{5}$

11. $\frac{7}{12}$

12. $\frac{9}{4}$

CHAPTER 12 USE WITH PAGES 356–357.

Decide if the ratios are equal. Write *yes* or *no.*

1. 2 to 1 and 1 to 2

2. 2:3 and 3:4

3. 5:2 and 10:4

4. 5:2 and 15:6

5. $\frac{1}{6}$ and $\frac{4}{24}$

6. $\frac{6}{24}$ and $\frac{3}{8}$

7. 10 to 1 and 5 to 1

8. 7:9 and 35:45

9. 12 to 15 and 4 to 5

Write the missing number.

10. 4 to 1 is the same as 12 to ▦.

11. 3 to 6 is the same as ▦ to 2.

12. $\frac{2}{5} = \frac{▦}{15}$

13. $\frac{18}{▦} = \frac{9}{2}$

14. $\frac{10}{8} = \frac{▦}{4}$

15. $\frac{▦}{6} = \frac{6}{18}$

16. $\frac{3}{9} = \frac{▦}{3}$

17. $\frac{7}{5} = \frac{14}{▦}$

18. $\frac{21}{24} = \frac{▦}{8}$

19. $\frac{▦}{4} = \frac{12}{16}$

20. $\frac{2}{7} = \frac{▦}{49}$

21. $\frac{9}{15} = \frac{3}{▦}$

22. $\frac{4}{5} = \frac{32}{▦}$

23. $\frac{8}{56} = \frac{▦}{7}$

24. $\frac{▦}{9} = \frac{40}{90}$

25. $\frac{24}{20} = \frac{▦}{10}$

26. $\frac{18}{81} = \frac{2}{▦}$

27. $\frac{4}{1} = \frac{▦}{18}$

28. $\frac{16}{12} = \frac{▦}{6}$

29. $\frac{36}{48} = \frac{▦}{8}$

30. $\frac{2}{7} = \frac{12}{▦}$

31. $\frac{5}{15} = \frac{1}{▦}$

Write each percent as a fraction in simplest form.

1. 15%   2. 3%   3. 25%   4. 10%   5. 8%

6. 16%   7. 55%   8. 40%   9. 34%   10. 2%

11. 75%   12. 9%   13. 12%   14. 5%   15. 45%

16. 4%   17. 64%   18. 37%   19. 18%   20. 89%

21. Write each percent in exercises 1–10 as a decimal.

Write each decimal as a percent.

22. 0.45   23. 0.5   24. 0.17   25. 0.21   26. 0.6

27. 0.9   28. 0.12   29. 0.8   30. 0.49   31. 0.05

32. 0.99   33. 0.02   34. 0.06   35. 0.7   36. 0.01

Write each fraction as a percent.

37. $\frac{7}{10}$ 38. $\frac{3}{5}$ 39. $\frac{1}{4}$ 40. $\frac{4}{25}$ 41. $\frac{9}{10}$

42. $\frac{4}{5}$ 43. $\frac{12}{25}$ 44. $\frac{2}{5}$ 45. $\frac{1}{10}$ 46. $\frac{8}{25}$

47. $\frac{9}{50}$ 48. $\frac{9}{20}$ 49. $\frac{3}{50}$ 50. $\frac{1}{20}$ 51. $\frac{24}{25}$

CHAPTER 12 USE WITH PAGES 368–369.

Find the percent of the number. Use mental math
when you can.

1. 20% of 60   2. 15% of 60   3. 6% of 60   4. 50% of 120

5. 4% of 200   6. 30% of 57   7. 25% of 120   8. 10% of 54

9. 65% of 220   10. 75% of 100   11. 80% of 300   12. 5% of 90

13. 50% of 90   14. 20% of 80   15. 25% of 400   16. 14% of 42

17. 10% of 38   18. 2% of 200   19. 25% of 800   20. 85% of 60

CHAPTER 12 USE WITH PAGES 374–375.

Write each probability in the form of a ratio.

1. What is the probability of spinning the number 5?

2. What is the probability of spinning a number less than 3?

3. What is the probability of spinning the number 10?

4. What is the chance of spinning an odd number?

5. What is the chance of spinning a number less than 7?

CHAPTER 13 USE WITH PAGES 386–387.

Write the area of each rectangle. Remember to use square units in your answer.

1.
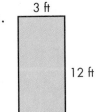
3 ft
12 ft

2.
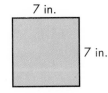
7 in.
7 in.

3.
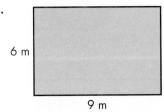
6 m
9 m

4.
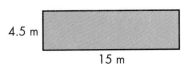
4.5 m
15 m

5.
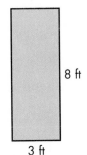
8 ft
3 ft

6.
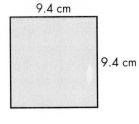
9.4 cm
9.4 cm

7. length = 18.75 m
   width = 3 m

8. length = 27 mi
   width = 13 mi

9. length = 10 ft
   width = 4 ft

10. length = 8.25 cm
    width = 2 cm

11. square side = 6.4 in.

12. square side = 12 ft

CHAPTER 13 USE WITH PAGES 388–389.

Estimate the area. Give your answer in square units.

1.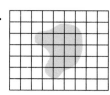

2.

3.

4.

CHAPTER 13 USE WITH PAGES 396–397.

Write the name of the polygon that is the base.

1.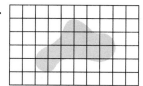
Triangular Pyramid

2.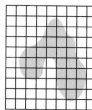
Cube

3.
Square Pyramid

4.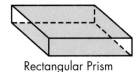
Rectangular Prism

5.
Triangular Prism

6.
Pentagonal Pyramid

CHAPTER 13 USE WITH PAGES 400–401.

Write the missing measurement for the rectangular prism.

	Length	Width	Height	Volume
1.	3 m	4 m		60 m³
2.	15 in.		3 in.	450 in.³
3.	8 ft	6 ft	12 ft	
4.	9 mm	20 mm		1260 mm³
5.		2 m	18 m	144 m³
6.	30 ft	7 ft	4 ft	

HANDBOOK

100 meter run - women

1976	A. Richter	W. Germany	11.08 sec.
1980	L. Kondratyeva	USSR	11.6 sec.
1984	E. Ashford	USA	10.97 sec.
1988	F. Griffith-Joyner	USA	10.54 sec.

Long jump - women

1976	A. Voigt,	E. Ger.	22 ft. $\frac{3}{4}$ in.
1980	T. Kolpakova,	USSR	23 ft. 2 in.
1984	A. Stanciu,	Romania	22 ft. 10 in.
1988	J. Joyner-Kersee,	USA	24 ft. $3\frac{3}{4}$ in.

OLYMPIC GOLD MEDAL WINNERS
TRACK & FIELD

Ball-Park Capacities and Recent Attendance Figures

Largest Capacities

Team	Home Park	Seating Capacity	Home Dates	Home Attendance
Cleveland (AL)	Municipal Stadium	74,208	79	1,411,610
California (AL)	Anaheim Stadium	64,573	80	2,340,865
Philadelphia (NL)	Veteran's Stadium	62,382	78	2,100,110

Smallest Capacities

Team	Home Park	Seating Capacity	Home Dates	Home Attendance
Boston (AL)	Fenway Park	33,583	79	2,464,851
Chicago Cubs (NL)	Wrigley Field	38,040	77	2,089,034
Kansas City (AL)	Royals Stadium	40,625	80	2,350,181

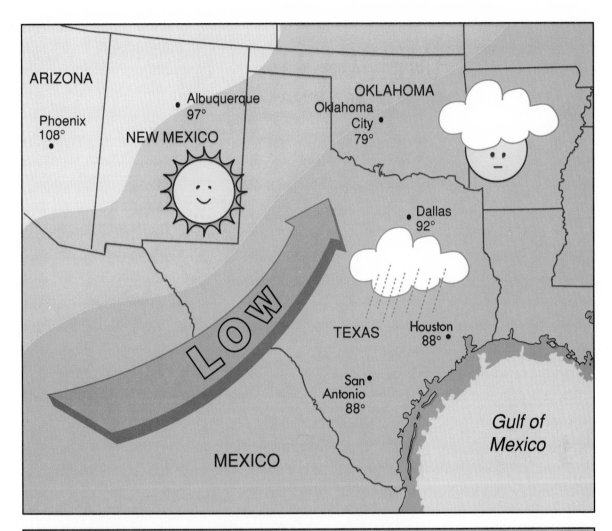

SOUTHWEST CITIES - AVERAGE DAILY HIGH TEMPERATURES (°F)

City	Average Yearly Rel Hum.	J	F	M	A	M	J	J	A	S	O	N	D
Albuquerque	43%	97	53	60	70	80	90	92	90	83	72	57	48
Dallas	67%	56	60	67	76	83	91	96	96	89	80	68	59
Houston	77%	63	66	72	79	86	91	94	94	90	84	73	66
Oklahoma City	65%	48	53	60	72	79	87	93	93	85	74	61	51
Phoenix	36%	65	69	75	84	93	102	105	102	98	88	75	66
San Antonio	67%	62	66	73	80	86	92	96	96	90	82	71	65

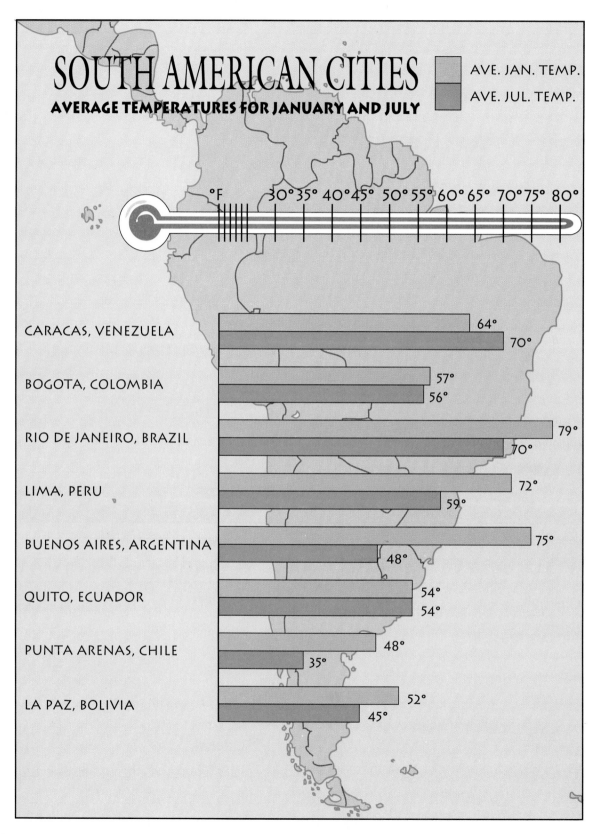

SOUTH AMERICAN CITIES
AVERAGE TEMPERATURES FOR JANUARY AND JULY

AVE. JAN. TEMP.
AVE. JUL. TEMP.

°F   30° 35° 40° 45° 50° 55° 60° 65° 70° 75° 80°

CARACAS, VENEZUELA
64°
70°

BOGOTA, COLOMBIA
57°
56°

RIO DE JANEIRO, BRAZIL
79°
70°

LIMA, PERU
72°
59°

BUENOS AIRES, ARGENTINA
75°
48°

QUITO, ECUADOR
54°
54°

PUNTA ARENAS, CHILE
48°
35°

LA PAZ, BOLIVIA
52°
45°

DATA BOOK

America's hot dogs

Top 10 breeds of dogs registered with the American Kennel Club (new registrations per year)

1986		1976	
1. Cocker spaniels	98,330	1. Poodles	126,799
2. Poodles	85,500	2. German shepherds	74,723
3. Labrador retrievers	77,371	3. Doberman pinschers	73,615
4. Golden retrievers	59,057	4. Irish setters	54,917
5. German shepherds	55,958	5. Cocker spaniels	46,862
6. Chow chows	43,026	6. Beagles	44,156
7. Beagles	39,849	7. Labrador retrievers	39,929
8. Miniature schnauzers	38,961	8. Dachshunds	38,927
9. Dachshunds	35,537	9. Miniature schnauzers	36,816
10. Shetland sheepdogs	35,064	10. Golden retrievers	27,612
Total (all registered breeds)	1,106,399	Total (all registered breeds)	1,048,648

1966		1956	
1. Poodles	235,536	1. Beagles	69,432
2. German shepherds	93,046	2. Boxers	39,502
3. Beagles	58,953	3. Chihuahuas	36,069
4. Dachshunds	53,022	4. Dachshunds	34,105
5. Chihuahuas	39,329	5. Cocker spaniels	32,003
6. Pekingese	26,712	6. German shepherds	29,126
7. Collies	22,748	7. Poodles	25,041
8. Miniature schnauzers	21,020	8. Collies	22,735
9. Cocker spaniels	17,433	9. Boston terriers	16,041
10. Basset hounds	16,140	10. Pekingese	15,540
Total (all registered breeds)	804,400	Total (all registered breeds)	430,900

DATA BOOK

World Time Zones

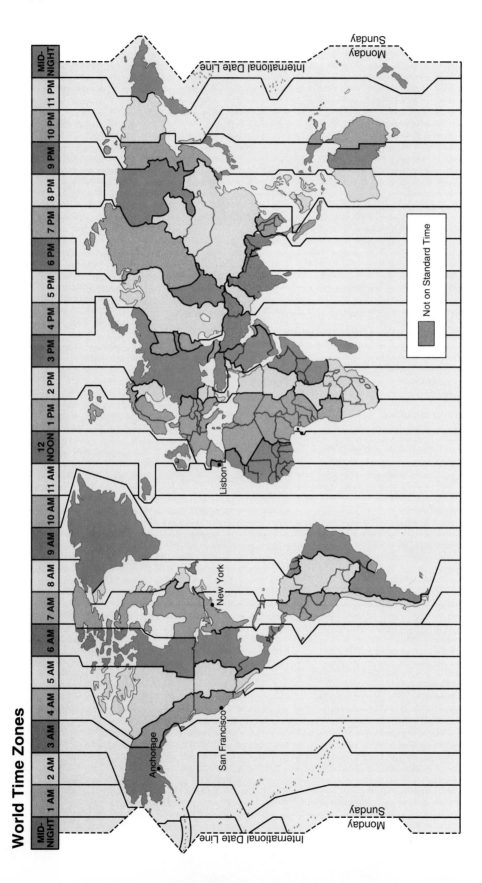

Not on Standard Time

CARIBBEAN SEA

Caracas ★

VENEZUELA

GUYANA

SURINAME

FRENCH
GUIANA

Georgetown

Paramaribo ★

Cayenne

Bogota ★

COLOMBIA

Equator

Quito ★

ECUADOR

B R A Z I L

PERU

★ Lima

BOLIVIA

★ La Paz

★ Brasilia

★

Sucre

PACIFIC
OCEAN

PARAGUAY

Rio de Janeiro ●

★ Asuncion

CHILE

ATLANTIC
OCEAN

ARGENTINA

URUGUAY

Santiago ★

Buenos Aires ★

★ Montevideo

N

W   E

S

**SOUTH
AMERICA**

0   400

miles

Punta
Arenas ●

443

DATA BOOK

FOOD CHART

Food	Approximate measure	Mass (g)	Calories	Protein (g)	Iron (mg)	Calcium (mg)
MEAT AND POULTRY, COOKED						
Bacon, crisp, dried	2 slices	16	95	4	0.5	2
Beef, chuck, pot-roasted	3 oz	85	245	23	2.9	10
Hamburger, commercial	3 oz	85	245	21	2.7	9
Ham, as luncheon meat	2 oz	57	170	13	1.5	5
VEGETABLES						
Asparagus, green	6 spears	96	18	1	1.7	18
Beans, green snap	1 cup	125	25	1	0.9	45
Corn, steamed	1 ear	100	92	3	0.5	4
FRUITS						
Apple juice, fresh or canned	1 cup	250	125	1	1.2	15
Apples, raw	1 medium	130	70	1	0.4	8
Orange juice	8 oz	250	112	2	0.5	2.7
Banana	1 medium	150	85	1	0.7	8
Apples, raw	1 medium	130	70	1	0.4	8

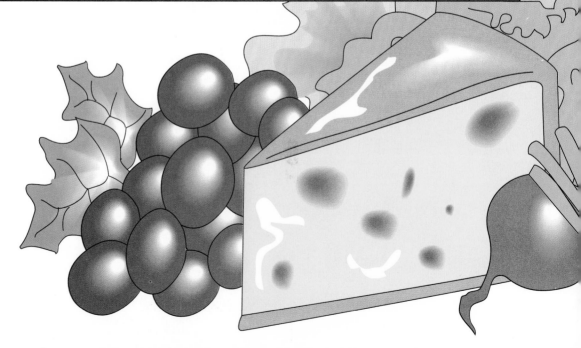

Food	Approximate measure	Mass (g)	Calories	Protein (g)	Iron (mg)	Calcium (mg)
DAIRY PRODUCTS						
Yogurt, of partially skim milk	1 cup	250	120	6	0.1	295
Egg, boiled, poached, or raw	2	100	150	12	2.3	54
Scrambled, omelet, or fried	2	128	220	13	2.2	60
BREADS, CEREALS, GRAINS AND GRAIN PRODUCTS						
Macaroni, cooked	1 cup	140	155	5	0.6	11
Baked with cheese	1 cup	220	475	18	2	394
Muffins of refined flour	1	48	135	4	0.7	74
Noodles	1 cup	160	200	7	1	16
Oatmeal or rolled oats	1 cup	236	150	5	1.7	21
Pizza	1 section	75	180	8	0.7	157

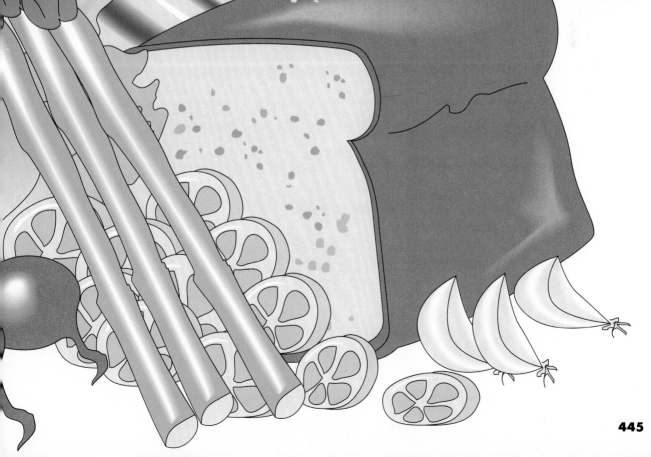

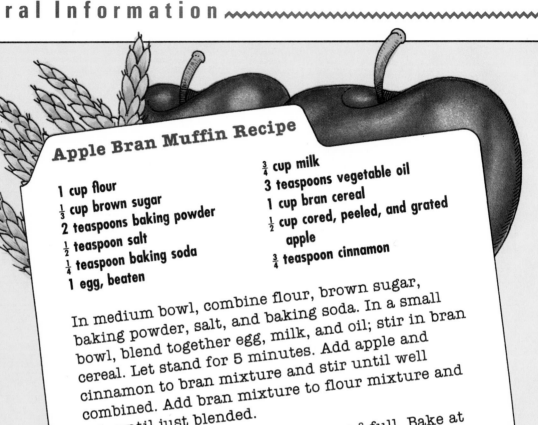

Apple Bran Muffin Recipe

1 cup flour
⅓ cup brown sugar
2 teaspoons baking powder
½ teaspoon salt
¼ teaspoon baking soda
1 egg, beaten

¾ cup milk
3 teaspoons vegetable oil
1 cup bran cereal
½ cup cored, peeled, and grated apple
¾ teaspoon cinnamon

In medium bowl, combine flour, brown sugar, baking powder, salt, and baking soda. In a small bowl, blend together egg, milk, and oil; stir in bran cereal. Let stand for 5 minutes. Add apple and cinnamon to bran mixture and stir until well combined. Add bran mixture to flour mixture and stir until just blended.

Fill 12–15 greased muffin pan cups ⅔ full. Bake at 400°F for 20–25 minutes or until done. Cool on wire rack.

Dental Chart

Percent of children that never had a cavity

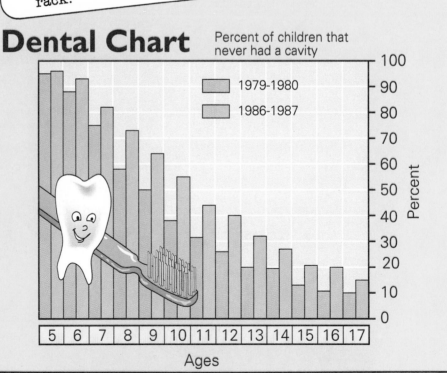

Legend:
- 1979-1980
- 1986-1987

Ages: 5 6 7 8 9 10 11 12 13 14 15 16 17

Percent axis: 0 10 20 30 40 50 60 70 80 90 100

DATA BOOK

TABLE OF MEASURES

Customary Measures

Length	1 foot (ft)	=	12 inches (in.)
	1 yard (yd)	=	3 feet
	1 yard	=	36 inches
	1 mile (mi)	=	5280 feet
	1 mile	=	1760 yards
Liquid	1 cup (c)	=	8 fluid ounces (fl oz)
	1 pint (pt)	=	2 cups
	1 quart (qt)	=	2 pints
	1 gallon (gal)	=	4 quarts
Weight	1 pound (lb)	=	16 ounces (oz)
	1 ton (t)	=	2000 pounds

Metric Measures

Length	1 centimeter (cm)	=	10 millimeters (mm)
	1 decimeter (dm)	=	10 centimeters
	1 meter (m)	=	10 decimeters
	1 meter	=	100 centimeters
	1 kilometer (km)	=	1000 meters
Liquid	1 liter (L)	=	1000 milliliters (mL)
Mass	1 gram (g)	=	1000 milligrams (mg)
	1 kilogram (kg)	=	1000 grams (g)

Time

1 minute (min)	=	60 seconds (s)
1 hour (h)	=	60 minutes
1 day	=	24 hours
1 week	=	7 days
1 year	=	12 months
1 year	=	52 weeks

Tips for Problem Solving

1. If you are stuck on a problem, that's all right. Problems aren't supposed to be easy, otherwise they wouldn't be problems.

2. There are no magic rules to take the place of thinking. These tips can help you get in the right frame of mind. They can't solve the problem for you.

3. Remember the Problem Solver's Guide.

   - **Understand** Make sure you know what is happening in the problem and what the problem is asking.

   - **Try** Don't give up. Keep trying different things. If one idea doesn't work, try another.

   - **Look back** Check over what you have done to see that it makes sense.

4. If you do *not* understand the problem, try these ideas:

   - Read the problem again slowly.

   - Picture in your mind what is happening in the problem.

   - Make notes or draw pictures.

   - Look up or ask about words you don't know.

5. If you understand the problem, but don't know what to try, you might try one or more of the strategies shown in your book.

Make Notes	See pages 60–61.
Work Backward	See pages 144–145 and 160–161.
Make a Plan	See pages 194–195.
Make a List	See pages 194–195.
Use Simpler Numbers	See pages 220–221.
Make a Diagram	See pages 252–253.
Make a Model	See pages 252–253.
Guess and Check	See pages 328–329.
Make a Table	See pages 328–329.
Write a Word Equation	See pages 358–359 and 376–377.

6. Take chances! Don't be afraid to explore. Have lots of scrap paper handy.

7. As you try to solve the problem, keep the following in mind:

    • Think clearly. Take your time.

    • Sometimes it helps to take a break after you have explored for a while. Then explore some more.

8. When you look back, ask yourself these questions:

    • Does my answer make sense?

    • Does it answer the question that the problem asked?

    • Are my computations correct?

    • Can I do the problem another way to see if I get the same answer?

INDEPENDENT STUDY

TIPS FOR DOING MENTAL MATH

Mental math is often faster and easier than using either a calculator or paper and pencil. When doing mental math, remember the following tips:

- There are special mental math strategies that work better than trying to use paper-and-pencil methods in your head.

- There are usually several good ways to do each problem.

- Be flexible; learn to see numbers as close to others; for example, $3.98 is 2 cents less than $4.00.

The mental math strategies shown on these pages will give you some ideas. Don't be afraid to invent methods of your own.

BREAKING NUMBERS APART

Replace numbers with other numbers that are easier to work with mentally.

$$76 + 89 = \blacksquare$$

Break apart 89.

$$76 + 80 + 9$$
$$156 + 9 = 165$$

OR

Break apart 76 and 89.

$$70 + 6 + 80 + 9$$
$$150 + 15 = 165$$

OR

Think of 89 as $90 - 1$.

$$76 + 90 = 166$$
$$166 - 1 = 165$$

The answer is 165.

$542 - 197 = $

Think of 197 as $200 - 3$.

> $542 - 200 = 342$
> You subtracted 3 too
> many. So add 3 to 342
> to get 345.

The answer is 345.

$27 \times 5 = $ ▦

Break 27 into $20 + 7$.

> $20 \times 5 = 100$
> $7 \times 5 = 35$
> $100 + 35 = 135$

The answer is 135.

$25 \times 16 = $ ▦

Replace 16 with 4×4.

> $25 \times 4 \times 4$
> 100×4
> 400

The answer is 400

OPERATING WITH MULTIPLES OF 10, 100, AND 1000

$$7000 - 500 = 6500 \qquad 320 \times 100 = 32,000$$

$$2800 \div 70 = 40$$

$6.8 \times 100 \longrightarrow$ (6.80) $\longrightarrow 680$ $\qquad 42 \div 10 \longrightarrow$ (4 2.) $\longrightarrow 4.2$

USING EQUIVALENT FORMS

To find the fractional part
of a number, divide.

$\frac{1}{4}$ of $24 = $ ▦

> $24 \div 4 = 6$

You will save $6 by
buying this kit on sale.

Change percents to
fractions.

50% of $40 = $ ▦

> $\frac{1}{2}$ of 40
>
> $40 \div 2 = 20$

So, 50% of 40 = 20.

TIPS FOR ESTIMATING

You can estimate when:

- you want to save time and work.

- an exact answer is not needed.

- you don't have paper and pencil or calculator with you.

- you want to see if an answer is reasonable.

The idea behind all estimation strategies is to use numbers close to the original numbers that *you* can work with mentally.

The estimation shown on these pages will give you some ideas. Don't be afraid to invent methods of your own.

> One dollar is worth 2833 pesos. I have $5.00. Is that enough to buy this piñata?
>
> 20,000 PESOS

Estimate 2833 × 5

3000 × 5 = 15,000

Since 2,833 < 3,000, $5 will give you less than 15,000 pesos. You do not have enough money.

Front-end Estimation

Add the front digits.	Look for groups of about 100 in the remaining digits.
185	185 ⟍ about 100
336	336 ⟋
352	352 ⟍ about 100
+457	+457 ⟋
Rough estimate: **1100**	Adjusted estimate: 1100 + 100 + 100 = 1300

Rounding

Round both numbers.	Round one number.	Round up and round down to get a range.
852 ⟶ 900	8.45 ⟶ 8.45	5 × $8.46
+287 ⟶ +300	−4.78 ⟶ −5.00	5 × $8 = $40
Estimate: 1200	Estimate: 3.45, or about $3\frac{1}{2}$	5 × $9 = $45
		Estimate: between $40 and $45

Compatible Numbers

Substitute numbers that are close to the original numbers and that are easy to work with mentally.

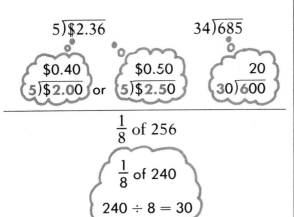

$5)\overline{\$2.36}$ $34)\overline{685}$

$\$0.40$
$5)\overline{\$2.00}$ or $\$0.50$
$5)\overline{\$2.50}$ 20
$30)\overline{600}$

$\frac{1}{8}$ of 256

$\frac{1}{8}$ of 240

$240 \div 8 = 30$

So, $\frac{1}{8}$ of 256 is about 30.

25% of 86

$\frac{1}{4}$ of 80

$80 \div 4 = 20$

So, 25% of 86 is about 20.

Clustering

$$\begin{array}{r} 5237 \\ 4952 \\ 5386 \\ 5024 \\ +4813 \end{array}$$

Each number is close to 5000. So, the sum is about 5 × 5000, or 25,000.

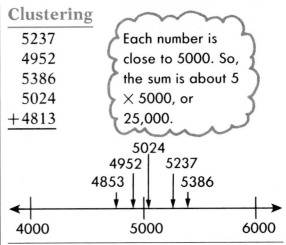

5024
4952   5237
4853   5386

4000 ——— 5000 ——— 6000

Benchmarks of 0, $\frac{1}{2}$, and 1

$\frac{9}{10} + \frac{1}{16} + \frac{5}{8}$

1   0 $\frac{1}{2}$

Estimate: $1 + 0 + \frac{1}{2} = 1\frac{1}{2}$

Remember: Be Flexible!

I could use the rounding rules.
$$\begin{array}{r} 25 \longrightarrow 30 \\ \times 45 \longrightarrow \times 50 \\ \hline 1500 \end{array}$$

25 × 45 is close to 25 × 40, which I can do mentally.

Since 25 × 4 = 100, then 25 × 40 = 1000.

Here are three good ways to estimate 25 × 45.

Since 25 and 45 are both in the middle, I could get a closer estimate by rounding one number up and one down.

$30 \times 40 = 1200$

All three estimates are reasonable: 1000, 1200, and 1500.

453

123456
234567
345678
456789
567891
678912
789123
912345
123456
234567
345678
456789
567891
678912
789123
891234
912345
123456
234567
345678
456789
567891
678912
789123
891234
912345
123456
234567
345678
456789
567891
678912
789123
891234
912345
123456
234567
345678
456789
567891
678912
789123
891234
912345
123456
234567
345678
567891

STUDY TIPS

HOMEWORK

Have you ever sat down to do your homework and discovered that you weren't sure how to do the problems?

This happens to all of us at some time. What can you do?

Understand a Math Book

How is a math book set up?

Most math lessons:
- cover two pages.
- begin on the left page and continue on the page on the right.
- start with an explanation of the lesson.
- show some examples.
- finish with exercises or problems.

Most math assignments:
- begin with easy problems.
- gradually get harder.

Use a Math Lesson

1. Read the explanation.

2. Go to the first example. Cover up the answer and do the problem.

INDEPENDENT STUDY

3. If you do not understand how to do the problem, or if your answer was different, try some of these strategies:

   • Look at the answer. Try to figure out why that is the correct answer.

   • Read the explanation and try again.

   • Ask someone in your family or call a friend.

   • Write down what you don't understand, and ask your teacher tomorrow.

4. If you did it *right*, go to the next example. Cover up the answer and do the problem. Continue to do this with each of the examples.

5. If you know how to do these you can do the exercises and problems that were assigned for your homework.

Take the time to check your homework when you finish. Make sure you did the exercises you were supposed to do. Look at each answer and make sure it is reasonable.

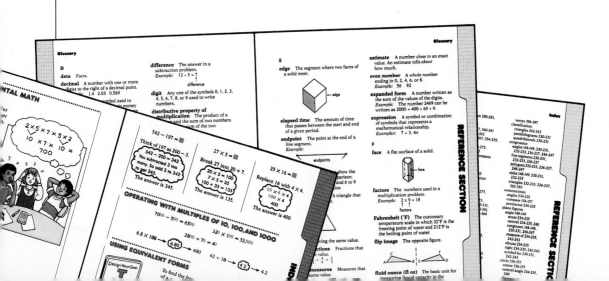

USING YOUR TEXTBOOK

Math can be a lot of fun, and your new book will help make it that way this year. In this book, you will find projects to do at home or in school, exercises to practice what you have learned, and challenging questions that ask you to think in new and different ways about things you already know.

Some lessons use calculators or computers. You will work with partners to make mathematical discoveries and to complete projects. You will be exploring many new ideas about math this year.

Knowing about your new book and how best to use it can help you. To get you started, here is a description of some features you'll find:

The **Connections** page of every chapter tells a story about mathematics that is related to the chapter's topic and to science, history, art, language, or another subject. From the story, you will understand how mathematics connects to the world and why the lessons in the chapter are important for you to learn. (See page 229.)

In the lessons, you will learn about new topics by doing activities and thinking, talking, and writing about what you're learning.

"Think" questions are part of many lessons. These are questions you will discuss in class with the help of your teacher. "Think" questions help you make sure you understand the lesson. (See page 114.)

The **Math Log** is also a part of many lessons. It gives you a chance to use your own words to describe what you are learning. (See page 193.)

INDEPENDENT STUDY

CHAPTER 3

Connections

Think

In many lessons in your book, you will be able to teach yourself something new about math based on what you already know. This is fun because you can be both the teacher and the student. You and your classmates will explore and make discoveries about mathematics by drawing diagrams, studying patterns, cutting out shapes, and measuring objects. A lesson of this type is on page 392.

Math is an important part of your life. You are often "doing" math and you may not even know it! Many lessons in your book show you how to use the math you have learned in a situation that you might find in your life today or in the future. You can find a lesson like this on page 164.

Many lessons contain **Projects.** Projects are math games for you to make and play, patterns for you to design and draw, objects for you to build, and other interesting things. Projects are a good way to practice and have some fun with the lesson. (See page 389.)

This Handbook section contains many helpful pages. The **Tips for Problem Solving** guide will help you solve word problems. Refer to it whenever you get stuck on a problem. (See page 448.)

The **Data Book** contains information on many topics, including sport, weather, maps, and population. You will use the Data Book to answer questions, draw graphs, and make predictions. (see page 438.)

You will find extra practice problems (called **More Practice**, page 410), sections on important **Estimation** skills (page 452) and **Mental Math** skills (page 450), and a **Glossary** (page 462) to use when you don't know or remember the meaning of a word.

INDEPENDENT STUDY

TIPS FOR WORKING TOGETHER

Cooperative learning helps you and your group develop important life skills. Here are some skills to work on:

MAKING CHOICES Decide who, when, what, where, and how to do the lesson.

COOPERATING Working together, everyone in the group takes part in the project.

BEING RESPONSIBLE Everyone is responsible for their part of the project and for seeing that the whole group finishes the project.

LISTENING Let others talk about their ideas—explain how they got an answer, or the methods they used —tell what they do or don't understand.

USING WORDS   Help your groupmates . . . praise a job well done or a good suggestion . . . ask questions when you are having difficulties . . . talk about your ideas.

THINKING   Be creative . . . apply what you already know to new concepts . . . look for patterns . . . develop rules, strategies . . . explore and make sense of new ideas.

BEING INDEPENDENT   Take charge of your learning . . . find resources, build a model, read books. There are no limits to what you and your groupmates can do!

USING A CALCULATOR

A calculator can be useful in many situations: at home, at school, at work, or at play. In order to use a calculator efficiently, you should know what it can do.

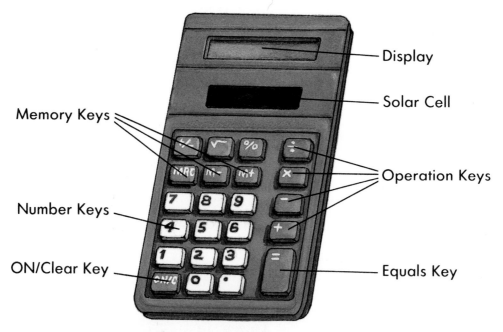

Display

Solar Cell

Memory Keys

Operation Keys

Number Keys

ON/Clear Key

Equals Key

Using the Memory Keys

The memory key, M+, saves a number for use later on.

Press 1 2 3 + 5 9 =. You should see *182* in the display. Pressing M+ will put 182 in the calculator's memory. The display should look like this:

$$\boxed{\mathrm{m} \qquad\qquad 182}$$

When you press M+ again, the calculator will add 182 to the number displayed. For example, press 3 6 × 7 M+. The display will show *252* and the calculator will add 252 to the number already in memory, 182.

MRC (memory recall key) is used to find out what number is in the calculator's memory or to clear the memory. Press **MRC**. The display should show *434* (182 + 252). **M−** is used to subtract a number from the number in the calculator's memory. For example, to remove 252 from the memory, press ③ ⑥ ✕ ⑦ **M−**. Now press **MRC**. You should see *182* (434 − 252).

To clear the memory, press **MRC** again. Notice that the small M in the display is gone. That tells you there is no number in memory.

The Multiplication Constant

You can use your calculator to multiply by the same number several times. For example, if you wanted to multiply the numbers 10, 36, and 48 by 8, you don't need to keep pressing ⑧.

To find how to use your calculator for the multiplication constant, press ② ✕ ④ ⬜. Then press ⑦ ⬜, If you see 14, that means your calculator uses the first number as the constant (2 × 7 = 14). If you see 28, your calculator uses the second number as the constant (4 × 7 = 28).

Use the multiplication constant feature to multiply each number below by 8. HINT: 8 is your constant, so will you input it first or second?

10   36   48   154

The information on these two pages applies to many, but not all, calculators. Your calculator may have different labels on the keys and may have different features. If your calculator is not like the one shown here, draw a picture of it and label the keys. As you try the activities, make notes about what your calculator can do and what it cannot do.

Glossary

A

acre   A unit of measure for an area of land equaling 43,560 square feet.

acute angle   An angle that measures less than 90°.

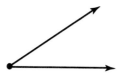

addend   A number added to another in an addition problem.
Example: 5 + 9 = 14
addends

angle   A figure formed by two rays that have a common endpoint.

area   The number of units needed to cover a surface.

associative property of addition
The sum stays the same when the grouping of addends is changed.
Example: 3.6 + (1.7 + 8.3) = 13.6
(3.6 + 1.7) + 8.3 = 13.6

associative property of multiplication   The product stays the same when the grouping of factors is changed.
Example: (1 x 2) x 5 = 10
1 x (2 x 5) = 10

B

bar graph   A graph that uses bars to show data.

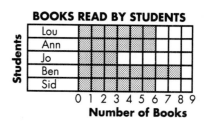

base   A special face of a solid. The bases in the two examples are shaded.

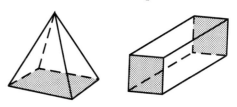

BASIC   A computer programming language.

C

capacity   The maximum amount that a container can hold.

Celsius (°C)   The metric temperature scale in which 0°C is the freezing point of water and 100°C is the boiling point of water.

centimeter (cm)   A metric unit of length; 100 centimeters equal 1 meter.

circle A closed plane curve with every point the same distance from the center.

circle graph A graph that shows all the parts of the whole.

AL'S BUDGET

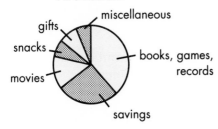

circumference The distance around the circle.

common factor A number that is a factor of two or more numbers.
Example: common factors of 18 and 24: 1, 2, 3, 6

common multiple A number that is a multiple of two or more numbers.
Example: common multiples of 2 and 3: 6, 12, 24, 30, 36

commutative property of addition The sum stays the same when the order of addends is change.
Example: 2.4 + 5.9 = 8.3
5.9 + 2.4 = 8.3

commutative property of multiplication The product stays the same when the order of factors is changed.
Example: 3 x 5 = 15
5 x 3 = 15

compatible numbers Numbers that are easy to work with mentally. Compatible numbers are used in place of actual numbers in computation to get an estimate. In the example, 60 and 240 are compatible numbers.
Example: 237 ÷ 62 → 240 ÷ 60
Estimate: 4

composite number A number that has more than two factors.
Example: 15 is a composite number because its factors are 1, 3, 5, and 15.

computer program A set of commands that tells a computer what to do.

congruent Having exactly the same size and shape.

congruent figures Figures that have exactly the same size and shape.

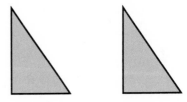

cube A solid having six square faces the same size.

cubit In ancient measurement, the distance from the elbow to the tip of the middle finger.

cup (c) A customary unit of capacity; 2 cups equal 1 pint.

customary system The measurement system that uses foot, quart, pound, and degree Fahrenheit.

D

data Facts.

decimal A number with one or more digits to the right of a decimal point.
Example: 1.4 2.03 0.569

decimal point A symbol used to separate dollars and cents in money amounts. A symbol used to separate ones and tenths in decimals.
Example: $1.50 3.2

decimal points

decimeter (dm) A metric unit of length. 10 decimeters equal 1 meter.

degree (angles) A unit for measuring angles.

degree (temperature) A unit for measuring temperature.

denominator The number written below the bar in a fraction.
Example: $\frac{1}{4}$ ← denominator

diagonal A line segment that joins two vertices of a polygon, but is not a side of the polygon.

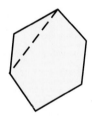

diameter The distance from any point on a circle, through the center, to another point on the circle.

diameter = 3 cm

difference The answer in a subtraction problem.
Example: 12 − 5 = 7

difference

digit Any one of the symbols 0, 1, 2, 3, 4, 5, 6, 7, 8, or 9 used to write numbers.

distributive property of multiplication The product of a number and the sum of two numbers is equal to the sum of the two products.
Example:
3 x (2 + 4) = (3 x 2) + (3 x 4)

dividend The number that is divided in a division problem.
Example: 36 ÷ 9 = 4

dividend

divisible When a number is capable of being divided into equal parts without a remainder.

divisor The number by which the dividend is divided in a division problem.
Example: 36 ÷ 9 = 4

divisor

double line graph A line graph that allows you to compare two sets of data.

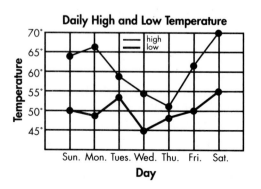

E

edge   The segment where two faces of a solid meet.

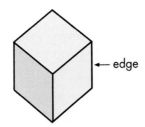
← edge

elapsed time   The amount of time that passes between the start and end of a given period.

endpoint   The point at the end of a line segment.
Example:

endpoints

equal ratios   Ratios that show the same relationship or comparison.
Example: 2 to 3, 4 to 6, and 6 to 9 are equal ratios.

equilateral triangle   A triangle that has all sides congruent.

equivalent   Having the same value.

equivalent fractions   Fractions that have the same value.
Example: $\frac{8}{12} = \frac{4}{6} = \frac{2}{3}$

equivalent measures   Measures that name the same value.
Example: 1 meter, 100 centimeters, and 1000 millimeters are equivalent measures.

estimate   A number close to an exact value. An estimate tells *about* how much.

even number   A whole number ending in 0, 2, 4, 6, or 8.
Examples: 56   92

expanded form   A number written as the sum of the values of the digits.
Example: The number 2469 can be written as 2000 + 400 + 60 + 9.

expression   A symbol or combination of symbols that represents a mathematical quantity.
Examples: $7 + 3, 4 \cdot n$

F

face   A flat surface of a solid.

— face

factors   The numbers used in a multiplication problem.
Example: $2 \times 9 = 18$
↑   ↑
factors

Fahrenheit (˚F)   The customary temperature scale in which 32˚F is the freezing point of water and 212˚F is the boiling point of water.

flip image   The position of a figure after a flip.

flip image

fluid ounce (fl oz)   The basic unit for measuring liquid capacity in the customary system; 16 fluid ounces equal 1 pint.

REFERENCE SECTION

REFERENCE SECTION

foot (ft) A customary unit of length; 12 inches equal 1 foot.

fraction A number that names a part of a whole or a part of a set.
Example: $\frac{1}{3}$ $\frac{2}{3}$ $\frac{2}{5}$

front-end estimation Estimate made by looking at the digits with the greatest place value to find *about* how much.

G

gallon (gal) A customary unit of capacity; 4 quarts equal 1 gallon.

gram (g) A metric unit of mass.

graph A picture that shows data by using bars, lines, or symbols.

greatest common factor The largest factor of two or more numbers.
Example: greatest common factor of 12, 18, and 30: 6

grouping property of addition See associative property of addition.

grouping property of multiplication See associative property of multiplication.

H

half turn A turn that causes a figure to face in the opposite direction. A 180° turn.

half-turn symmetry If a figure matches itself after a half turn about its center point, then the figure has half-turn symmetry.

hexagon A polygon with six sides.

hour A unit of time; 60 minutes equal 1 hour.

I

inch (in.) A customary unit of length; 12 inches equal 1 foot.

intersecting lines Lines that cross or meet.

intersecting planes Planes that intersect to form a line.

isosceles triangle A triangle that has two sides congruent

K

kilogram (kg) A metric unit of mass; 1000 grams equal 1 kilogram.

kilometer (km) A metric unit of length; 1000 meters equal 1 kilometer.

L

least common denominator The smallest common denominator for a set of fractions.

least common multiple   The smallest common multiple of a set of numbers.
Example: least common multiple of 2 and 3: 6

line   A collection of points along a straight path that goes on forever.

line graph   A graph that displays data by using connected line segments.

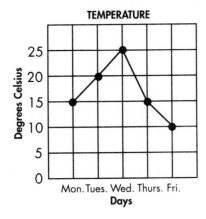

TEMPERATURE

line of symmetry   A line along which you could fold a figure so that both halves match.

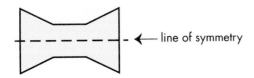

line of symmetry

line segment   Part of a line having two endpoints.

A •————————————• Z

line symmetry   A figure has line symmetry when it can be folded along a line so that the two halves match exactly.

liter (L)   A metric unit of capacity; 1000 milliliters equal 1 liter.

M

mass   The amount of matter in an object.

mean   The average of a set of numbers, found by adding the numbers in the set and dividing by the number of addends.

median   The middle number in a set when the numbers are ordered from least to greatest.

mental math   Finding an exact answer to a math problem without using paper and pencil.

meter (m)   A metric unit of length; 100 centimeters equal 1 meter.

metric system   The measurement system that uses meter, liter, gram, and degree Celsius.

migrate   To move from one place to another.

mile (mi)   A customary unit of length; 5280 feet equal 1 mile.

miles per hour (mph)   The rate of speed travelled.

milliliter (mL)   A metric unit of capacity; 1000 milliliters equal 1 liter.

millimeter (mm)   A metric unit of length; 10 millimeters equal 1 centimeter.

minute (min)   A unit of time; 60 seconds equal 1 minute.

mixed number   A number that has a whole number part and a fraction part.
Example: $2\frac{1}{6}$

multiple   A product of two whole numbers.
Example: $4 \times 2 = 8$
The number 8 is a multiple of 4 and 2.

REFERENCE SECTION

multiplication property of one   If any factor is multiplied by one, the product is the same as that factor.
Example: 4 x 1 = 4   51 x 1 = 51

multiplication property of zero
If any factor is multiplied by zero, the product is zero.
Example: 7 x 0 = 0   0 x 238 = 0

N

net   A flat pattern that folds into a solid.

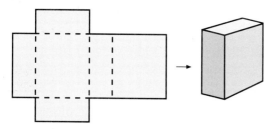

numerator   The number written above the bar in a fraction.
Example: $\frac{1}{4}$ ← numerator

O

obtuse angle   An angle that measures more than 90° and less than 180°.

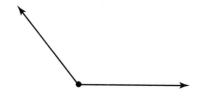

odd number   A whole number ending in 1, 3, 5, 7, or 9.
Example: 67   99

ordered pair   A pair of numbers that gives the coordinates of a point on a grid.

order property of addition   See commutative property of addition.

order property of multiplication   See commutative property of multiplication.

ounce (oz)   A customary measure of weight; 16 ounces equal 1 pound.

P

palm   In ancient measurement, the width of the four fingers. 7 palms was equal to 1 cubit.

parallel   Planes or lines extending in the same direction and always the same distance apart.

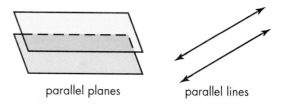

parallel planes   parallel lines

parallelogram   A quadrilateral with two pairs of parallel sides.

pentagon   A polygon with five sides.

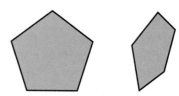

percent   A ratio based on 100.

468

perimeter   The distance around a figure.

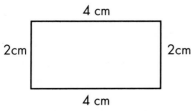

4 cm + 2 cm + 4 cm + 2 cm = 12 cm

perpendicular   Two lines or line segments that cross to form right angles.

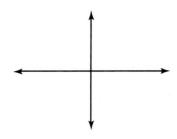

pint (pt)   A customary unit of capacity; 2 pints equal 1 quart.

place value   The value of a position in a number.
Example: In 7949, the 7 is in the thousands place.

plane   A flat surface that goes on forever in all directions.

point   An exact place or position in space, represented by a dot.

polygon   A closed figure formed by line segments.

pound (lb)   A customary unit of weight; 16 ounces equal 1 pound.

prediction   Something that is guessed in advance, based on known facts.

prime factorization   The expression of a number as the product of prime factors.
Example: The prime factorization of 56 is 7 x 2 x 2 x 2.

prime number   A number greater than 1 that has exactly two factors, itself and 1.
Example: 2, 3, 7, 11, and 17 are prime numbers

prism   A solid having two faces that are parallel and congruent.

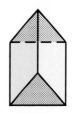

probability   A measure of chance.

product   The answer in a multiplication problem.
Example: 5 x 3 = 15
                          ↑
                       product

pyramid   A solid that has a polygon for a base and whose other faces are triangles that share a common vertex.

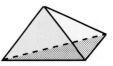

Q

quadrilateral   A polygon with four sides.

quart (qt)   A customary unit of capacity; 4 quarts equal 1 gallon.

quarter   Another name for 25¢, one fourth, or $\frac{1}{4}$.

quarter inch   One fourth of an inch.

quarter turn   A 90° turn.

quotient   The answer in a division problem.
Example: 36 ÷ 9 = 4
                            ↑
                        quotient

R

radius   The distance from the center of a circle to any point on the circle.

radius = 1.3 cm

range   The difference between the greatest number and least number in a set.

ratio   A comparison of two quantities by division.

reciprocal   The inverse of a fraction.
Example: $\frac{4}{5}$ is the reciprocal of $\frac{5}{4}$.

rectangle   A quadrilateral having four sides and four right angles.

rectangular prism   A prism having 6 faces. Each side is a rectangle.

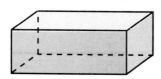

rhombus   A quadrilateral with four congruent sides.

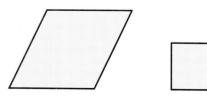

right angle   An angle measuring 90°.

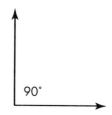
90°

right triangle   A triangle with a 90° angle.

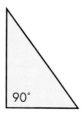
90°

S

scalene triangle   A triangle that has no congruent sides.

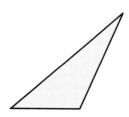

second (s)   A unit of time; 60 seconds equal 1 minute.

side   A line segment forming part of a plane figure.

similar figures   Figures that have the same shape, but are not necessarily the same size.

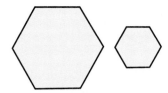

simplest form   A fraction whose numerator and denominator have no common factor other than 1.
Example: $\frac{2}{3}$ is the simplest form of $\frac{8}{12}$

slide   A motion in which every point of a figure moves the same distance and in the same direction.

slide image   A figure after it has moved to a different location.

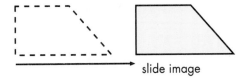

slide image

square   A figure with four right angles and four equal sides.

square centimeter (cm^2)   A metric unit used to measure area.

square inch (in^2)   A customary unit used to measure area.

standard   A measurement that is agreed upon generally.

standard form   The usual, or common, way of writing a number using digits.
Example: The standard form of twenty-seven is 27.

sum   The answer in an addition problem.
Example: 5 + 4 = 9
                              ↑
                            sum

surface area   The number of units needed to cover the entire surface of a solid.

survey   A way to collect data by asking questions of many persons.

T

tessellate   To fit plane figures together without overlapping or leaving gaps.

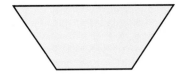

tessellation   The pattern formed by tessellating figures.

trapezoid   A quadrilateral with only one pair of parallel sides.

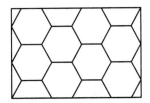

triangle   A polygon with three sides and three vertices.

turn   To move or cause to move around a center or axis.

turn center   The point around which a figure is turned.

turn image The position of a figure after a turn.

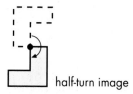

half-turn image

U

uncia In ancient measurements, the width of the thumb; 12 uncias was equal to 1 foot.

unit price The cost of one item.

V

value In 324, the digit 2 is in the tens place; its *value* is 20.

Venn diagram A drawing that shows relationships among sets of objects.

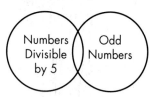

vertex (vertices) The corner point of an angle, polygon, or solid.

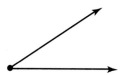

volume The number of cubic units that could fit inside a container.

W

whole number Any of the numbers 0, 1, 2, 3, 4, 5, and so on.

Y

yard (yd) A customary unit of length; 3 feet equal 1 yard.

Z

zero property of addition The sum of zero and any addend is the addend.
Example: $4.9 + 0 = 4.9$
                $0 + 6.7 = 6.7$

Index

REFERENCE SECTION

REFERENCE SECTION

Index

REFERENCE SECTION

REFERENCE SECTION

REFERENCE SECTION

REFERENCE SECTION

Index

REFERENCE SECTION

480